Under the General Editorship of

Gordon N. Ray

The University of Illinois

TWENTY-
NINE
STORIES

Edited by

William Peden

The University of Missouri

HOUGHTON MIFFLIN COMPANY • BOSTON
The Riverside Press Cambridge

The Riverside Press • Cambridge, Massachusetts • Printed in the U.S.A.

✿ CONTENTS

v

❦ INTRODUCTION

The stories in this anthology have been selected with three main purposes in view: (1) to indicate the historical development of the short story from the great beginnings of Poe and Hawthorne, through the turn-of-the-century achievements of Chekhov, Henry James, and James Joyce, up to and including the contributions of contemporary authors in America, England, and elsewhere; (2) to indicate to the student the extreme variety of the form, ranging as it does from the narration of a single incident or anecdote to the fully plotted story involving subtle, complex, and sophisticated techniques; (3) to provide a rich and varied reading experience for both beginner and specialized student. Though some of the stories in this book have never been previously anthologized and are not well known, all of them are *good* stories, and many of them deserve to be called great.

The short story is a literary form which eludes strict definition and defies attempts at arbitrary classification. Story-telling, like singing and dancing, has been a pleasure shared by almost all peoples and cultures; written narrative sketches, anecdotes, and tales are among the oldest of literary forms, and are found in all the major works of antiquity, including the Hindu collection of fables known as the Panchatantra and the Hebraic Bible. As a consciously contrived piece of literature, however, the short story is considered essentially a *modern* form.

The modern short story has developed in two different directions: in one, because of its suitability to periodical publication; in the other, because of its inherent possibilities as an

vii

art form. The rise of periodicals in the nineteenth century and the growth of the reading public acted reciprocally to create for the first time a mass market for reading matter. Thus in one line of development the short story became a means of popular entertainment, with standards set by mass-circulation media. At the same time, however, in another direction of growth, it was coming to be recognized as one of the most subtle, varied, and demanding of literary forms, laying siege to the talents of the best writers — and sometimes, as in the years since World War II, giving them their major outlet. To its practitioners and its multitudes of readers, then, the short story has meant many things. To the untutored reader, it may mean the ever-popular cliché of "boy-meets-girl, boy-chases-girl, boy-catches-girl" or "hero-triumphs-over-all-obstacles" as purveyed by the "pulps" — the magazines of "true confessions," westerns, sports stories, and the like. On a somewhat higher plane, though still for general consumption, it may follow the basic pattern of "conflict-com-plication-climax-and-conclusion" which for many years has been the most popular commodity in the "slick" mass-circulation magazines. Or, at its highest level, the short story can edify as well as give pleasure, and it can be an art form worthy of the greatest writers.

"Pulp" and "slick" stories are in the main produced by formula to provide mindless entertainment and leave no residue, no after-math of deeply stirred emotion, no moral implications to think over later, no particular insights into life, behavior, or human character. Short stories of more sophisticated kinds than these tend to be overwhelmingly serious; very few humorists are short story writers, and a serious purpose underlies the humor of many of those that are. This is true for several reasons, some of them historical. Edgar Allan Poe, the first great practitioner of the modern short story, was fascinated by the literary tradition known as Gothic. Popular well into the nineteenth century, Gothic fiction delighted in horror. Among its standard machinery were ruined castles, dank dungeons, clanking chains, apparitions, and mysterious screams in the middle of moonless nights. Poe found these trappings conveniently at hand for his use in ex-ploring the dark labyrinths of human consciousness, in trans-mitting to the reader the experience of the abnormal mind, in creating through a highly wrought atmosphere that unity of effect which he believed was the essence of the short story as an art form. Poe's greater contemporary, Nathaniel Hawthorne, shared to some extent this fascination for the strange and the marvelous, but he made quite different use of it. For Hawthorne's concern with moral issues, and the brooding sense of guilt implicit in so much that he wrote, stemmed from the high seriousness of his Puritan background and gave to many of his stories an abiding richness to be found in relatively few of Poe's. In any event, seriousness has always been part of the tradition of the modern short story.

This element of seriousness was reinforced by the somber trend of thought in the late nineteenth and early twentieth centuries. For example, the literary philosophy known as "naturalism," carrying over into fiction the theory and method of scientific observation, contributed its view of man at the mercy of uncontrollable and indifferent natural forces, the hapless victim in a tragedy that conceded him no more status than any other bit of matter adrift in the universe. At the same time, Freudian psychology and psychoanalysis were beginning to provide clinical documentation of those deeps and disorientations of the human psyche that Poe and Hawthorne had intuitively recognized, and that their successors in the short story tradition would continue to explore.

There are other reasons why the quality of seriousness has persisted. The very brevity of the short story demands that its effect be made quickly: there simply isn't time to explore by-paths, however pleasant and entertaining, which do not lead directly to the destination. For this purely practical reason it is often said that the short story must have unity of tone. If it is true that any significant insight, or comment on life, is essentially serious, then any story which makes such a comment must be essentially serious; although it may use humor, satire (ridicule of folly), or irony (statement by opposites), these are but means to a serious end. Even humorous writers such as Mark Twain and Frank O'Connor, when they wrote short stories that attained stature, had serious things to say. O. Henry generally did not, but then his stories seldom attained such stature. If there is to be anything left to think about or reflect upon after the fun is over, it appears that this residue must be some meaning which is essentially not comic, but serious.

Hence it is understandable that so many short story writers have gone to deliberate extremes to intensify impact by dealing in violence, in the grotesque and the macabre. Ernest Hemingway explained that in trying to learn to write, he deliberately sought contact with the most serious fact of life, which is death; that for this reason he became interested in bullfighting, a sport in which each encounter ends in death. Conceivably the writer can go too far in his quest for impact, and the reader may feel that some of the stories in this book are less successful than they might be for this reason. It is nonetheless true that the story as a form is preponderantly serious and that humor plays but a small part in it.

Whatever the tone, mood, or intent, a short story is, almost by definition, a type of prose fiction designed to be read "at one sitting" — perhaps fifteen to forty minutes, more or less. Further, a short story usually contains the following elements: plot, character, setting, and idea or theme. We can add that it is a piece of imaginative writing in which a human being gets "from here to there." The here-to-there progression may be dimensional, physical, material, and objective, or psychological, spiritual, emotional, and subjective. The point is that in getting from here to there something happens to the character which has meaning for him as a human being, and hence for the reader as well. It is this core of meaning, as we have seen, that gives the short story its quality or seriousness. Beyond this, any formal attempt to confine the short story within the bounds of a definition is a waste of time and effort.

For variety is perhaps the outstanding characteristic of the short story — variety of subject matter, character, setting, mood, theme, and narrative method; variety that stems also from differences of vision or intent among authors and from trends or fashions in the form itself. A short story can be an account of violent physical action, or a psychological study of character with almost no external movement or action. It can be a vehicle for social protest, or a study in mood or atmosphere more akin to lyric poetry than to traditional fiction. The form is comprehensive enough, and flexible enough, to include both the sparse understatement of Hemingway's "Indian Camp" and the leisurely narrative of Pritchett's "The Sailor," the slice-of-life realism of Anderson's "Adventure" and the symbolism of de la Mare's "The

Riddle" and Kafka's "A Country Doctor." This variety is perhaps the chief reason why the short story as a literary form has appealed to so many major writers.

Another reason for the wide appeal of the short story is that it challenges the writer in the controlled exercise of his powers. Like a surgeon performing an operation or a quarterback directing a football team, he must continuously be in command of the situation. Within the limited boundaries of the short story, there is no room for lapses, false moves, or mistakes, no room for discursiveness, irrelevance, or extravagance. Compression, careful selectivity, and technical mastery are essential to success — every incident and narrative detail, every line of dialogue, and every element of description must work toward the author's goal. The short story writer, in effect, walks a precarious tightrope between failure and success. A single false move may lead to disaster; there simply is no opportunity to recoup one's losses or compensate for one's mistakes.

If the variety and the technical demands of the short story are a challenge to the author, they sometimes present difficulties to the reader, particularly one accustomed only to the superficialities of most popular magazine stories or television scripts. To such a reader the narrative complexities of Henry James, the subtleties of Katherine Mansfield, and the grotesque symbols of A. E. Coppard may seem insurmountable obstacles; he is tempted to throw up his hands in despair or cry out in exasperation: Why can't these authors say what they mean? One of the purposes of this book is to enable such a reader to perceive, through the detailed study of a number of short stories, that complexity, indirection, and symbolism may be a necessary, integral part of the "saying" and the "meaning."

This anthology is based on the assumption that there are differences in quality among stories, just as there are differences in the quality of, let us say, various kinds of cloth or cheese. To help the student recognize, understand, enjoy, and ultimately prefer a story of genuine literary quality to a piece of competent trash, some remarks concerning basic structural elements, narrative methods, and literary techniques are necessary. Additional details, as well as approaches to individual stories, will be suggested in the comments and questions following each story in the text. Readers who wish to pursue further these and similar matters will find a source of information in the books and articles listed on pages xix-xx.

From an author's point of view, every story represents a series of technical problems over which he must triumph or by which he will be defeated. In what way will he relate a particular story? How will he reveal a certain character? To what extent and purpose will he employ atmosphere and setting? How will he determine the relation between incident and idea, between subject matter and structure? There are no ready-made answers to such questions. An author learns something about the craft of fiction from every story he writes, just as a reader should learn something about it from every story he reads.

With only occasional exceptions, the most important elements in a short story are plot and characters. In Poe's "The Black Cat," the most important thing is *what happens;* this story turns primarily on plot. On the other hand, in James's "Brooksmith," what happens is less important than the person *to whom* it happens; this is essentially a story of character. At the risk of oversimplifying a complex and controversial matter, we may take *plot* to mean the chain of incidents or events in which the character or characters are involved, the story-element of a piece of fiction. The way the author arranges the incidents, the method by which he relates or reveals them, suggests or determines the structure of his story. Structure (or form or pattern) in short fiction varies considerably. One story may be a series of loosely joined episodes, like the tales of Washington Irving, which are more properly called narrative sketches than short stories. Another may depict a single incident or re-create a "slice of life" which is more akin to a news story or to the "simple art of narration," as one critic has termed it, than to the "comprehensive art of fiction." Or, as it so often is, a short story may be a completely unified work of art, with a beginning, middle, and end, in which plot, characters, setting, and theme are so closely linked together that nothing could be added or removed without changing or damaging the effect and harmony of the whole; "Young Goodman Brown" and "The Open Boat" are stories of this kind. No one of these structures, or variations of them, is necessarily superior to the others *as a form,* since each gives opportunity for perfection or artistry within its particular limits. The story in which all elements are fully integrated, however, is generally the superior *work of fiction,* for the interplay of plot, characters, setting, theme, fact, and symbol gives to the imaginative re-creation of life a richness of texture, a symphonic quality, and a depth of meaning that the simpler or looser structures do not achieve.

The final success or failure of a short story often depends on the author's ability to create realistic, understandable human beings. Even the most bizarre, sensational, or moving events are unlikely to stir an adult reader unless they concern individuals with whom the reader can, through the writer's art, temporarily identify himself. The effective short story focuses a pinpoint of light upon man's history: a moment, an incident, a situation, a detail, a life, isolated from the repetitious and meaningless round of daily living, and illuminated with a significance beyond every-day reality. At its center is man himself, man engaged in a quest, search, struggle, or conflict, striving to "get from here to there."

Time is another important element, and one closely related to the author's management of plot and development of char-acter. Not without reason has Frank O'Connor said that "Every great short story represents a struggle with Time." Until com-paratively late in the nineteenth century, writers of fiction tended to unfold their stories in straightforward chronological fashion: a novel like Defoe's *Moll Flanders* or Dickens's *David Copper-field* begins at a specific point in historical time, usually with the birth or early childhood of the protagonist, and proceeds in order of occurrence through a series of episodes and events to a subsequent point in time, usually the old age or death of the protagonist, at which point the narrative ends. Later writers, however, such as Henry James, James Joyce, Virginia Woolf, and William Faulkner, increasingly concerned with form and technique, experimented in various ways with time and chron-ology, particularly in relation to a character's thought process or stream-of-consciousness. As for the time-span, the action of a short story can be compressed into a few hours, as in Bierce's "Chickamauga" and Saroyan's "Snake," or may extend over a period of years as in Anderson's "Adventure," or even over a lifetime. Sometimes an author, working within a brief span, interrupts his chronology to thrust back into time by references to the past or direct scenes from the past, as Coppard does in

"Arabesque" and Faulkner in "A Bear Hunt." A straightforward time-progression and a limited time-span may at first be easier for the less experienced reader to follow, but he will be able to move with understanding and enjoyment to more complex treatments if he keeps constantly on the lookout for what some critics have called the clock or hourglass implicit in the story.

It has been said that the art of fiction, technically speaking, is the manipulation of a few basic narrative methods and literary devices. The oldest, the most dependable, and perhaps the most important narrative method is that which depicts action as it takes place, sometimes called the "scenic" method. This is the method of the ballad, the nursery rhyme, the folk tale, and most oral narrative as well as much sophisticated literary narrative. Its major virtue is immediacy; the reader watches the direct enactment of the story through the actions, words, or thoughts of the characters. Regardless of the nature of the action — whether primarily physical, as in Crane's "The Open Boat," or emotional or intellectual, as in Joyce's "Araby" or James's "Brooksmith" — the scenic method creates the illusion that the reader is sharing or participating in the drama which is unfolding as he reads. In effect, then, the scenic narrative is similar to the action of a play — the curtain rises (the story begins); the characters speak their lines and go into action (the story unfolds); the final curtain falls (the story ends). Frequently the writer must halt the action to establish the physical setting or other externals, such as the characters' appearance; when he does, he is writing description. Or he may need to interrupt the action to refer to incidents or events which occurred prior to the time-limits of the story proper; this is sometimes called flashback or retrospect.

The point of view, the way in which the author chooses to tell the story, has been an important area of experiment in the modern short story. A widely used narrative point of view has been the traditional one of the "omniscient observer"—the author who sees and knows everything in the fictional world he has created, as though he were equipped with a psychic camera that follows the characters everywhere and penetrates the minds and emotions of all of them. Or the author can filter his story through the mind and consciousness of one of his characters, the "I" of many stories, who may be the major character, a minor participant, or a bystander. This mode of telling adds dramatic intensity and gives the reader an immediate point of contact with persons and events, almost as though he too were on the scene. But in choosing this point of view the author is limited to presenting only the things which this character can reasonably be expected to have seen, experienced, been told by other characters, or deduced for himself. It is as though the author were using a filter over the camera lens — he picks up some things he would not ordinarily get, but drops out others. Some writers and critics insist that the point of view should never shift, but should remain constant throughout; others, including Joyce and Faulkner, have felt that consistency in this respect is not a condition of artistry in the short story, but a restriction on it. Finally, it should be noted that point of view includes more than the technical problems of the author's angle of presentation; it is also the way he sees the world, encompassing his set of values and their moral implications.

Much of the enduring value and interest of a piece of fiction lies in the author's ability to depict or suggest the universal in terms of the specific — that is, in the symbolic or allegorical quality of the story.* In literature, a symbol is something that has both a literal and a non-literal meaning; it suggests or implies more than it actually says or represents; it suggests the nature of something in terms of something else. It can be, for example, an inanimate object like the tower of "The Open Boat" or the elaborately carved chest of "The Riddle"; a person, like the alcoholic young woman of "The Sailors"; a non-human living thing, like the withering flowers of "Rappaccini's Daughter" or

---

*Allegory, in the more limited definition of the term, is a literary device concerned with the personification of abstract qualities. Obvious examples are the characters of the medieval morality plays, who represent specific attributes, such as one or another of the Seven Deadly Sins — Gluttony, Sloth, and so forth. That is, each character has a definite, fixed, assigned meaning on the level of allegory. A short story can loosely be called an allegory when its whole meaning is implied in terms of symbols, or metaphors, or both, rather than being directly stated. Ray B. West, Jr. and Robert W. Stallman have summed up the distinction between symbol and allegory as follows: "Strictly speaking, a story is an allegory only when all the details of its action relate directly to the details of the historical or mythical events or ideas to which it refers. A distinction between allegory and symbolism in fiction might then be made by saying that a story becomes allegorical only when the symbols are used consistently to signify a second series of events *is all its important details.*"

the reptile of "Snake"; or a detail like the crack in the House of Usher.

Symbols are used in many different ways. In stories like Kafka's "A Country Doctor" or de la Mare's "The Riddle," for example, symbols become what might be called basic structural or architectural elements, as necessary to the successful functioning of the story as hub and spokes are necessary to the wheel. Such stories cannot be read literally. The individual reader's ability to understand this kind of story on the symbolic level will determine its success or failure, at least so far as he is concerned. At the other extreme, symbols can be used so sparingly, or so subtly, as to constitute a kind of embroidery or patina on action, situation, character, or idea. Again, they may be so closely integrated with the other structural and narrative elements that the story can be read with equal success on either a literal or a symbolic level. Symbols may be as obvious as the brooding atmospheric conditions with which Poe begins "The Fall of the House of Usher" or as elusive as the pink ribbon of Faith which flutters to the feet of young Goodman Brown after his experience in the haunted wood.

Regardless of how they are employed, symbols urge (or, in some cases, force) upon even the least perceptive reader a more than literal interpretation of a piece of fiction; they suggest to him the allegorical or symbolic meaning. The individual symbols of a story may be susceptible of more than one meaning or interpretation; Kafka's "A Hunger Artist," for example, can be variously read in terms of the artist in contemporary society, the role of religion in the modern world, or the eternal conflict between the spiritual and the physical. Indeed, the story may be interpreted or experienced on all these levels simultaneously; the floating quality of the symbol, its evasion of a one-to-one correspondence with a specific referent, makes multiple meaning possible in all its richness and depth. Over such matters of interpretation, there is bound to be considerable disagreement and controversy. The average reader is not likely to gain a great deal from arguing about definitions, correspondences, or origins and influences. Reading short stories, like reading poetry or listening to music, can be an intensely *personal* experience; what brings insight or illumination to one person may leave another untouched. The best way to understand what short stories mean and are, is to read them.

The student will soon find, however, that to become a good reader of short stories he must learn to read critically and analytically. As he reads these and other stories, he should cultivate the habit of asking himself certain questions:

How, for example, does the author reveal and develop the *characters?* Does the reader learn about them by what they say? Or by what they do? Or by what they think, or what other characters in the story say, do, or think about them? Remember that frequently more can be learned from what a character does *not* do than from what he actually does. Do the characters seem convincing? What are the dominant traits of the individual people in the story? To what extent does the author contrast the various characters? Are all the characters necessary? How are they motivated — why do they act, or fail to act, as they do? Are they unusual, bizarre, abnormal, commonplace?

What is the relationship between *plot* and characters? Do the incidents seem to be the logical or inevitable outgrowth of the problem, situation, predicament, or conflict around which the story is built? What is the nature of this conflict — is it physical, psychological, emotional? Does the story have a beginning, middle, and end? Does the ending seem to be compatible with what has gone before? Are the characters and events closely related? To what extent do surprise endings, tricks, coincidence, and contrivance affect the development of the story? What devices does the author use to whet your curiosity, or to foreshadow the ending, dénouement, climax, or conclusion? Is the story primarily one of plot or of character?

What is the *theme* or motivating idea? Is the theme implicit in the action and the characters, as it is in most good stories, or is it obtrusively "tacked on" to the story? Is the theme significant? Is it one that applies specifically to one particular group of people, or is it universally applicable? Did you learn anything significant about mankind, life, or human nature from the story? What sort of emotional effect, if any, did you derive from it? If it "left you cold," can you analyze the reasons for this? Are symbols used; and if so, how? To what extent does the author employ irony, suspense, or paradox? Is the theme dependent upon such factors?

From what or whose *point of view* is the story narrated? Does the point of view shift? If so, do you think the shifts are effective? Why, in your own opinion, has the author made these shifts?

What part does *setting*, background, atmosphere, or description play?

What is the *time-sequence or chronology*? To what extent, if at all, are flashbacks employed? How much time supposedly elapses during the course of the story? How many shifts in time occur?

How does the author use *dialogue* — as a means of developing character, as a narrative method, or both? Does dialogue serve any other purposes? How much of the story is told by means of dialogue? Does the dialogue seem natural or stilted? Is it in keeping with the characters, with the setting, with the background of time and place?

What can be said about the author's *style*? Is he a meticulous craftsman? How does he vary his sentence patterns? What kind of words is he particularly fond of? What part do style and structure play in the story? What is there about an author's work which makes it specifically, definitely, and inevitably *his*, so that the reader recognizes at once a story by Hemingway, Kafka, Henry James, etc.?

By constantly asking himself these and similar questions, the reader will grow steadily in understanding and enjoyment. Like an architect poring over blueprints, or a football coach studying movies of next week's opponent, the student must learn to recognize the elements that make up the whole, isolate the component parts, examine the way they are put together, recognize and account for the many details which have gone into the completed work. Only then will he be able to enjoy to the full the rich and varied world of what V. S. Pritchett has aptly called the "brief, quickly moving, epigrammatic, allusive habit of the short story."

SUGGESTIONS FOR FURTHER READING

Aldridge, John W., ed. *Critiques and Essays on Modern Fiction, 1920-1951.* New York: Ronald Press, 1952.

Bates, H. E. *The Modern Short Story, a Critical Survey.* Boston: The Writer, 1949.

Bentley, Phyllis. *Some Observations on the Art of Narrative.* New York: Macmillan, 1947.

Birmingham, Frederic A., ed. *The Writer's Craft.* New York: Hawthorn Books, 1958.

Brickell, Herschel, ed. *Writers on Writing.* New York: Doubleday, 1949.

Brooks, Cleanth, and Robert Penn Warren, eds. *Understanding Fiction.* New York: F. S. Crofts, 1947.

Burack, A. S., ed. *The Writer's Handbook.* Boston: The Writer, 1959.

Campbell, Walter S. *Writing: Advice and Devices.* New York: Doubleday, 1950.

Chekhov, Anton. *Letters on the Short Story, the Drama and Other Literary Topics.* New York: Minton, Balch, 1924.

Chekhov, Anton. *Note Book of Anton Chekhov.* New York: B. W. Huebsch, 1921.

Conrad, Joseph. *Conrad's Prefaces to his Works.* London: J. M. Dent, 1937.

Cowden, Roy, ed. *The Writer and His Craft.* Ann Arbor: University of Michigan Press, 1956.

Edel, Leon. *The Psychological Novel, 1900-1950.* Philadelphia: Lippincott, 1955.

Forster, E. M. *Aspects of the Novel.* New York: Harcourt, Brace, 1927.

Glasgow, Ellen. *A Certain Measure. An Interpretation of Prose Fiction.* New York: Harcourt, Brace, 1943.

Gordon, Caroline, and Allen Tate, eds. *The House of Fiction: An Anthology of the Short Story with Commentary.* New York: Scribner's, 1950.

James, Henry. *The Art of the Novel. Critical Prefaces.* Ed. R. P. Blackmur. New York: Scribner's, 1934.

Lubbock, Percy. *The Craft of Fiction.* New York: Cape and Smith, 1929.

McHugh, Vincent. *A Primer of the Novel.* New York: Doubleday, 1950.

Mansfield, Katherine. *The Journals of Katherine Mansfield.* New York: Knopf, 1927.

Maugham, W. Somerset. *The Summing Up.* New York: Doubleday, Doran, 1938.

O'Connor, William Van, ed. *Forms of Modern Fiction.* Minneapolis: University of Minnesota Press, 1948.

O'Faolain, Sean. *The Short Story.* New York: Devin-Adair, 1951.

Schorer, Mark, ed. *The Story: A Critical Anthology.* New York: Prentice-Hall, 1950.

West, Ray B., and Robert Wooster Stallman, eds. *The Art of Modern Fiction.* New York: Rinehart, 1949.

TWENTY-
NINE
STORIES

EDGAR ALLAN POE

The Fall of the House of Usher

Son coeur est un luth suspendu;
Sitôt qu'on le touche il résonne.
DE BÉRANGER

DURING the whole of a dull, dark, and soundless day in the autumn of the year, when the clouds hung oppressively low in the heavens, I had been passing alone, on horseback, through a singularly dreary tract of country; and at length found myself, as the shades of the evening drew on, within view of the melancholy House of Usher. I know not how it was — but, with the first glimpse of the building, a sense of insufferable gloom pervaded my spirit. I say insufferable; for the feeling was unrelieved by any of that half-pleasurable, because poetic, sentiment with which the mind usually receives even the sternest natural images of the desolate or terrible. I looked upon the scene before me — upon the mere house, and the simple landscape features of the domain, upon the bleak walls, upon the vacant eye-like windows, upon a few rank sedges, and upon a few white trunks of decayed trees — with an utter depression of soul which I can compare to no earthly sensation more properly than to the after-dream of the reveler upon opium; the bitter lapse into everyday life, the hideous dropping off of the veil. There was an iciness, a sinking, a sickening of the heart, an unredeemed dreariness of thought which no goading of

3

the imagination could torture into aught of the sublime. What was it — I paused to think — what was it that so unnerved me in the contemplation of the House of Usher? It was a mystery all insoluble; nor could I grapple with the shadowy fancies that crowded upon me as I pondered. I was forced to fall back upon the unsatisfactory conclusion, that while, beyond doubt, there *are* combinations of very simple natural objects which have the power of thus affecting us, still the analysis of this power lies among considerations beyond our depth. It was possible, I reflected, that a mere different arrangement of the particulars of the scene, of the details of the picture, would be sufficient to modify, or perhaps to annihilate, its capacity for sorrowful impression; and, acting upon this idea, I reined my horse to the precipitous brink of a black and lurid tarn that lay in unruffled luster by the dwelling, and gazed down — but with a shudder even more thrilling than before — upon the remodeled and inverted images of the gray sedge, and the ghastly tree stems, and the vacant and eye-like windows.

Nevertheless, in this mansion of gloom I now proposed to myself a sojourn of some weeks. Its proprietor, Roderick Usher, had been one of my boon companions in boyhood; but many years had elapsed since our last meeting. A letter, however, had lately reached me in a distant part of the country — a letter from him — which in its wildly importunate nature had admitted of no other than a personal reply. The MS. gave evidence of nervous agitation. The writer spoke of acute bodily illness, of a mental disorder which oppressed him, and of an earnest desire to see me, as his best and indeed his only personal friend, with a view of attempting, by the cheerfulness of my society, some alleviation of his malady. It was the manner in which all this, and much more, was said — it was the apparent *heart* that went with his request — which allowed me no room for hesitation; and I accordingly obeyed forthwith what I still considered a very singular summons.

Although as boys we had been even intimate associates, yet I really knew little of my friend. His reserve had been always excessive and habitual. I was aware, however, that his very ancient family had been noted, time out of mind, for a peculiar sensibility of temperament, displaying itself, through long ages, in many works of exalted art, and manifested of late in repeated deeds of munificent yet unobtrusive charity, as well as in a passionate devotion to the intricacies, perhaps even more than to the orthodox and easily recognizable beauties, of musical science. I had learned, too, the very remarkable fact that the stem of the Usher race, all time-honored as it was, had put forth at no period any enduring branch; in other words, that the entire family lay in the direct line of descent, and had always, with very trifling and very temporary variation, so lain. It was this deficiency, I considered, while running over in thought the perfect keeping of the character of the premises with the accredited character of the people, and while speculating upon the possible influence which the one, in the long lapse of centuries, might have exercised upon the other — it was this deficiency, perhaps, of collateral issue, and the consequent undeviating transmission from sire to son of the patrimony with the name, which had, at length, so identified the two as to merge the original title of the estate in the quaint and equivocal appellation of the "House of Usher" — an appellation which seemed to include, in the minds of the peasantry who used it, both the family and the family mansion.

I have said that the sole effect of my somewhat childish experiment, that of looking down within the tarn, had been to deepen the first singular impression. There can be no doubt that the consciousness of the rapid increase of my superstition — for why should I not so term it? — served mainly to accelerate the increase itself. Such, I have long known, is the paradoxical law of all sentiments having terror as a basis. And it might have been for this reason only, that, when I again uplifted my eyes to the house itself, from its image in the pool, there grew in my mind a strange fancy — a fancy so ridiculous, indeed, that I but mention it to show the vivid force of the sensations which oppressed me. I had so worked upon my imagination as really to believe that about the whole mansion and domain there hung an atmosphere peculiar to themselves and their immediate vicinity: an atmosphere which had no affinity with the air of heaven, but which had reeked up from the decayed trees, and the gray wall, and the silent tarn: a pestilent and mystic vapor, dull, sluggish, faintly discernible, and leaden-hued.

Shaking off from my spirit what *must* have been a dream, I scanned more narrowly the real aspect of the building. Its principal feature seemed to be that of an excessive antiquity. The discoloration of ages had been great. Minute fungi overspread the whole exterior, hanging in a fine tangled webwork from the eaves. Yet all this was apart from any extraordinary dilapidation. No portion of the masonry had fallen; and there appeared to be a wild inconsistency between its still perfect adaptation of parts and the crumbling condition of the individual stones. In this there was much that reminded me of the specious totality of old woodwork which has rotted for long years in some neglected vault, with no disturbance from the breath of the external air. Beyond this indication of excessive decay, however, the fabric gave little token of instability. Perhaps the eye of a scrutinizing observer might have discovered a barely perceptible fissure, which, extending from the roof of the building in front, made its way down the wall in a zigzag direction, until it became lost in the sullen waters of the tarn.

Noticing these things, I rode over a short causeway to the house. A servant in waiting took my horse, and I entered the Gothic archway of the hall. A valet, of stealthy step, thence conducted me, in silence, through many dark and intricate passages in my progress to the studio of his master. Much that I encountered on the way contributed, I know not how, to heighten the vague sentiments of which I have already spoken. While the objects around me — while the carvings of the ceilings, the somber tapestries of the walls, the ebon blackness of the floors, and the phantasmagoric armorial trophies which rattled as I strode, were but matters to which, or to such as which, I had been accustomed from my infancy — while I hesitated not to acknowledge how familiar was all this — I still wondered to find how unfamiliar were the fancies which ordinary images were stirring up. On one of the staircases, I met the physician of the family. His countenance, I thought, wore a mingled expression of low cunning and perplexity. He accosted me with trepidation and passed on. The valet now threw open a door and ushered me into the presence of his master.

The room in which I found myself was very large and lofty. The windows were long, narrow, and pointed, and at so vast a distance from the black oaken floor as to be altogether inaccessible from within. Feeble gleams of encrimsoned light made their way through the trellised panes, and served to render sufficiently distinct the more prominent objects around; the eye, however, struggled in vain to reach the remoter angles of the chamber, or the recesses of the vaulted and fretted ceiling. Dark draperies hung upon the walls. The general furniture was profuse, comfortless, antique, and tattered. Many books and musical instruments lay scattered about, but failed to give any vitality to the scene. I felt that I breathed an atmosphere of sorrow. An air of stern, deep, and irredeemable gloom hung over and pervaded all.

Upon my entrance, Usher arose from a sofa on which he had been lying at full length, and greeted me with a vivacious warmth which had much in it, I at first thought, of an overdone cordiality — of the constrained effort of the *ennuyé* man of the world. A glance, however, at his countenance, convinced me of his perfect sincerity. We sat down; and for some moments, while he spoke not, I gazed upon him with a feeling half of pity, half of awe. Surely man had never before so terribly altered in so brief a period as had Roderick Usher! It was with difficulty that I could bring myself to admit the identity of the wan being before me with the companion of my early boyhood. Yet the character of his face had been at all times remarkable. A cadaverousness of complexion; an eye large, liquid, and luminous beyond comparison; lips somewhat thin and very pallid, but of a surpassingly beautiful curve; a nose of a delicate Hebrew model, but with a breadth of nostril unusual in similar formations; a finely molded chin, speaking, in its want of prominence, of a want of moral energy; hair of a more than weblike softness and tenuity; these features, with an inordinate expansion above the regions of the temple, made up altogether a countenance not easily to be forgotten. And now in the mere exaggeration of the prevailing character of these features, and of the expression they were wont to convey, lay so much of change that I doubted to whom I spoke. The now ghostly pallor of the skin, and the now miraculous luster of the eye, above all things startled and even awed me. The silken hair, too, had been suffered to grow all unheeded, and as, in its wild gossamer texture, it floated rather than fell about the face, I could not, even with effort, connect its arabesque expression with any idea of simple humanity.

In the manner of my friend I was at once struck with an incoherence, an inconsistency; and I soon found this to arise from a series of feeble and futile struggles to overcome an habitual trepidancy, an excessive nervous agitation. For something of this nature I had indeed been prepared, no less by his letter than by

reminiscences of certain boyish traits, and by conclusions deduced
from his peculiar physical conformation and temperament. His
action was alternatively vivacious and sullen. His voice varied
rapidly from a tremulous indecision (when the animal spirits
seemed utterly in abeyance) to that species of energetic concision
— that abrupt, weighty, unhurried, and hollow-sounding enun-
ciation — that leaden, self-balanced and perfectly modulated gut-
tural utterance — which may be observed in the lost drunkard, or
the irreclaimable eater of opium, during the periods of his most
intense excitement.

It was thus that he spoke of the object of my visit, of his earnest
desire to see me, and of the solace he expected me to afford him.
He entered, at some length, into what he conceived to be the
nature of his malady. It was, he said, a constitutional and a
family evil, and one for which he despaired to find a remedy — a
mere nervous affection, he immediately added, which would undoubtedly soon pass off. It displayed itself in a host of unnatural
sensations. Some of these, as he detailed them, interested and
bewildered me: although, perhaps, the terms and the general
manner of the narration had their weight. He suffered much
from a morbid acuteness of the senses; the most insipid food was
alone endurable; he could wear only garments of a certain texture; the odors of all flowers were oppressive; his eyes were
tortured by even a faint light; and there were but peculiar
sounds, and these from stringed instruments, which did not in-
spire him with horror.

To an anomalous species of terror I found him a bounden
slave. "I shall perish," said he, "I *must* perish in this deplorable
folly. Thus, thus, and not otherwise, shall I be lost. I dread the
events of the future, not in themselves, but in their results. I
shudder at the thought of any, even the most trivial, incident,
which may operate upon this intolerable agitation of soul. I
have, indeed, no abhorrence of danger, except in its absolute
effect — in terror. In this unnerved — in this pitiable condition —
I feel that the period will sooner or later arrive when I must
abandon life and reason together, in some struggle with the grim
phantasm, FEAR."

I learned moreover at intervals, and through broken and equivocal hints, another singular feature of his mental condition. He

was enchained by certain superstitious impressions in regard to the dwelling which he tenanted, and whence, for many years, he had never ventured forth — in regard to an influence whose supposititious force was conveyed in terms too shadowy here to be restated —an influence which some peculiarities in the mere form and substance of his family mansion, had, by dint of long sufferance, he said, obtained over his spirit — an effect which the physique of the gray walls and turrets, and of the dim tarn into which they all looked down, had, at length, brought about upon the morale of his existence.

He admitted, however, although with hesitation, that much of the peculiar gloom which thus afflicted him could be traced to a more natural and far more palpable origin — to the severe and long-continued illness, indeed to the evidently approaching dissolution, of a tenderly beloved sister — his sole companion for long years, his last and only relative on earth. "Her decease," he said, with a bitterness which I can never forget, "would leave him (him the hopeless and the frail) the last of the ancient race of the Ushers." While he spoke, the lady Madeline (for so was she called) passed slowly through a remote portion of the apartment, and, without having noticed my presence, disappeared. I regarded her with an utter astonishment not unmingled with dread, and yet I found it impossible to account for such feelings. A sensation of stupor oppressed me, as my eyes followed her retreating steps. When a door, at length, closed upon her, my glance sought instinctively and eagerly the countenance of the brother, but he had buried his face in his hands, and I could only perceive that a far more than ordinary wanness had overspread the emaciated fingers through which trickled many passionate tears.

The disease of the lady Madeline had long baffled the skill of her physicians. A settled apathy, a gradual wasting away of the person, and frequent although transient affections of a partially cataleptical character, were the unusual diagnosis. Hitherto she had steadily borne up against the pressure of her malady, and had not betaken herself finally to bed; but, on the closing in of the evening of my arrival at the house, she succumbed (as her brother told me at night with inexpressible agitation) to the prostrating power of the destroyer; and I learned that the glimpse

I had obtained of her person would thus probably be the last I should obtain — that the lady, at least while living, would be seen by me no more.

For several days ensuing, her name was unmentioned by either Usher or myself; and during this period I was busied in earnest endeavors to alleviate the melancholy of my friend. We painted and read together; or I listened, as if in a dream, to the wild improvisation of his speaking guitar. And thus, as a closer and still closed intimacy admitted me more unreservedly into the recesses of his spirit, the more bitterly did I perceive the futility of all attempt at cheering a mind from which darkness,, as if an inherent positive quality, poured forth upon all objects of the moral and physical universe, in one unceasing radiation of gloom.

I shall ever bear about me a memory of the many solemn hours I thus spent alone with the master of the House of Usher. Yet I should fail in any attempt to convey an idea of the exact character of the studies, or of the occupations, in which he involved me, or led me the way. An excited and highly distempered ideality threw a sulphurous luster over all. His long improvised dirges will ring forever in my ears. Among other things, I hold painfully in mind a certain singular perversion and amplification of the wild air of the last waltz of Von Weber. From the paintings over which his elaborate fancy brooded, and which grew, touch by touch, into vagueness at which I shuddered the more thrillingly because I shuddered knowing not why; — from these paintings (vivid as their images now are before me) I would in vain endeavor to educe more than a small portion which should lie within the compass of merely written words. By the utter simplicity, by the nakedness of his designs, he arrested and overawed attention. If ever mortal painted an idea, that mortal was Roderick Usher. For me at least, in the circumstances then surrounding me, there arose, out of the pure abstractions which the hypochondriac contrived to throw upon his canvas, an intensity of intolerable awe, no shadow of which felt I ever yet in the contemplation of the certainly glowing yet too concrete reveries of Fuseli.

One of the phantasmagoric conceptions of my friend, partaking not so rigidly of the spirit of abstraction, may be shadowed forth, although feebly, in words. A small picture presented the interior of an immensely long and rectangular vault or tunnel, with low walls, smooth, white, and without interruption or device. Certain accessory points of the design served well to convey the idea that this excavation lay at an exceeding depth below the surface of the earth. No outlet was observed in any portion of its vast extent, and no torch or other artificial source of light was discernible; yet a flood of intense rays rolled throughout, and bathed the whole in a ghastly and inappropriate splendor.

I have just spoken of that morbid condition of the auditory nerve which rendered all music intolerable to the sufferer, with the exception of certain effects of stringed instruments. It was, perhaps, the narrow limits to which he thus confined himself upon the guitar, which gave birth, in great measure, to the fantastic character of his performances. But the fervid *facility* of his *impromptus* could not be so accounted for. They must have been, and were, in the notes, as well as in the words of his wild fantasias (for he not unfrequently accompanied himself with rhymed verbal improvisations), the result of that intense mental collectedness and concentration to which I have previously alluded as observable only in particular moments of the highest artificial excitement. The words of one of these rhapsodies I have easily remembered. I was, perhaps, the more forcibly impressed with it, as he gave it, because, in the under or mystic current of its meaning, I fancied that I perceived, and for the first time, a full consciousness, on the part of Usher, of the tottering of his lofty reason upon her throne. The verses, which were entitled "The Haunted Palace," ran very nearly, if not accurately, thus:

I

In the greenest of our valleys,
By good angels tenanted,
Once a fair and stately palace —
Radiant palace — reared its head.
In the monarch Thought's dominion,
It stood there!
Never seraph spread a pinion
Over fabric half so fair.

II

Banners yellow, glorious, golden,
On its roof did float and flow,
(This — all this — was in the olden
Time long ago)

And every gentle air that dallied,
   In that sweet day,
Along the ramparts plumed and pallid,
   A wingèd odor went away.

III

Wanderers in that happy valley
   Through two luminous windows saw
Spirits moving musically
   To a lute's well-tunèd law,
Round about a throne where, sitting,
   (Porphyrogene!)
In state his glory well befitting,
   The ruler of the realm was seen.

IV

And all with pearl and ruby glowing
   Was the fair palace door,
Through which came flowing, flowing, flowing,
   And sparkling evermore,
A troop of Echoes whose sweet duty
   Was but to sing,
In voices of surpassing beauty,
   The wit and wisdom of their king.

V

But evil things, in robes of sorrow,
   Assailed the monarch's high estate;
(Ah, let us mourn, for never morrow
   Shall dawn upon him, desolate!)
And round about his home the glory
   That blushed and bloomed
Is but a dim-remembered story
   Of the old time entombed.

VI

And travellers now within that valley
   Through the red-litten windows see
Vast forms that move fantastically
   To a discordant melody;
While, like a rapid ghastly river,
   Through the pale door,
A hideous throng rush out forever,
   And laugh — but smile no more.

I well remember that suggestions arising from this ballad led us into a train of thought, wherein there became manifest an opinion of Usher's which I mention not so much on account of its novelty (for other men have thought thus) as on account of the pertinacity with which he maintained it. This opinion, in its general form, was that of the sentience of all vegetable things. But in his disordered fancy the idea had assumed a more daring character, and trespassed, under certain conditions, upon the kingdom of inorganization. I lack words to express the full extent, or the earnest *abandon* of his persuasion. The belief, however, was connected (as I have previously hinted) with the gray stones of the home of his forefathers. The conditions of the sentience had been here, he imagined, fulfilled in the method of collocation of these stones — in the order of their arrangement, as well as in that of the many fungi which overspread them, and of the decayed trees which stood around — above all, in the long undisturbed endurance of this arrangement, and in its reduplication in the still waters of the tarn. Its evidence — the evidence of the sentience — was to be seen, he said (and I here started as he spoke), in the gradual yet certain condensation of an atmosphere of their own about the waters and the walls. The result was discoverable, he added, in that silent, yet importunate and terrible influence which for centuries had molded the destinies of his family, and which made *him* what I now saw him — what he was. Such opinions need no comment, and I will make none.

Our books — the books which, for years, had formed no small portion of the mental existence of the invalid — were, as might be supposed, in strict keeping with this character of phantasm. We pored together over such works as the Ververt and Chartreuse of Gresset; the Belphegor of Machiavelli; the Heaven and Hell of Swedenborg; the Subterranean Voyage of Nicholas Klimm by Holberg; the Chiromancy of Robert Flud, of Jean D'Indaginé, and of De la Chambre; the Journey into the Blue Distance of Tieck; and the City of the Sun of Campanella. One favorite volume was a small octavo edition of the *Directorium Inquisitorium,* by the Dominican Eymeric de Gironne; and there were passages in Pomponius Mela, about the old African Satyrs and Ægipans, over which Usher would sit dreaming for hours. His chief delight, however, was found in the perusal of an exceedingly rare and curious book in quarto Gothic — the manual of a forgotten church — the *Vigiliæ Mortuorum Secundum Chorum Ecclesiæ Maguntinæ.*

I could not help thinking of the wild ritual of this work, and of its probable influence upon the hypochondriac, when one evening, having informed me abruptly that the lady Madeline was no more, he stated his intention of preserving her corpse for a fortnight (previously to its final interment) in one of the numerous vaults within the main walls of the building. The worldly reason, however, assigned for this singular proceeding was one which I did not feel at liberty to dispute. The brother had been led to his resolution (so he told me) by consideration of the unusual character of the malady of the deceased, of certain obtrusive and eager inquiries on the part of her medical men, and of the remote and exposed situation of the burial-ground of the family. I will not deny that when I called to mind the sinister countenance of the person whom I met upon the staircase, on the day of my arrival at the house, I had no desire to oppose what I regarded as at best but a harmless, and by no means an unnatural, precaution.

At the request of Usher, I personally aided him in the arrangements for the temporary entombment. The body having been encoffined, we two alone bore it to its rest. The vault in which we placed it (and which had been so long unopened that our torches, half smothered in its oppressive atmosphere, gave us little opportunity for investigation) was small, damp, and entirely without means of admission for light; lying, at great depth, immediately beneath that portion of the building in which was my own sleeping apartment. It had been used, apparently, in remote feudal times, for the worst purposes of a donjon-keep, and in later days as a place of deposit for powder, or some other highly combustible substance, as a portion of its floor, and the whole interior of a long archway through which we reached it, were carefully sheathed with copper. The door, of massive iron, had been also similarly protected. Its immense weight caused an unusually sharp grating sound, as it moved upon its hinges.

Having deposited our mournful burden upon trestles within this region of horror, we partially turned aside the yet unscrewed lid of the coffin, and looked upon the face of the tenant. A striking similitude between the brother and sister now first arrested my attention; and Usher divining, perhaps, my thoughts, murmured out some few words from which I learned that the deceased and himself had been twins, and that sympathies of a scarcely intelligible nature had always existed between them. Our glances, however, rested not long upon the dead — for we could not regard her unawed. The disease which had thus entombed the lady in the maturity of youth, had left, as usual in all maladies of a strictly cataleptical character, the mockery of a faint blush upon the bosom and the face, and that suspiciously lingering smile upon the lip which is so terrible in death. We replaced and screwed down the lid, and, having secured the door of iron, made our way, with toil, into the scarcely less gloomy apartments of the upper portion of the house.

And now, some days of bitter grief having elapsed, an observable change came over the features of the mental disorder of my friend. His ordinary manner had vanished. His ordinary occupations were neglected or forgotten. He roamed from chamber to chamber with hurried, unequal, and objectless step. The pallor of his countenance had assumed, if possible, a more ghastly hue — but the luminousness of his eye had utterly gone out. The once occasional huskiness of his tone was heard no more; and a tremulous quaver, as if of extreme terror, habitually characterized his utterance. There were times, indeed, when I thought his unceasingly agitated mind was laboring with some oppressive secret, to divulge which he struggled for the necessary courage. At times, again, I was obliged to resolve all into the mere inexplicable vagaries of madness, for I beheld him gazing upon vacancy for long hours, in an attitude of the profoundest attention, as if listening to some imaginary sound. It was no wonder that his condition terrified — that it infected me. I felt creeping upon me, by slow yet certain degrees, the wild influences of his own fantastic yet impressive superstitions.

It was, especially, upon retiring to bed late in the night of the seventh or eighth day after the placing of the lady Madeline within the donjon, that I experienced the full power of such feelings. Sleep came not near my couch, while the hours waned and waned away. I struggled to reason off the nervousness which had dominion over me. I endeavored to believe that much, if not all, of what I felt was due to the bewildering influence of the gloomy furniture of the room — of the dark and tattered draperies which, tortured into motion by the breath of a rising tempest, swayed fitfully to and fro upon the walls, and rustled

uneasily about the decorations of the bed. But my efforts were
fruitless. An irrepressible tremor gradually pervaded my frame;
and at length there sat upon my very heart an incubus of utterly
causeless alarm. Shaking this off with a gasp and a struggle, I
uplifted myself upon the pillows, and, peering earnestly within
the intense darkness of the chamber, hearkened — I know not
why, except that an instinctive spirit prompted me — to certain
low and indefinite sounds which came, through the pauses of the
storm, at long intervals, I knew not whence. Overpowered by
an intense sentiment of horror, unaccountable yet unendurable, I
threw on my clothes with haste (for I felt that I should sleep no
more during the night) and endeavored to arouse myself from
the pitiable condition into which I had fallen, by pacing rapidly
to and fro through the apartment.

I had taken but few turns in this manner, when a light step
on an adjoining staircase arrested my attention. I presently recognized it as that of Usher. In an instant afterward he rapped with
a gentle touch at my door, and entered, bearing a lamp. His
countenance was, as usual, cadaverously wan — but, moreover,
there was a species of mad hilarity in his eyes — an evidently
restrained *hysteria* in his whole demeanor. His air appalled me
— but anything was preferable to the solitude which I had so
long endured, and I even welcomed his presence as a relief.

"And you have not seen it?" he said abruptly, after having
stared about him for some moments in silence — "you have not
then seen it? — but, stay! you shall." Thus speaking, and having
carefully shaded his lamp, he hurried to one of the casements,
and threw it freely open to the storm.

The impetuous fury of the entering gust nearly lifted us from
our feet. It was, indeed, a tempestuous yet sternly beautiful
night, and one wildly singular in its terror and its beauty. A
whirlwind had apparently collected its force in our vicinity; for

there were frequent and violent alterations in the direction of the
wind; and the exceeding density of the clouds (which hung so
low as to press upon the turrets of the house) did not prevent our
perceiving the lifelike velocity with which they flew careering
from all points against each other, without passing away into the
distance. I say that even their exceeding density did not prevent
our perceiving this; yet we had no glimpse of the moon or stars,

nor was there any flashing forth of the lightning. But the under surfaces of the huge masses of agitated vapor, as well as all terrestrial objects immediately around us, were glowing in the unnatural light of a faintly luminous and distinctly visible gaseous exhalation which hung about and enshrouded the mansion.

"You must not — you shall not behold this!" said I, shudderingly, to Usher, as I led him with a gentle violence from the window to a seat. "These appearances, which bewilder you, are merely electrical phenomena not uncommon — or it may be that they have their ghastly origin in the rank miasma of the tarn. Let us close this casement; the air is chilling and dangerous to your frame. Here is one of your favorite romances. I will read, and you shall listen; — and so we will pass away this terrible night together."

The antique volume which I had taken up was the *Mad Trist* of Sir Launcelot Canning; but I had called it a favorite of Usher's more in sad jest than in earnest; for, in truth, there is little in its uncouth and unimaginative prolixity which could have had interest for the lofty and spiritual ideality of my friend. It was, however, the only book immediately at hand; and I indulged a vague hope that the excitement which now agitated the hypochondriac might find relief (for the history of mental disorder is full of similar anomalies) even in the extremeness of the folly which I should read. Could I have judged, indeed, by the wild overstrained air of vivacity with which he hearkened, or apparently hearkened, to the words of the tale, I might well have congratulated myself upon the success of my design.

I had arrived at that well-known portion of the story where Ethelred, the hero of the Trist, having sought in vain for peaceable admission into the dwelling of the hermit, proceeds to make good an entrance by force. Here, it will be remembered, the words of the narrative run thus:

"And Ethelred, who was by nature of a doughty heart, and who was now mighty withal, on account of the powerfulness of the wine which he had drunken, waited no longer to hold parley with the hermit, who, in sooth, was of an obstinate and maliceful turn, but, feeling the rain upon his shoulders, and fearing the rising of the tempest, uplifted his mace outright, and, with blows, made quickly room in the plankings of the door for his gauntleted hand; and now pulling there-

with sturdily, he so cracked, and ripped, and tore all asunder, that the
noise of the dry and hollow-sounding wood alarummed and reverber-
ated throughout the forest."

At the termination of this sentence I started, and for a moment
paused; for it appeared to me (although I at once concluded that
my excited fancy had deceived me) — it appeared to me that
from some very remote portion of the mansion there came, in-
distinctly, to my ears, what might have been, in its exact similarity of character, the echo (but a stifled and dull one certainly)
of the very cracking and ripping sound which Sir Launcelot had
so particularly described. It was, beyond doubt, the coincidence
alone which had arrested my attention; for, amid the rattling of
the sashes of the casements, and the ordinary commingled noises
of the still increasing storm, the sound, in itself, had nothing,
surely, which should have interested or disturbed me. I continued the story:

"But the good champion Ethelred, now entering within the door,
was sore enraged and amazed to perceive no signal of the maliceful
hermit; but, in the stead thereof, a dragon of a scaly and prodigious
demeanor, and of a fiery tongue, which sate in guard before a palace
of gold, with a floor of silver; and upon the wall there hung a shield
of shining brass with this legend enwritten —
       Who entereth herein, a conqueror hath bin;
       Who slayeth the dragon, the shield he shall win.
And Ethelred uplifted his mace, and struck upon the head of the
dragon, which fell before him, and gave up his pesty breath, with a
shriek so horrid and harsh, and withal so piercing, that Ethelred had
fain to close his ears with his hands against the dreadful noise of it,
the like whereof was never before heard."

Here again I paused abruptly, and now with a feeling of wild
amazement; for there could be no doubt whatever that, in this
instance, I did actually hear (although from what direction it
proceeded I found it impossible to say) a low and apparently
distant, but harsh, protracted, and most unusual screaming or
grating sound — the exact counterpart of what my fancy had
already conjured up for the dragon's unnatural shriek as described
by the romancer.
Oppressed, as I certainly was, upon the occurrence of this
second and most extraordinary coincidence, by a thousand con-

flicting sensations, in which wonder and extreme terror were predominant, I still retained sufficient presence of mind to avoid exciting, by any observation, the sensitive nervousness of my companion. I was by no means certain that he had noticed the sounds in question; although, assuredly, a strange alteration had during the last few minutes taken place in his demeanor. From a position fronting my own, he had gradually brought round his chair, so as to sit with his face to the door of the chamber; and thus I could but partially perceive his features, although I saw that his lips trembled as if he were murmuring inaudibly. His head had dropped upon his breast — yet I knew that he was not asleep, from the wide and rigid opening of the eye as I caught a glance of it in profile. The motion of his body, too, was at variance with this idea — for he rocked from side to side with a gentle yet constant and uniform sway. Having rapidly taken notice of all this, I resumed the narrative of Sir Launcelot, which thus proceeded:

"And now, the champion having escaped from the terrible fury of the dragon, bethinking himself of the brazen shield, and of the breaking up of the enchantment which was upon it, removed the carcass from out of the way before him, and approached valorously over the silver pavement of the castle to where the shield was upon the wall; which in sooth tarried not for his full coming, but fell down at his feet upon the silver floor, with a mighty great and terrible ringing sound."

No sooner had these syllables passed my lips, than — as if a shield of brass had indeed, at the moment, fallen heavily upon a floor of silver — I became aware of a distinct, hollow, metallic and clangorous, yet apparently muffled reverberation. Completely unnerved, I leaped to my feet; but the measured rocking movement of Usher was undisturbed. I rushed to the chair in which he sat. His eyes were bent fixedly before him, and throughout his whole countenance there reigned a stony rigidity. But, as I placed my hand upon his shoulder, there came a strong shudder over his whole person; a sickly smile quivered about his lips; and I saw that he spoke in a low, hurried, and gibbering murmur, as if unconscious of my presence. Bending closely over him, I at length drank in the hideous import of his words.

"Not hear it? — yes, I hear it, and *have* heard it. Long — long — long — many minutes, many hours, many days, have I heard it

— yet I dared not — oh, pity me, miserable wretch that I am! — I dared not — *I dared not speak!* *We have put her living in the tomb!* Said I not that my senses were acute? I *now* tell you that I heard her first feeble movements in the hollow coffin. I heard them — many, many days ago — yet I dared not — *I dared not speak!* And now — tonight — Ethelred — ha! ha! — the breaking of the hermit's door, and the death-cry of the dragon, and the clangor of the shield! — say, rather, the rending of her coffin, and the grating of the iron hinges of her prison, and her struggles within the coppered archway of the vault! Oh, whither shall I fly? Will she not be here anon? Is she not hurrying to upbraid me for my haste? Have I not heard her footsteps on the stair? Do I not distinguish that heavy and horrible beating of her heart? Madman!" — here he sprang furiously to his feet, and shrieked out his syllables, as if in the effort he were giving up his soul — *"Madman! I tell you that she now stands without the door!"*

As if in the superhuman energy of his utterance there had been found the potency of a spell, the huge antique panels to which the speaker pointed drew slowly back, upon the instant, their ponderous and ebony jaws. It was the work of the rushing gust — but then without the doors there *did* stand the lofty and enshrouded figure of the lady Madeline of Usher. There was blood upon her white robes, and the evidence of some bitter struggle upon every portion of her emaciated frame. For a moment she remained trembling and reeling to and fro upon the threshold — then, with a low moaning cry, fell heavily inward upon the person of her brother, and, in her violent and now final death-agonies, bore him to the floor a corpse, and a victim to the terrors he had anticipated.

From that chamber, and from that mansion, I fled aghast. The storm was still abroad in all its wrath as I found myself crossing the old causeway. Suddenly there shot along the path a wild light, and I turned to see whence a gleam so unusual could have issued; for the vast house and its shadows were alone behind me. The radiance was that of the full, setting, and blood-red moon, which now shone vividly through that once barely discernible fissure, of which I have before spoken as extending from the roof of the building, in a zigzag direction, to the base. While I gazed, this fissure rapidly widened — there came a fierce breath of the whirlwind — the entire orb of the satellite burst at once upon my sight — my brain reeled as I saw the mighty walls rushing asunder — there was a long tumultuous shouting sound like the voice of a thousand waters — and the deep and dank tarn at my feet closed sullenly and silently over the fragments of the House of Usher.

Edgar Allan Poe (1809-1849)   Edgar Allan Poe was born in Boston; both his English mother and his Maryland father were traveling actors. Orphaned before the age of three, he was raised by foster parents in Richmond, Virginia, and attended the University of Virginia, leaving without a degree in 1826. His first volume of poems was published in 1827, his first stories a few years later. From this time until his unexplained death in Baltimore in 1849, his stature and reputation increased steadily; as editor, critic, poet, and fiction writer, he is perhaps the most influential figure in this first great period of American literature.

Poe can justly be called the "father of the short story." His contributions to the genre are many and varied. He was the first American writer to define what he thought a short story should be, and he formulated certain patterns and rules governing it. His conception of the short story as a tightly organized piece of short fiction, with a beginning, middle, and end, designed to achieve one overwhelming impression — or "totality of effect" — was essentially new. A master of technique, he popularized and at his best attained real literary distinction in creating tales in which the basic elements of character, setting, atmosphere, idea or theme, and plot are closely or inseparably related. In a story like "The Fall of the House of Usher" he drew on the elements of shock, terror, and horror that had been made familiar to the reading public through the so-called "Gothic" romances which flourished in the late eighteenth and early nineteenth centuries, but he transformed them into something far removed from the Gothic achievements of his predecessors.

Poe insisted again and again — and his own stories frequently illustrated his theories — that the short story was not a vulgar upstart but a literary type which deserved respect both as art and as entertainment. He was a hard-working and talented, if uneven craftsman, and the popularity of his short stories in periodicals like *Graham's Magazine* helped create an ever-increasing and enthusiastic audience for this "new" American literary form.

Among the good one-volume collections of Poe's stories are: *Selected Writings of Edgar Allan Poe* (ed. Edward H. Davidson, Houghton

Mifflin Riverside Edition); *The Selected Poetry and Prose of Edgar Allan Poe* (ed. T. O. Mabbott, Modern Library College Edition); *The Portable Poe* (ed. Philip Van Doren Stern, Viking).

Questions   1. The opening paragraph of this story has been praised as a very effective prelude to the sombre events which follow. Do you think this praise is justfied? In what ways, if any, does it remind you of the opening scenes of classic "horror" moving pictures you may have seen?   2. In a recent adaptation of this story for television, the destruction of the Usher mansion was scientifically explained, in an epilogue, as the result of a tornado. In what ways, if any, does this strengthen or weaken the story? In what ways does it violate what might be called Poe's basic conception of the story? 3. Would you call this essentially a story of character, of incident, of mood? Is there in it any clearly defined theme? If so, what is the theme?   4. For what reasons does Poe include in this story the poem, "The Haunted Palace"? What, in your opinion, is the significance of the story, read by the narrator of the "good champion Ethelred"? 5. "The Fall of the House of Usher" is an effective example of the story narrated in the first person by an observer-participant, "I." Could it conceivably have been written more effectively from some other point of view?

EDGAR ALLAN POE

The
Black Cat

FOR THE MOST WILD, yet most homely narrative which I am about
to pen, I neither expect nor solicit belief. Mad indeed would I
be to expect it, in a case where my very senses reject their own
evidence. Yet, mad am I not — and very surely do I not dream.
But to-morrow I die, and to-day I would unburthen my soul. My
immediate purpose is to place before the world, plainly, suc-
cinctly, and without comment, a series of mere household events.
In their consequences, these events have terrified — have tortured
— have destroyed me. Yet I will not attempt to expound them.
To me, they have presented little but Horror — to many they will
seem less terrible than *baroques*. Hereafter, perhaps, some intellect may be found which will reduce my phantasm to the
common-place — some intellect more calm, more logical, and far
less excitable than my own, which will perceive, in the circumstances I detail with awe, nothing more than an ordinary succes-
sion of very natural causes and effects.

From my infancy I was noted for the docility and humanity of
my disposition. My tenderness of heart was even so conspicuous
as to make me the jest of my companions. I was especially fond
of animals, and was indulged by my parents with a great variety
of pets. With these I spent most of my time, and never was so
happy as when feeding and caressing them. This peculiarity of
character grew with my growth, and, in my manhood, I derived

from it one of my principal sources of pleasure. To those who have cherished an affection for a faithful and sagacious dog, I need hardly be at the trouble of explaining the nature or the intensity of the gratification thus derivable. There is something in the unselfish and self-sacrificing love of a brute, which goes directly to the heart of him who has had frequent occasion to test the paltry friendship and gossamer fidelity of mere *Man*.

I married early, and was happy to find in my wife a disposition not uncongenial with my own. Observing my partiality for domestic pets, she lost no opportunity of procuring those of the most agreeable kind. We had birds, goldfish, a fine dog, rabbits, a small monkey, and *a cat.*

This latter was a remarkably large and beautiful animal, entirely black, and sagacious to an astonishing degree. In speaking of his intelligence, my wife, who at heart was not a little tinctured with superstition, made frequent allusion to the ancient popular notion, which regarded all black cats as witches in disguise. Not that she was ever *serious* upon this point — and I mention the matter at all for no better reason than that it happens, just now, to be remembered.

Pluto — this was the cat's name — was my favorite pet and playmate. I alone fed him, and he attended me wherever I went about the house. It was even with difficulty that I could prevent him from following me through the streets.

Our friendship lasted, in this manner, for several years, during which my general temperament and character — through the instrumentality of the Fiend Intemperance — had (I blush to confess it) experienced a radical alteration for the worse. I grew, day by day, more moody, more irritable, more regardless of the feelings of others. I suffered myself to use intemperate language to my wife. At length, I even offered her personal violence. My pets, of course, were made to feel the change in my disposition. I not only neglected, but ill-used them. For Pluto, however, I still retained sufficient regard to restrain me from maltreating him, as I made no scruple of maltreating the rabbits, the monkey, or even the dog, when by accident, or through affection, they came in my way. But my disease grew upon me — for what disease is like Alcohol! — and at length even Pluto, who was now becoming old, and consequently somewhat peevish — even Pluto began to experience the effects of my ill temper.

One night, returning home, much intoxicated, from one of my haunts about town, I fancied that the cat avoided my presence. I seized him; when, in his fright at my violence, he inflicted a slight wound upon my hand with his teeth. The fury of a demon instantly possessed me. I knew myself no longer. My original soul seemed, at once, to take its flight from my body; and a more than fiendish malevolence, gin-nurtured, thrilled every fibre of my frame. I took from my waistcoat-pocket a penknife, opened it, grasped the poor beast by the throat, and deliberately cut one of its eyes from the socket! I blush, I burn, I shudder, while I pen the damnable atrocity.

When reason returned with the morning — when I had slept off the fumes of the night's debauch — I experienced a sentiment half of horror, half of remorse, for the crime of which I had been guilty; but it was, at least, a feeble and equivocal feeling, and the soul remained untouched. I again plunged into excess, and soon drowned in wine all memory of the deed.

In the meantime the cat slowly recovered. The socket of the lost eye presented, it is true, a frightful appearance, but he no longer appeared to suffer any pain. He went about the house as usual, but, as might be expected, fled in extreme terror at my approach. I had so much of my old heart left, as to be at first grieved by this evident dislike on the part of a creature which had once so loved me. But this feeling soon gave place to irritation. And then came, as if to my final and irrevocable overthrow, the spirit of PERVERSENESS. Of this spirit philosophy takes no account. Yet I am not more sure that my soul lives, than I am that perverseness is one of the primitive impulses of the human heart — one of the indivisible primary faculties, or sentiments, which give direction to the character of Man. Who has not, a hundred times, found himself committing a vile or a silly action, for no other reason than because he knows he should *not*? Have we not a perpetual inclination, in the teeth of our best judgment, to violate that which is *Law*, merely because we understand it to be such? This spirit of perverseness, I say, came to my final overthrow. It was this unfathomable longing of the soul *to vex itself* — to offer violence to its own nature — to do wrong for the wrong's sake only — that urged me to continue and finally to consummate the injury I had inflicted upon the unoffending brute. One morning, in cool blood, I slipped a noose about its neck and hung it to the limb of a tree; — hung it with the tears streaming from my eyes, and with the bitterest remorse at my heart; — hung it *because* I knew that it had loved me, and *because* I felt it had given me no reason of offence; — hung it *because* I knew that in so doing I was committing a sin — a deadly sin that would so jeopardize my immortal soul as to place it — if such a thing were possible — even beyond the reach of the infinite mercy of the Most Merciful and Most Terrible God.

On the night of the day on which this cruel deed was done, I was aroused from sleep by the cry of fire. The curtains of my bed were in flames. The whole house was blazing. It was with great difficulty that my wife, a servant, and myself, made our escape from the conflagration. The destruction was complete. My entire worldly wealth was swallowed up, and I resigned myself thenceforward to despair.

I am above the weakness of seeking to establish a sequence of cause and effect, between the disaster and the atrocity. But I am detailing a chain of facts — and wish not to leave even a possible link imperfect. On the day succeeding the fire, I visited the ruins. The walls, with one exception, had fallen in. This exception was found in a compartment wall, not very thick, which stood about the middle of the house, and against which had rested the head of my bed. The plastering had here, in great measure, resisted the action of the fire — a fact which I attributed to its having been recently spread. About this wall a dense crowd were collected, and many persons seemed to be examining a particular portion of it with very minute and eager attention. The words "strange!" "singular!" and other similar expressions, excited my curiosity. I approached and saw, as if graven in *bas relief* upon the white surface, the figure of a gigantic *cat*. The impression was given with an accuracy truly marvellous. There was a rope about the animal's neck.

When I first beheld this apparition — for I could scarcely regard it as less — my wonder and my terror were extreme. But at length reflection came to my aid. The cat, I remembered, had been hung in a garden adjacent to the house. Upon the alarm of fire, this garden had been immediately filled by the crowd — by some one of whom the animal must have been cut from the tree and thrown, through an open window, into my chamber. This had probably been done with the view of arousing me from sleep. The falling of other walls had compressed the victim of my cruelty into the substance of the freshly-spread plaster; the lime of which, with the flames, and the *ammonia* from the carcass, had then accomplished the portraiture as I saw it.

Although I thus readily accounted to my reason, if not altogether to my conscience, for the startling fact just detailed, it did not the less fail to make a deep impression upon my fancy. For months I could not rid myself of the phantasm of the cat; and, during this period, there came back into my spirit a half-sentiment that seemed, but was not, remorse. I went so far as to regret the loss of the animal, and to look about me, among the vile haunts which I now habitually frequented, for another pet of the same species, and of somewhat similar appearance, with which to supply its place.

One night as I sat, half stupefied, in a den of more than infamy, my attention was suddenly drawn to some black object, reposing upon the head of one of the immense hogsheads of Gin, or of Rum, which constituted the chief furniture of the apartment. I had been looking steadily at the top of this hogshead for some minutes, and what now caused me surprise was the fact that I had not sooner perceived the object thereupon. I approached it, and touched it with my hand. It was a black cat — a very large one — fully as large as Pluto, and closely resembling him in every respect but one. Pluto had not a white hair upon any portion of his body; but this cat had a large, although indefinite splotch of white, covering nearly the whole region of the breast.

Upon my touching him, he immediately arose, purred loudly, rubbed against my hand, and appeared delighted with my notice. This, then, was the very creature of which I was in search. I at once offered to purchase it of the landlord; but this person made no claim to it — knew nothing of it — had never seen it before.

I continued my caresses, and, when I prepared to go home, the animal evinced a disposition to accompany me. I permitted it to do so; occasionally stooping and patting it as I proceeded. When it reached the house it domesticated itself at once, and became immediately a great favorite with my wife.

For my own part, I soon found a dislike to it arising within me. This was just the reverse of what I had anticipated; but I know not how or why it was — its evident fondness for myself rather disgusted and annoyed. By slow degrees, these feelings of disgust and annoyance rose into the bitterness of hatred. I avoided the creature; a certain sense of shame, and the remembrance of my former deed of cruelty, preventing me from physically abusing it. I did not, for some weeks, strike, or otherwise violently ill use it; but gradually — very gradually — I came to look upon it with unutterable loathing, and to flee silently from its odious presence, as from the breath of a pestilence.

What added, no doubt, to my hatred of the beast, was the discovery, on the morning after I brought it home, that, like Pluto, it also had been deprived of one of its eyes. This circumstance, however, only endeared it to my wife, who, as I have already said, possessed, in a high degree, that humanity of feeling which had once been my distinguishing trait, and the source of many of my simplest and purest pleasures.

With my aversion to this cat, however, its partiality for myself seemed to increase. It followed my footsteps with a pertinacity which it would be difficult to make the reader comprehend. Whenever I sat, it would crouch beneath my chair, or spring upon my knees, covering me with its loathsome caresses. If I arose to walk it would get between my feet and thus nearly throw me down, or, fastening its long and sharp claws in my dress, clamber, in this manner, to my breast. At such times, although I longed to destroy it with a blow, I was yet withheld from so doing, partly by a memory of my former crime, but chiefly — let me confess it at once — by absolute *dread* of the beast.

This dread was not exactly a dread of physical evil — and yet I should be at a loss how otherwise to define it. I am almost ashamed to own — yes, even in this felon's cell, I am almost ashamed to own — that the terror and horror with which the animal inspired me, had been heightened by one of the merest chimæras it would be possible to conceive. My wife had called my attention, more than once, to the character of the mark of white hair, of which I have spoken, and which constituted the sole visible difference between the strange beast and the one I had destroyed. The reader will remember that this mark, although large, had been originally very indefinite; but, by slow degrees — degrees nearly imperceptible, and which for a long time my Reason struggled to reject as fanciful — it had, at length, assumed a rigorous distinctness of outline. It was now the representation of an object that I shudder to name — and for this, above all, I loathed, and dreaded, and would have rid myself of the monster *had I dared* — it was now, I say, the image of a hideous — of a ghastly thing — of the GALLOWS! — oh, mournful and terrible engine of Horror and of Crime — of Agony and of Death!

And now was I indeed wretched beyond the wretchedness of mere Humanity. And a *brute beast* — whose fellow I had contemptuously destroyed — *a brute beast* to work out for *me* — for me a man, fashioned in the image of the High God — so much of insufferable wo! Alas! neither by day nor by night knew I the blessing of Rest any more! During the former the creature left me no moment alone; and, in the latter, I started, hourly, from dreams of unutterable fear, to find the hot breath of *the thing* upon my face, and its vast weight — an incarnate Night-Mare that I had no power to shake off — incumbent eternally upon my *heart!*

Beneath the pressure of torments such as these, the feeble remnant of the good within me succumbed. Evil thoughts became my sole intimates — the darkest and most evil of thoughts. The moodiness of my usual temper increased to hatred of all things and of all mankind; while, from the sudden, frequent, and ungovernable outbursts of a fury to which I now blindly abandoned myself, my uncomplaining wife, alas! was the most usual and the most patient of sufferers.

One day she accompanied me, upon some household errand, into the cellar of the old building which our poverty compelled us to inhabit. The cat followed me down the steep stairs, and, nearly throwing me headlong, exasperated me to madness. Uplifting an axe, and forgetting, in my wrath, the childish dread which had hitherto stayed my hand, I aimed a blow at the animal which, of course, would have proved instantly fatal had it descended as I wished. But this blow was arrested by the hand of my wife. Goaded, by the interference, into a rage more than demoniacal, I withdrew my arm from her grasp and buried the axe in her brain. She fell dead upon the spot, without a groan.

This hideous murder accomplished, I set myself forthwith, and with entire deliberation, to the task of concealing the body. I knew that I could not remove it from the house, either by day or by night, without the risk of being observed by the neighbors.

Many projects entered my mind. At one period I thought of cutting the corpse into minute fragments, and destroying them by fire. At another, I resolved to dig a grave for it in the floor of the cellar. Again, I deliberated about casting it in the well in the yard — about packing it in a box, as if merchandize, with the usual arrangements, and so getting a porter to take it from the house. Finally I hit upon what I considered a far better expedient than either of these. I determined to wall it up in the cellar — as the monks of the middle ages are recorded to have walled up their victims.

For a purpose such as this the cellar was well adapted. Its walls were loosely constructed, and had lately been plastered throughout with a rough plaster, which the dampness of the atmosphere had prevented from hardening. Moreover, in one of the walls was a projection, caused by a false chimney, or fireplace, that had been filled up, and made to resemble the rest of the cellar. I made no doubt that I could readily displace the bricks at this point, insert the corpse, and wall the whole up as before, so that no eye could detect anything suspicious.

And in this calculation I was not deceived. By means of a crow-bar I easily dislodged the bricks, and, having carefully deposited the body against the inner wall, I propped it in that position, while, with little trouble, I re-laid the whole structure as it originally stood. Having procured mortar, sand, and hair, with every possible precaution, I prepared a plaster which could not be distinguished from the old, and with this I very carefully went over the new brick-work. When I had finished, I felt satisfied that all was right. The wall did not present the slightest appearance of having been disturbed. The rubbish on the floor was picked up with the minutest care. I looked around triumphantly, and said to myself — "Here at least, then, my labor has not been in vain."

My next step was to look for the beast which had been the cause of so much wretchedness; for I had, at length, firmly resolved to put it to death. Had I been able to meet with it, at the moment, there could have been no doubt of its fate, but it appeared that the crafty animal had been alarmed at the violence of my previous anger, and forebore to present itself in my present mood. It is impossible to describe, or to imagine, the deep, the blissful sense of relief which the absence of the detested creature

occasioned in my bosom. It did not make its appearance during
the night — and thus for one night at least, since its introduction
into the house, I soundly and tranquilly slept; aye, *slept* even with
the burden of murder upon my soul!

The second and the third day passed, and still my tormentor
came not. Once again I breathed as a freeman. The monster, in
terror, had fled the premises forever! I should behold it no more!
My happiness was supreme! The guilt of my dark deed disturbed
me but little. Some few inquiries had been made, but these had
been readily answered. Even a search had been instituted — but
of course nothing was to be discovered. I looked upon my future
felicity as secured.

Upon the fourth day of the assassination, a party of police
came, very unexpectedly, into the house, and proceeded again to
make rigorous investigation of the premises. Secure, however, in
the inscrutability of my place of concealment, I felt no embarrassment whatever. The officers bade me accompany them in their
search. They left no nook or corner unexplored. At length, for
the third or fourth time, they descended into the cellar. I quivered not in a muscle. My heart beat calmly as that of one who
slumbers in innocence. I walked the cellar from end to end. I
folded my arms upon my bosom, and roamed easily to and fro.
The police were thoroughly satisfied and prepared to depart.
The glee at my heart was too strong to be restrained. I burned
to say if but one word, by way of triumph, and to render doubly
sure their assurance of my guiltlessness.

"Gentlemen," I said at last, as the party ascended the steps, "I
delight to have allayed your suspicions. I wish you all health,
and a little more courtesy. By the bye, gentlemen, this — this is a
very well-constructed house." [In the rabid desire to say something easily, I scarcely knew what I uttered at all.] — "I may say
an *excellently* well-constructed house. These walls — are you
going, gentlemen? — these walls are solidly put together;" and
here, through the mere phrenzy of bravado, I rapped heavily,
with a cane which I held in my hand, upon that very portion of
the brick-work behind which stood the corpse of the wife of my
bosom.

But may God shield and deliver me from the fangs of the
Arch-Fiend! No sooner had the reverberation of my blows sunk
into silence, than I was answered by a voice from within the

tomb! — by a cry, at first muffled and broken, like the sobbing
of a child, and then quickly swelling into one long, loud, and
continuous scream, utterly anomalous and inhuman — a howl! —
a wailing shriek, half of horror and half of triumph, such as
might have arisen only out of hell, conjointly from the throats
of the damned in their agony and of the demons that exult in
the damnation.

Of my own thoughts it is folly to speak. Swooning, I staggered
to the opposite wall. For one instant the party upon the stairs
remained motionless, through extremity of terror and of awe. In
the next, a dozen stout arms were toiling at the wall. It fell
bodily. The corpse, already greatly decayed and clotted with
gore, stood erect before the eyes of the spectators. Upon its
head, with red extended mouth and solitary eye of fire, sat the
hideous beast whose craft had seduced me into murder, and
whose informing voice had consigned me to the hangman. I had
walled the monster up within the tomb!

Questions   1. In what ways does the "I" of this story resemble
the narrator of "The Fall of the House of Usher"? Is he a sympathetic
character? Is he convincing? Do you think he, or Poe, is joking or
being ironic when he states, early in the story, that "My tenderness of
heart was even so conspicuous as to make me the jest of my companions"? It has often been said that weakness in characterization is
Poe's most conspicuous limitation as a fiction writer; do you feel that
this statement is relevant in connection with "The Black Cat"? With
"The Fall of the House of Usher"?   2. Are the incidents in this story
a logical outgrowth of character and setting? Are you convinced or
emotionally moved by the narrator's initial act of violence, the cutting
out of the cat's eye? Are the events which follow a convincing outgrowth of this action? What do you think of the ending?   3. Which
do you consider the greater work of art, "The Black Cat" or "The Fall
of the House of Usher"?   4. Henry James once commented that
"the figures in any picture, the agents in any drama, are interesting
only in proportion as they feel their respective situations. . . . Their
being finely aware — as Hamlet and Lear, say, are finely aware —
makes absolutely the intensity of their adventure, gives the maximum
of sense to what befalls them." Does this comment have any influence
on your final evaluation of this story; does it, perhaps, lead you to
conclude that "The Black Cat" is not a great story but is, rather, an
effective but melodramatic "shocker"?

NATHANIEL HAWTHORNE

Young Goodman Brown

YOUNG GOODMAN BROWN came forth at sunset into the street at Salem village; but put his head back, after crossing the threshold, to exchange a parting kiss with his young wife. And Faith, as the wife was aptly named, thrust her own pretty head into the street, letting the wind play with the pink ribbons of her cap while she called to Goodman Brown.

"Dearest heart," whispered she, softly and rather sadly, when her lips were close to his ear, "prithee put off your journey until sunrise and sleep in your own bed to-night. A lone woman is troubled with such dreams and such thoughts that she's afeard of herself sometimes. Pray tarry with me this night, dear husband, of all nights in the year."

"My love and my Faith," replied young Goodman Brown, "of all nights in the year, this one night must I tarry away from thee. My journey, as thou callest it, forth and back again, must needs be done 'twixt now and sunrise. What, my sweet, pretty wife, dost thou doubt me already, and we but three months married?"

"Then God bless you!" said Faith, with the pink ribbons; "and may you find all well when you come back."

"Amen!" cried Goodman Brown. "Say thy prayers, dear Faith, and go to bed at dusk, and no harm will come to thee."

So they parted; and the young man pursued his way until, being about to turn the corner by the meeting-house, he looked

33

back and saw the head of Faith still peeping after him with a melancholy air, in spite of her pink ribbons.

"Poor little Faith!" thought he, for his heart smote him. "What a wretch am I to leave her on such an errand! She talks of dreams, too. Methought as she spoke there was trouble in her face, as if a dream had warned her what work is to be done tonight. But no, no; 'twould kill her to think it. Well, she's a blessed angel on earth; and after this one night I'll cling to her skirts and follow her to heaven."

With this excellent resolve for the future, Goodman Brown felt himself justified in making more haste on his present evil purpose. He had taken a dreary road, darkened by all the gloomiest trees of the forest, which barely stood aside to let the narrow path creep through, and closed immediately behind. It was all as lonely as could be; and there is this peculiarity in such a solitude, that the traveller knows not who may be concealed by the innumerable trunks and the thick boughs overhead; so that with lonely footsteps he may yet be passing through an unseen multitude.

"There may be a devilish Indian behind every tree," said Goodman Brown to himself; and he glanced fearfully behind him as he added, "What if the devil himself should be at my very elbow!"

His head being turned back, he passed a crook of the road, and, looking forward again, beheld the figure of a man, in grave and decent attire, seated at the foot of an old tree. He arose at Goodman Brown's approach and walked onward side by side with him.

"You are late, Goodman Brown," said he. "The clock of the Old South was striking as I came through Boston, and that is full fifteen minutes agone."

"Faith kept me back awhile," replied the young man, with a tremor in his voice, caused by the sudden appearance of his companion, though not wholly unexpected.

It was now deep dusk in the forest, and deepest in that part of it where these two were journeying. As nearly as could be discerned, the second traveller was about fifty years old, apparently in the same rank of life as Goodman Brown, and bearing a considerable resemblance to him, though perhaps more in expression than features. Still they might have been taken for father and son. And yet, though the elder person was as simply clad as the younger, and as simple in manner too, he had an indescribable air of one who knew the world, and who would not have felt abashed at the governor's dinner table or in King William's court, were it possible that his affairs should call him thither. But the only thing about him that could be fixed upon as remarkable was his staff, which bore the likeness of a great black snake, so curiously wrought that it might almost be seen to twist and wriggle itself like a living serpent. This, of course, must have been an ocular deception, assisted by the uncertain light.

"Come, Goodman Brown," cried his fellow-traveler, "this is a dull pace for the beginning of a journey. Take my staff, if you are so soon weary."

"Friend," said the other, exchanging his slow pace for a full stop, "having kept covenant by meeting thee here, it is my purpose now to return whence I came. I have scruples touching the matter thou wot'st of."

"Sayest thou so?" replied he of the serpent, smiling apart. "Let us walk on, nevertheless, reasoning as we go; and if I convince thee not thou shalt turn back. We are but a little way in the forest yet."

"Too far! too far!" exclaimed the goodman, unconsciously resuming his walk. "My father never went into the woods on such an errand, nor his father before him. We have been a race of honest men and good Christians since the days of the martyrs; and shall I be the first of the name of Brown that ever took this path and kept — "

"Such company, thou wouldst say," observed the elder person, interpreting his pause. "Well said, Goodman Brown! I have been as well acquainted with your family as with ever a one among the Puritans; and that's no trifle to say. I helped your grandfather, the constable, when he lashed the Quaker women so smartly through the streets of Salem; and it was I that brought your father a pitch-pine knot, kindled at my own hearth, to set fire to an Indian village, in King Philip's war. They were my good friends, both; and many a pleasant walk have we had along this path, and returned merrily after midnight. I would fain be friends with you for their sake."

"If it be as thou sayest," replied Goodman Brown, "I marvel they never spoke of these matters; or, verily, I marvel not, seeing that the least rumor of the sort would have driven them from New England. We are a people of prayer, and good works to boot, and abide no such wickedness."

"Wickedness or not," said the traveller with the twisted staff, "I have a very general acquaintance here in New England. The deacons of many a church have drunk the communion wine with me; the selectmen of divers towns make me their chairman; and a majority of the Great and General Court are firm supporters of my interest. The governor and I, too — But these are state secrets."

"Can this be so?" cried Goodman Brown, with a stare of amazement at his undisturbed companion. "Howbeit, I have nothing to do with the governor and his council; they have their own ways, and are no rule for a simple husbandman like me. But, were I to go on with thee, how should I meet the eye of that good old man, our minister, at Salem village? Oh, his voice would make me tremble both Sabbath day and lecture day."

Thus far the elder traveller had listened with due gravity; but now burst into a fit of irrepressible mirth, shaking himself so violently that his snake-like staff actually seemed to wriggle in sympathy.

"Ha! ha! ha!" shouted he again and again; then composing himself, "Well, go on, Goodman Brown, go on; but, prithee, don't kill me with laughing."

"Well, then, to end the matter at once," said Goodman Brown, considerably nettled, "there is my wife, Faith. It would break her dear little heart; and I'd rather break my own."

"Nay, if that be the case," answered the other, "e'en go thy ways, Goodman Brown. I would not for twenty old women like the one hobbling before us that Faith should come to any harm."

As he spoke he pointed his staff at a female figure on the path, in whom Goodman Brown recognized a very pious and exemplary dame, who had taught him his catechism in youth, and was still his moral and spiritual adviser, jointly with the minister and Deacon Gookin.

"A marvel, truly, that Goody Cloyse should be so far in the wilderness at nightfall," said he. "But with your leave, friend, I shall take a cut through the woods until we have left this Christian women behind. Being a stranger to you, she might ask whom I was consorting with and whither I was going."

"Be it so," said his fellow-traveller. "Betake you to the woods, and let me keep the path."

Accordingly the young man turned aside, but took care to watch his companion, who advanced softly along the road until he had come within a staff's length of the old dame. She, meanwhile, was making the best of her way, with singular speed for so aged a woman, and mumbling some indistinct words — a prayer, doubtless — as she went. The traveller put forth his staff and touched her withered neck with what seemed the serpent's tail.

"The devil!" screamed the pious old lady.

"Then Goody Cloyse knows her old friend?" observed the traveller, confronting her and leaning on his writhing stick.

"Ah, forsooth, and is it your worship indeed?" cried the good dame. "Yea, truly it is, and in the very image of my old gossip, Goodman Brown, the grandfather of the silly fellow that now is. But — would your worship believe it? — my broomstick hath strangely disappeared, stolen, as I suspect, by that unhanged witch, Goody Cory, and that, too, when I was all anointed with the juice of smallage, and cinquefoil, and wolf's bane — "

"Mingled with fine wheat and the fat of a new-born babe," said the shape of old Goodman Brown.

"Ah, your worship knows the recipe," cried the old lady, cackling aloud. "So, as I was saying, being all ready for the meeting, and no horse to ride on, I made up my mind to foot it; for they tell me there is a nice young man to be taken into communion to-night. But now your good worship will lend me your arm, and we shall be there in a twinkling."

"That can hardly be," answered her friend. "I may not spare you my arm, Goody Cloyse; but here is my staff, if you will."

So saying, he threw it down at her feet, where, perhaps, it assumed life, being one of the rods which its owner had formerly lent to the Egyptian magi. Of this fact, however, Goodman Brown could not take cognizance. He had cast up his eyes in astonishment, and, looking down again, beheld neither Goody Cloyse nor the serpentine staff, but his fellow-traveller alone, who waited for him as calmly as if nothing had happened.

"That old woman taught me my catechism," said the young man; and there was a world of meaning in this simple comment.

They continued to walk onward, while the elder traveller exhorted his companion to make good speed and persevere in the path, discoursing so aptly that his arguments seemed rather to spring up in the bosom of his auditor than to be suggested by himself. As they went, he plucked a branch of maple to serve for a walking stick, and began to strip it of the twigs and little boughs, which were wet with evening dew. The moment his fingers touched them they became strangely withered and dried up as with a week's sunshine. Thus the pair proceeded, at a good free pace, until suddenly, in a gloomy hollow of the road, Goodman Brown sat himself down on the stump of a tree and refused to go any farther.

"Friend," said he, stubbornly, "my mind is made up. Not another step will I budge on this errand. What if a wretched old woman do choose to go to the devil when I thought she was going to heaven: is that any reason why I should quit my dear Faith and go after her?"

"You will think better of this by and by," said his acquaintance, composedly. "Sit here and rest yourself awhile; and when you feel like moving again, there is my staff to help you along."

Without more words, he threw his companion the maple stick, and was as speedily out of sight as if he had vanished into the deepening gloom. The young man sat a few moments by the roadside, applauding himself greatly, and thinking with how clear a conscience he should meet the minister in his morning walk, nor shrink from the eye of good old Deacon Gookin. And what calm sleep would be his that very night, which was to have been spent so wickedly, but so purely and sweetly now, in the arms of Faith! Amidst these pleasant and praiseworthy meditations, Goodman Brown heard the tramp of horses along the road, and deemed it advisable to conceal himself within the verge of the forest, conscious of the guilty purpose that had brought him thither, though now so happily turned from it.

On came the hoof tramps and the voices of the riders, two grave old voices, conversing soberly as they drew near. These mingled sounds appeared to pass along the road, within a few yards of the young man's hiding-place; but, owing doubtless to the depth of the gloom at that particular spot, neither the travellers nor their steeds were visible. Though their figures brushed the small boughs by the wayside, it could not be seen that they intercepted, even for a moment, the faint gleam from the strip of bright sky athwart which they must have passed. Goodman

Brown alternately crouched and stood on tiptoe, pulling aside the branches and thrusting forth his head as far as he durst without discerning so much as a shadow. It vexed him the more, because he could have sworn, were such a thing possible, that he recognized the voices of the minister and Deacon Gookin, jogging along quietly, as they were wont to do, when bound to some ordination or ecclesiastical council. While yet within hearing, one of the riders stopped to pluck a switch.

"Of the two, reverend sir," said the voice like the deacon's, "I had rather miss an ordination dinner than to-night's meeting. They tell me that some of our community are to be here from Falmouth and beyond, and others from Connecticut and Rhode Island, besides several of the Indian powwows, who, after their fashion, know almost as much deviltry as the best of us. Moreover, there is a goodly young woman to be taken into communion."

"Mighty well, Deacon Gookin!" replied the solemn old tones of the minister. "Spur up, or we shall be late. Nothing can be done, you know, until I get on the ground."

The hoofs clattered again; and the voices, talking so strangely in the empty air, passed on through the forest, where no church had ever been gathered or solitary Christian prayed. Whither, then, could these holy men be journeying so deep into the heathen wilderness? Young Goodman Brown caught hold of a tree for support, being ready to sink down on the ground, faint and overburdened with the heavy sickness of his heart. He looked up to the sky, doubting whether there really was a heaven above him. Yet there was the blue arch, and the stars brightening in it.

"With heaven above and Faith below, I will yet stand firm against the devil!" cried Goodman Brown.

While he still gazed upward into the deep arch of the firmament and had lifted his hands to pray, a cloud, though no wind was stirring, hurried across the zenith and hid the brightening stars. The blue sky was still visible, except directly overhead, where this black mass of cloud was sweeping swiftly northward. Aloft in the air, as if from the depths of the cloud, came a confused and doubtful sound of voices. Once the listener fancied that he could distinguish the accents of townspeople of his own, men and women, both pious and ungodly, many of whom he had

hears Faith's voice in a cloud overhead

met at the communion table, and had seen others rioting at the tavern. The next moment, so indistinct were the sounds, he doubted whether he had heard aught but the murmur of the old forest, whispering without a wind. Then came a stronger swell of those familiar tones, heard daily in the sunshine at Salem village, but never until now from a cloud of night. There was one voice, of a young woman, uttering lamentations, yet with an uncertain sorrow, and entreating for some favor, which, perhaps, it would grieve her to obtain; and all the unseen multitude, both saints and sinners, seemed to encourage her onward.

"Faith!" shouted Goodman Brown, in a voice of agony and desperation; and the echoes of the forest mocked him, crying, "Faith! Faith!" as if bewildered wretches were seeking her all through the wilderness.

The cry of grief, rage, and terror was yet piercing the night, when the unhappy husband held his breath for a response. There was a scream, drowned immediately in a louder murmur of voices, fading into far-off laughter, as the dark cloud swept away, leaving the clear and silent sky above Goodman Brown. But something fluttered lightly down through the air and caught on the branch of a tree. The young man seized it, and beheld a pink ribbon.

"My Faith is gone!" cried he, after one stupefied moment. "There is no good on earth; and sin is but a name. Come, devil; for to thee is this world given."

And, maddened with despair, so that he laughed loud and long, did Goodman Brown grasp his staff and set forth again, at such a rate that he seemed to fly along the forest path rather than to walk or run. The road grew wilder and drearier and more faintly traced, and vanished at length, leaving him in the heart of the dark wilderness, still rushing onward with the instinct that guides mortal men to evil. The whole forest was peopled with frightful sounds — the creaking of the trees, the howling of wild beasts, and the yell of Indians; while sometimes the wind tolled like a distant church bell, and sometimes gave a broad roar around the traveller, as if all Nature were laughing him to scorn. But he was himself the chief horror of the scene, and shrank not from its other horrors.

"Ha! ha! ha!" roared Goodman Brown when the wind laughed at him. "Let us hear which will laugh loudest. Think not to frighten me with your deviltry. Come witch, come wizard, Indian powwow, come devil himself, and here comes Goodman Brown. You may as well fear him as he fear you."

In truth, all through the haunted forest there could be nothing more frightful than the figure of Goodman Brown. On he flew among the black pines, brandishing his staff with frenzied gestures, now giving vent to an inspiration of horrid blasphemy, and now shouting forth such laughter as set all the echoes of the forest laughing like demons around him. The fiend in his own shape is less hideous than when he rages in the breast of man. Thus sped the demoniac on his course, until, quivering among the trees, he saw a red light before him, as when the felled trunks and branches of a clearing have been set on fire, and throw up their lurid blaze against the sky, at the hour of midnight. He paused, in a lull of the tempest that had driven him onward, and heard the swell of what seemed a hymn, rolling solemnly from a distance with the weight of many voices. He knew the tune; it was a familiar one in the choir of the village meeting-house. The verse died heavily away, and was lengthened by a chorus, not of human voices, but of all the sounds of the benighted wilderness pealing in awful harmony together. Goodman Brown cried out, and his cry was lost to his own ear by its unison with the cry of the desert.

In the interval of silence he stole forward until the light glared full upon his eyes. At one extremity of an open space, hemmed in by the dark wall of the forest, arose a rock, bearing some rude, natural resemblance either to an altar or a pulpit, and surrounded by four blazing pines, their tops aflame, their stems untouched, like candles at an evening meeting. The mass of foliage that had overgrown the summit of the rock was all on fire, blazing high into the night and fitfully illuminating the whole field. Each pendent twig and leafy festoon was in a blaze. As the red light arose and fell, a numerous congregation alternately shone forth, then disappeared in shadow, and again grew, as it were, out of the darkness, peopling the heart of the solitary woods at once.

"A grave and dark-clad company," quoth Goodman Brown.

In truth they were such. Among them, quivering to and fro between gloom and splendor, appeared faces that would be seen next day at the council board of the province, and others which, Sabbath after Sabbath, looked devoutly heavenward, and be-

nignantly over the crowded pews, from the holiest pulpits in
the land. Some affirm that the lady of the governor was there.
At least there were high dames well known to her, and wives of
honored husbands, and widows, a great multitude, and ancient
maidens, all of excellent repute, and fair young girls, who
trembled lest their mothers should espy them. Either the sudden
gleams of light flashing over the obscure field bedazzled Goodman Brown, or he recognized a score of the church members of
Salem village famous for their especial sanctity. Good old Deacon Gookin had arrived, and waited at the skirts of that venerable
saint, his revered pastor. But, irreverently consorting with these
grave, reputable, and pious people, these elders of the church,
these chaste dames and dewy virgins, there were men of dissolute
lives and women of spotted fame, wretches given over to all
mean and filthy vice, and suspected even of horrid crimes. It
was strange to see that the good shrank not from the wicked, nor
were the sinners abashed by the saints. Scattered also among
their pale-faced enemies were the Indian priests, or powwows,
who had often scared their native forest with more hideous in-
cantations than any known to English witchcraft.

"But where is Faith?" thought Goodman Brown; and, as hope
came into his heart, he trembled.

Another verse of the hymn arose, a slow and mournful strain,
such as the pious love, but joined to the words which expressed
all that our nature can conceive of sin, and darkly hinted at far
more. Unfathomable to mere mortals is the lore of fiends. Verse
after verse was sung; and still the chorus of the desert swelled
between like the deepest tone of a mighty organ; and with the
final peal of that dreadful anthem there came a sound, as if the
roaring wind, the rushing streams, the howling beasts, and every
other voice of the unconcerted wilderness were mingling and
according with the voice of guilty man in homage to the prince
of all. The four blazing pines threw up a loftier flame, and ob-
scurely discovered shapes and visages of horror on the smoke
wreaths above the impious assembly. At the same moment the
fire on the rock shot redly forth and formed a glowing arch above
its base, where now appeared a figure. With reverence be it
spoken, the figure bore no slight similitude, both in garb and
manner, to some grave divine of the New England churches.

"Bring forth the converts!" cried a voice that echoed through the field and rolled into the forest.

At the word, Goodman Brown stepped forth from the shadow of the trees and approached the congregation, with whom he felt a loathful brotherhood by the sympathy of all that was wicked in his heart. He could have well-nigh sworn that the shape of his own dead father beckoned him to advance, looking downward from a smoke wreath, while a woman, with dim features of despair, threw out her hand to warn him back. Was it his mother? But he had no power to retreat one step, nor to resist, even in thought, when the minister and good old Deacon Gookin seized his arms and led him to the blazing rock. Thither came also the slender form of a veiled female, led between Goody Cloyse, that pious teacher of the catechism, and Martha Carrier, who had received the devil's promise to be queen of hell. A rampant hag was she. And there stood the proselytes beneath the canopy of fire.

"Welcome, my children," said the dark figure, "to the communion of your race. Ye have found thus young your nature and your destiny. My children, look behind you!"

They turned; and flashing forth, as it were, in a sheet of flame, the fiend worshippers were seen; the smile of welcome gleamed darkly on every visage.

"There," resumed the sable form, "are all whom ye have reverenced from youth. Ye deemed them holier than yourselves, and shrank from your own sin, contrasting it with their lives of righteousness and prayerful aspirations heavenward. Yet here are they all in my worshipping assembly. This night it shall be granted you to know their secret deeds: how hoary-bearded elders of the church have whispered wanton words to the young maids of their households; how many a woman, eager for widows' weeds, has given her husband a drink at bedtime and let him sleep his last sleep in her bosom; how beardless youths have made haste to inherit their fathers' wealth; and how fair damsels — blush not, sweet ones — have dug little graves in the garden, and bidden me, the sole guest, to an infant's funeral. By the sympathy of your human hearts for sin ye shall scent out all the places — whether in church, bedchamber, street, field, or forest — where crime has been committed, and shall exult to behold the whole earth one stain of guilt, one mighty blood spot. Far more than this. It shall be yours to penetrate, in every bosom, the deep mystery of sin, the fountain of all wicked arts, and which inexhaustibly supplies more evil impulses than human power — than my power at its utmost — can make manifest in deeds. And now, my children, look upon each other."

They did so; and, by the blaze of the hell-kindled torches, the wretched man beheld his Faith, and the wife her husband, trembling before that unhallowed altar.

"Lo, there ye stand, my children," said the figure, in a deep and solemn tone, almost sad with its despairing awfulness, as if his once angelic nature could yet mourn for our miserable race. "Depending upon one another's hearts, ye had still hoped that virtue were not all a dream. Now are ye undeceived. Evil is the nature of mankind. Evil must be your only happiness. Welcome again, my children, to the communion of your race."

"Welcome," repeated the fiend worshippers, in one cry of despair and triumph.

And there they stood, the only pair, as it seemed, who were yet hesitating on the verge of wickedness in this dark world. A basin was hollowed, naturally, in the rock. Did it contain water, reddened by the lurid light? or was it blood? or, perchance, a liquid flame? Herein did the shape of evil dip his hand and prepare to lay the mark of baptism on their foreheads, that they might be partakers of the mystery of sin, more conscious of the secret guilt of others, both in deed and thought, than they could now be of their own. The husband cast one look at his pale wife, and Faith at him. What polluted wretches would the next glance show them to each other, shuddering alike at what they disclosed and what they saw!

"Faith! Faith!" cried the husband, "look up to heaven, and resist the wicked one."

Whether Faith obeyed he knew not. Hardly had he spoken when he found himself amid calm night and solitude, listening to a roar of the wind which died heavily away through the forest. He staggered against the rock, and felt it chill and damp; while a hanging twig, that had been all on fire, besprinkled his cheek with the coldest dew.

The next morning young Goodman Brown came slowly into the street of Salem village, staring around him like a bewildered man. The good old minister was taking a walk along the grave-yard to get an appetite for breakfast and meditate his sermon, and bestowed a blessing, as he passed, on Goodman Brown. He shrank from the venerable saint as if to avoid an anathema. Old Deacon Gookin was at domestic worship, and the holy words of his prayer were heard through the open window. "What God doth the wizard pray to?" quoth Goodman Brown. Goody Cloyse, that excellent old Christian, stood in the early sunshine at her own lattice, catechizing a little girl who had brought her a pint of morning's milk. Goodman Brown snatched away the child as from the grasp of the fiend himself. Turning the corner by the meeting-house, he spied the head of Faith, with the pink ribbons, gazing anxiously forth, and bursting into such joy at the sight of him that she skipped along the street and almost kissed her husband before the whole village. But Goodman Brown looked sternly and sadly into her face, and passed on without a greeting.

Had Goodman Brown fallen asleep in the forest and only dreamed a wild dream of a witch-meeting?

Be it so if you will; but, alas! it was a dream of evil omen for young Goodman Brown. A stern, a sad, a darkly meditative, a distrustful, if not a desperate man did he become from the night of that fearful dream. On the Sabbath day, when the congregation were singing a holy psalm, he could not listen because an anthem of sin rushed loudly upon his ear and drowned all the blessed strain. When the minister spoke from the pulpit with power and fervid eloquence, and, with his hand on the open Bible, of the sacred truths of our religion, and of saint-like lives and triumphant deaths, and of future bliss or misery unutterable, then did Goodman Brown turn pale, dreading lest the roof should thunder down upon the gray blasphemer and his hearers. Often, awaking suddenly at midnight, he shrank from the bosom of Faith; and at morning or eventide, when the family knelt down at prayer, he scowled and muttered to himself, and gazed sternly at his wife, and turned away. And when he had lived long, and was borne to his grave a hoary corpse, followed by Faith, an aged woman, and children and grandchildren, a goodly procession, besides neighbors not a few, they carved no hopeful verse upon his tombstone, for his dying hour was gloom.

Nathaniel Hawthorne (1804-1864)   Nathaniel Hawthorne was
born in Salem, Massachusetts; his sea-captain father, who died when
Hawthorne was four years old, and his mother were members of prominent New England families. After being graduated from Bowdoin
College in 1825, Hawthorne lived in semi-retirement in Salem for
several years, writing his first novel, *Fanshawe,* and sketches, anecdotes, and tales about New England, many of which were published
anonymously in *The Token* and collected in book form as *Twice-Told
Tales* in 1837. Except for his consulship at Liverpool during the
Presidency of his college companion and lifelong friend Franklin
Pierce, Hawthorne dedicated himself to a literary career. Among his
outstanding works of fiction are *Mosses from an Old Manse,* which included "Young Goodman Brown" and "Rappaccini's Daughter," and
several distinguished novels: *The Scarlet Letter* (1850), *The House
of the Seven Gables* (1851), *The Blithedale Romance* (1852), and
The Marble Faun (1860).

Like his contemporary, Poe, Hawthorne is a painstaking artist and
innovator. Although Poe, in a well-known review of *Twice-Told Tales,*
commented that many of Hawthorne's pieces were not tales at all, but
were "pure essays," Hawthorne's later stories, like "Young Goodman
Brown" and "Rappaccini's Daughter," are carefully wrought around a
single intense situation and display a very close interdependence of
characters, theme, setting, and incidents. Preoccupied with problems
of sin and guilt, Hawthorne effectively uses symbols to suggest or
sometimes force upon the reader a more than literal, or allegorical, interpretation of a story. In one form or another, symbolism is almost
as old as literature itself; Hawthorne's modernity, however, lies in his
use of symbols as fundamental structural elements in a story, and in
his conceiving certain stories in terms of deliberate or conscious ambiguity. Both "Young Goodman Brown" and "Rappaccini's Daughter,"
for example, are fictional inquiries into the nature of sin and wrong-
doing; both exist simultaneously on more than one level — the one
literal and specific, the other non-literal, allegorical, symbolic, and
universal. Yet Hawthorne avoids any dogmatic conclusions concerning
religious or moral beliefs; rather, he presents a picture and leaves the
ultimate interpretation to the individual. Although an untrained
reader can derive enjoyment from reading such stories on a purely
literal level, it is difficult for the adult reader to do so. To remove
the ideas behind the characters and events, to eliminate the symbols,
is to destroy, as it were, the soul of the story.

Convenient one-volume collections of Hawthorne's stories include *The Short Stories of Nathaniel Hawthorne* (ed. Newton Arvin, Vintage); *The Complete Novels and Selected Tales of Nathaniel Hawthorne* (ed. Norman Holmes Pearson, Modern Library); *Nathaniel Hawthorne: Selected Tales and Sketches* (ed. Hyatt W. Waggoner, Rinehart Edition); *The Portable Hawthorne* (ed. Malcolm Cowley, Viking).

Questions   **1.** In this story, Hawthorne poses the question "Had Goodman Brown fallen asleep in the forest and only dreamed a wild dream of a witch-meeting?" Why does Hawthorne ask this question? In your opinion are the events of Brown's ordeal in the forest a dream, a product of his imagination, or do they actually occur? Do these events seem to you to be a convincing outgrowth of the beginning of the story? Are you convinced by the ending of the story?   **2.** Do you sympathize with young Goodman Brown? Is he an admirable character? Or do you think him an evil man? Is his wife an evil woman?   **3.** By what means is the character of Brown revealed to the reader (i.e., through action, dialogue, description, revelation of Brown's innermost thoughts, through other characters)?   **4.** What does Faith's pink ribbon signify? Make a list of other symbols in the story. How do you interpret these symbols?   **5.** Is this a story primarily of plot, character, theme, mood, or atmosphere?   **6.** In his introduction to *The House of the Seven Gables*, Hawthorne differentiated between a Novel and a Romance; a novelist, he said, was obliged to aim at a "very minute fidelity . . . to the probable and ordinary course of man's experience." The writer of Romance, on the other hand, has a right to depict "truth under circumstances . . . of the writer's own choosing or creation." In what ways, according to this distinction, would "Young Goodman Brown" be classified as a Romance?   **7.** Hawthorne's works are permeated with the atmosphere of old New England; this gives, in effect, a kind of additional dimension to his work. In his use of native legends, his preoccupation with New England idiosyncrasies of character and temperament, and his fondness for local settings, Hawthorne differs from many earlier American writers who were inclined to ignore the literary possibilities inherent in their native section or region. Could "Young Goodman Brown" have a different setting, or is its specific setting necessary to the effect of the story as a whole?

NATHANIEL HAWTHORNE

Rappaccini's Daughter

A YOUNG MAN, named Giovanni Guasconti, came, very long ago, from the more southern region of Italy, to pursue his studies at the University of Padua. Giovanni, who had but a scanty supply of gold ducats in his pocket, took lodgings in a high and gloomy chamber of an old edifice which looked not unworthy to have been the palace of a Paduan noble, and which, in fact, exhibited over its entrance the armorial bearings of a family long since extinct. The young stranger, who was not unstudied in the great poem of his country, recollected that one of the ancestors of this family, and perhaps an occupant of this very mansion, had been pictured by Dante as a partaker of the immortal agonies of his Inferno. These reminiscences and associations, together with the tendency to heartbreak natural to a young man for the first time out of his native sphere, caused Giovanni to sigh heavily as he looked around the desolate and ill-furnished apartment.

"Holy Virgin, signor!" cried old Dame Lisabetta, who, won by the youth's remarkable beauty of person, was kindly endeavoring to give the chamber a habitable air, "what a sigh was that to come out of a young man's heart! Do you find this old mansion gloomy? For the love of Heaven, then, put your head out of the window, and you will see as bright sunshine as you have left in Naples."

Guasconti mechanically did as the old woman advised, but

48

could not quite agree with her that the Paduan sunshine was as
cheerful as that of southern Italy. Such as it was, however, it fell
upon a garden beneath the window, and expended its fostering
influences on a variety of plants, which seemed to have been
cultivated with exceeding care.

"Does this garden belong to the house?" asked Giovanni.

"Heaven forbid, signor, unless it were fruitful of better pot
herbs than any that grow there now," answered old Lisabetta.
"No; that garden is cultivated by the own hands of Signor Giacomo Rappaccini, the famous doctor, who, I warrant him, has
been heard of as far as Naples. It is said that he distills these
plants into medicines that are as potent as a charm. Oftentimes
you may see the signor doctor at work, and perchance the signora,
his daughter, too, gathering the strange flowers that grow in the
garden."

The old woman had now done what she could for the aspect of
the chamber; and, commending the young man to the protection
of the saints, took her departure.

Giovanni still found no better occupation than to look down
into the garden beneath his window. From its appearance, he
judged it to be one of those botanic gardens which were of earlier
date in Padua than elsewhere in Italy, or in the world. Or, not
improbably, it might once have been the pleasure-place of an
opulent family; for there was the ruin of a marble fountain in
the centre, sculptured with rare art, but so wofully shattered that
it was impossible to trace the original design from the chaos of
remaining fragments. The water, however, continued to gush
and sparkle into the sunbeams as cheerfully as ever. A little
gurgling sound ascended to the young man's window, and made
him feel as if the fountain were an immortal spirit that sung its
song unceasingly and without heeding the vicissitudes around it,
while one century embodied it in marble and another scattered
the perishable garniture on the soil. All about the pool into which
the water subsided grew various plants, that seemed to require a
plentiful supply of moisture for the nourishment of gigantic
leaves, and, in some instances, flowers gorgeously magnificent.
There was one shrub in particular, set in a marble vase in the
midst of the pool, that bore a profusion of purple blossoms, each
of which had the lustre and richness of a gem; and the whole
together made a show so resplendent that it seemed enough to

illuminate the garden, even had there been no sunshine. Every portion of the soil was peopled with plants and herbs, which, if less beautiful, still bore tokens of assiduous care, as if all had their individual virtues, known to the scientific mind that fostered them. Some were placed in urns, rich with old carving, and others in common garden pots; some crept serpent-like along the ground or climbed on high, using whatever means of ascent was offered them. One plant had wreathed itself round a statue of Vertumnus, which was thus quite veiled and shrouded in a drapery of hanging foliage, so happily arranged that it might have served a sculptor for a study.

While Giovanni stood at the window he heard a rustling behind a screen of leaves, and became aware that a person was at work in the garden. His figure soon emerged into view, and showed itself to be that of no common laborer, but a tall, emaciated, sallow, and sickly-looking man dressed in a scholar's garb of black. He was beyond the middle term of life, with gray hair, a thin, gray beard, and a face singularly marked with intellect and cultivation, but which could never, even in his more youthful days, have expressed much warmth of heart.

Nothing could exceed the intentness with which this scientific gardener examined every shrub which grew in his path: it seemed as if he was looking into their inmost nature, making observations in regard to their creative essence, and discovering why one leaf grew in this shape and another in that, and wherefore such and such flowers differed among themselves in hue and perfume. Nevertheless, in spite of this deep intelligence on his part, there was no approach to intimacy between himself and these vegetable existences. On the contrary, he avoided their actual touch or the direct inhaling of their odors with a caution that impressed Giovanni most disagreeably; for the man's demeanor was that of one walking among malignant influences, such as savage beasts, or deadly snakes, or evil spirits, which, should he allow them one moment of license, would wreak upon him some terrible fatality. It was strangely frightful to the young man's imagination to see this air of insecurity in a person cultivating a garden, that most simple and innocent of human toils, and which had been alike the joy and labor of the unfallen parents of the race. Was this garden, then, the Eden of the present world? and this man, with such a perception of harm in what his own hands caused to grow, — was he the Adam?

The distrustful gardener, while plucking away the dead leaves or pruning the too luxuriant growth of the shrubs, defended his hands with a pair of thick gloves. Nor were these his only armor. When, in his walk through the garden, he came to the magnificent plant that hung its purple gems beside the marble fountain, he placed a kind of mask over his mouth and nostrils, as if all this beauty did but conceal a deadlier malice; but, finding his task still too dangerous, he drew back, removed the mask, and called loudly, but in the infirm voice of a person affected with inward disease.

"Beatrice! Beatrice!"

"Here am I, my father. What would you?" cried a rich and youthful voice from the window of the opposite house — a voice as rich as a tropical sunset, and which made Giovanni, though he knew not why, think of deep hues of purple or crimson and of perfumes heavily delectable. "Are you in the garden?"

"Yes, Beatrice," answered the gardener, "and I need your help."

Soon there emerged from under a sculptured portal the figure of a young girl, arrayed with as much richness of taste as the most splendid of the flowers, beautiful as the day, and with a bloom so deep and vivid that one shade more would have been too much. She looked redundant with life, health, and energy; all of which attributes were bound down and compressed as it were, and girdled tensely, in their luxuriance, by her virgin zone. Yet Giovanni's fancy must have grown morbid while he looked down into the garden; for the impression which the fair stranger made upon him was as if here were another flower, the human sister of those vegetable ones, as beautiful as they, more beautiful than the richest of them, but still to be touched only with a glove, not to be approached without a mask. As Beatrice came down the garden path, it was observable that she handled and inhaled the odor of several of the plants which her father had most sedulously avoided.

"Here, Beatrice," said the latter, "see how many needful offices require to be done to our chief treasure. Yet, shattered as I am, my life might pay the penalty of approaching it so closely as circumstances demand. Henceforth, I fear, this plant must be consigned to your sole charge."

"And gladly will I undertake it," cried again the rich tones of the young lady, as she bent toward the magnificent plant and opened her arms as if to embrace it. "Yes, my sister, my splendor, it shall be Beatrice's task to nurse and serve thee; and thou shalt reward her with thy kisses and perfumed breath, which to her is as the breath of life."

Then, with all the tenderness in her manner that was so strikingly expressed in her words, she busied herself with such attentions as the plant seemed to require; and Giovanni, at his lofty window, rubbed his eyes and almost doubted whether it were a girl tending her favorite flower, or one sister performing the duties of affection to another.

The scene soon terminated. Whether Dr. Rappaccini had finished his labors in the garden or that his watchful eye had caught the stranger's face, he now took his daughter's arm and retired. Night was already closing in; oppressive exhalations seemed to proceed from the plants and steal upward past the open window; and Giovanni, closing the lattice, went to his couch and dreamed of a rich flower and beautiful girl. Flower and maiden were different, and yet the same, and fraught with some strange peril in either shape.

But there is an influence in the light of morning that tends to rectify whatever errors of fancy, or even of judgment, we may have incurred during the sun's decline, or among the shadows of the night, or in the less wholesome glow of moonshine. Giovanni's first movement, on starting from sleep, was to throw open the window and gaze down into the garden which his dreams had made so fertile of mysteries. He was surprised and a little ashamed to find how real and matter-of-fact an affair it proved to be, in the first rays of the sun which gilded the dew-drops that hung upon leaf and blossom, and, while giving a brighter beauty to each rare flower, brought everything within the limits of ordinary experience. The young man rejoiced that, in the heart of the barren city, he had the privilege of overlooking this spot of lovely and luxuriant vegetation. It would serve, he said to himself, as a symbolic language to keep him in communion with Nature. Neither the sickly and thought-worn Dr. Giacomo Rappaccini, it is true, nor his brilliant daughter, were now visible; so that Giovanni could not determine how much of the singularity which he attributed to both was due to their own qualities and how much to his wonder-working fancy; but he was inclined to take a most rational view of the whole matter.

In the course of the day he paid his respects to Signor Pietro Baglioni, professor of medicine in the university, a physician of eminent repute, to whom Giovanni had brought a letter of introduction. The professor was an elderly personage, apparently of genial nature, and habits that might almost be called jovial. He kept the young man to dinner, and made himself very agreeable by the freedom and liveliness of his conversation, especially when warmed by a flask or two of Tuscan wine. Giovanni, conceiving that men of science, inhabitants of the same city, must needs be on familiar terms with one another, took an opportunity to mention the name of Dr. Rappaccini. But the professor did not respond with so much cordiality as he had anticipated.

"Ill would it become a teacher of the divine art of medicine," said Professor Pietro Baglioni, in answer to a question of Giovanni, "to withhold due and well-considered praise of a physician so eminently skilled as Rappaccini; but, on the other hand, I should answer it but scantily to my conscience were I to permit a worthy youth like yourself, Signor Giovanni, the son of an ancient friend, to imbibe erroneous ideas respecting a man who might hereafter chance to hold your life and death in his hands. The truth is, our worshipful Dr. Rappaccini has as much science as any member of the faculty — with perhaps one single exception — in Padua, or all Italy; but there are certain grave objections to his professional character."

"And what are they?" asked the young man.

"Has my friend Giovanni any disease of body or heart, that he is so inquisitive about physicians?" said the professor, with a smile. "But as for Rappaccini, it is said of him — and I, who know the man well, can answer for its truth — that he cares infinitely more for science than for mankind. His patients are interesting to him only as subjects for some new experiment. He would sacrifice human life, his own among the rest, or whatever else was dearest to him, for the sake of adding so much as a grain of mustard seed to the great heap of his accumulated knowledge."

"Methinks he is an awful man indeed," remarked Guasconti, mentally recalling the cold and purely intellectual aspect of Rappaccini. "And yet, worshipful professor, is it not a noble spirit?

Are there many men capable of so spiritual a love of science?"

"God forbid," answered the professor, somewhat testily; "at least, unless they take sounder views of the healing art than those adopted by Rappaccini. It is his theory that all medicinal virtues are comprised within those substances which we term vegetable poisons. These he cultivates with his own hands, and is said even to have produced new varieties of poison, more horribly deleterious than Nature, without the assistance of this learned person, would ever have plagued the world withal. That the signor doctor does less mischief than might be expected with such dangerous substances is undeniable. Now and then, it must be owned, he has effected, or seemed to effect, a marvelous cure; but, to tell you my private mind, Signor Giovanni, he should receive little credit for such instances of success, — they being probably the work of chance, — but should be held strictly accountable for his failures, which may justly be considered his own work."

The youth might have taken Baglioni's opinions with many grains of allowance had he known that there was a professional warfare of long continuance between him and Dr. Rappaccini, in which the latter was generally thought to have gained the advantage. If the reader be inclined to judge for himself, we refer him to certain black-letter tracts on both sides, preserved in the medical department of the University of Padua.

"I know not, most learned professor," returned Giovanni, after musing on what had been said of Rappaccini's exclusive zeal for science, — "I know not how dearly this physician may love his art; but surely there is one object more dear to him. He has a daughter."

"Aha!" cried the professor, with a laugh. "So now our friend Giovanni's secret is out. You have heard of this daughter, whom all the young men in Padua are wild about, though not half a dozen have ever had the good hap to see her face. I know little of the Signora Beatrice save that Rappaccini is said to have instructed her deeply in his science, and that, young and beautiful as fame reports her, she is already qualified to fill a professor's chair. Perchance her father destines her for mine! Other absurd rumors there be, not worth talking about or listening to. So now, Signor Giovanni, drink off your glass of lachryma."

Guasconti returned to his lodgings somewhat heated with the

wine he had quaffed, and which caused his brain to swim with strange fantasies in reference to Dr. Rappaccini and the beautiful Beatrice. On his way, happening to pass by a florist's he bought a fresh bouquet of flowers.

Ascending to his chamber, he seated himself near the window, but within the shadow thrown by the depth of the wall, so that he could look down into the garden with little risk of being discovered. All beneath his eye was a solitude. The strange plants were basking in the sunshine, and now and then nodding gently to one another, as if in acknowledgment of sympathy and kindred. In the midst, by the shattered fountain, grew the magnificent shrub, with its purple gems clustering all over it; they glowed in the air, and gleamed back again out of the depths of the pool, which thus seemed to overflow with colored radiance from the rich reflection that was steeped in it. At first, as we have said, the garden was a solitude. Soon, however, — as Giovanni had half hoped, half feared, would be the case, — a figure appeared beneath the antique sculptured portal, and came down between the rows of plants, inhaling their various perfumes as if she were one of those beings of old classic fables that lived upon sweet odors. On again beholding Beatrice, the young man was even startled to perceive how much her beauty exceeded his recollection of it; so brilliant, so vivid, was its character, that she glowed amid the sunlight, and, as Giovanni whispered to himself, positively illuminated the more shadowy intervals of the garden path. Her face being now more revealed than on the former occasion, he was struck by its expression of simplicity and sweetness, — qualities that had not entered into his idea of her character, and which made him ask anew what manner of mortal she might be. Nor did he fail again to observe, or imagine, an analogy between the beautiful girl and the gorgeous shrub that hung its gemlike flowers over the fountain, — a resemblance which Beatrice seemed to have indulged a fantastic humor in heightening, both by the arrangement of her dress and the selection of its hues.

Approaching the shrub, she threw open her arms, as with a passionate ardor, and drew its branches into an intimate embrace —so intimate that her features were hidden in its leafy bosom and her glistening ringlets all intermingled with the flowers.

"Give me thy breath, my sister," exclaimed Beatrice; "for I am faint with common air. And give me this flower of thine, which I

separate with gentlest fingers from the stem and place it close beside my heart."

With these words the beautiful daughter of Rappaccini plucked
one of the richest blossoms of the shrub, and was about to fasten
it in her bosom. But now, unless Giovanni's draughts of wine
had bewildered his senses, a singular incident occurred. A small
orange-colored reptile of the lizard or chameleon species, chanced
to be creeping along the path just at the feet of Beatrice. It
appeared to Giovanni, — but at the distance from which he
gazed, he could scarcely have seen anything so minute, — it
appeared to him, however, that a drop or two of moisture from
the broken stem of the flower descended upon the lizard's head.
For an instant the reptile contorted itself violently, and then lay
motionless in the sunshine. Beatrice observed this remarkable
phenomenon, and crossed herself, sadly, but without surprise;
nor did she therefore hesitate to arrange the fatal flower in her
bosom. There it blushed, and almost glimmered with the dazzling
effect of a precious stone, adding to her dress and aspect the one
appropriate charm which nothing else in the world could have
supplied. But Giovanni, out of the shadow of his window, bent
forward and shrank back, and murmured and trembled.

"Am I awake? Have I my senses?" said he to himself. "What
is this being? Beautiful shall I call her, or inexpressibly terrible?"

Beatrice now strayed carelessly through the garden, approaching closer beneath Giovanni's window, so that he was compelled
to thrust his head quite out of its concealment in order to gratify
the intense and painful curiosity which she excited. At this
moment there came a beautiful insect over the garden wall; it
had, perhaps, wandered through the city and found no flowers or
verdure among those antique haunts of men until the heavy perfumes of Dr. Rappaccini's shrubs had lured it from afar. Without
alighting on the flowers, this winged brightness seemed to be
attracted by Beatrice, and lingered in the air and fluttered about
her head. Now, here it could not be but that Giovanni Guasconti's eyes deceived him. Be that as it might, he fancied that,
while Beatrice was gazing at the insect with childish delight, it
grew faint and fell at her feet; its bright wings shivered; it was
dead — from no cause that he could discern, unless it were the
atmosphere of her breath. Again Beatrice crossed herself and
sighed heavily as she bent over the dead insect.

An impulsive movement of Giovanni drew her eyes to the window. There she beheld the beautiful head of the young man — rather a Grecian than an Italian head, with fair, regular features, and a glistening of gold among his ringlets — gazing down upon her like a being that hovered in mid air. Scarcely knowing what he did, Giovanni threw down the bouquet which he had hitherto held in his hand.

"Signora," said he, "there are pure and healthful flowers. Wear them for the sake of Giovanni Guasconti."

"Thanks, signor," replied Beatrice, with her rich voice, that came forth as it were like a gush of music, and with a mirthful expression half childish and half woman-like. "I accept your gift, and would fain recompense it with this precious purple flower; but if I toss it into the air it will not reach you. So Signor Guasconti must even content himself with my thanks."

She lifted the bouquet from the ground, and then, as if inwardly ashamed at having stepped aside from her maidenly reserve to respond to a stranger's greeting, passed swiftly homeward through the garden. But few as the moments were, it seemed to Giovanni, when she was on the point of vanishing beneath the sculptured portal, that his beautiful bouquet was already beginning to wither in her grasp. It was an idle thought; there could be no possibility of distinguishing a faded flower from a fresh one at so great a distance.

For many days after this incident the young man avoided the window that looked into Dr. Rappaccini's garden, as if something ugly and monstrous would have blasted his eyesight had he been betrayed into a glance. He felt conscious of having put himself, to a certain extent, within the influence of an unintelligible power by the communication which he had opened with Beatrice. The wisest course would have been, if his heart were in any real danger, to quit his lodgings and Padua itself at once; the next wiser, to have accustomed himself, as far as possible, to the familiar and daylight view of Beatrice, — thus bringing her rigidly and systematically within the limits of ordinary experience. Least of all, while avoiding her sight, ought Giovanni to have remained so near this extraordinary being that the proximity and possibility even of intercourse should give a kind of substance and reality to the wild vagaries which his imagination ran riot continually in producing. Guasconti had not a deep heart — or, at all events, its depths were not sounded now; but he had a quick fancy, and an ardent southern temperament which rose every instant to a higher fever pitch. Whether or no Beatrice possessed those terrible attributes, that fatal breath, the affinity with those so beautiful and deadly flowers which were indicated by what Giovanni had witnessed, she had at least instilled a fierce and subtle poison into his system. It was not love, although her rich beauty was a madness to him; nor horror, even while he fancied her spirit to be imbued with the same baneful essence that seemed to pervade her physical frame; but a wild offspring of both love and horror that had each parent in it, and burned like one and shivered like the other. Giovanni knew not what to dread; still less did he know what to hope; yet hope and dread kept a continual warfare in his breast, alternately vanquishing one another and starting up afresh to renew the contest. Blessed are all simple emotions, be they dark or bright! It is the lurid intermixture of the two that produces the illuminating blaze of the infernal regions.

Sometimes he endeavored to assuage the fever of his spirit by a rapid walk through the streets of Padua or beyond its gates: his footsteps kept time with the throbbings of his brain, so that the walk was apt to accelerate itself to a race. One day he found himself arrested; his arm was seized by a portly personage who had turned back on recognizing the young man and expended much breath in overtaking him.

"Signor Giovanni! Stay, my young friend!" cried he. "Have you forgotten me? That might well be the case if I were as much altered as yourself."

It was Baglioni, whom Giovanni had avoided ever since their first meeting, from a doubt that the professor's sagacity would look too deeply into his secrets. Endeavoring to recover himself, he stared forth wildly from his inner world into the outer one and spoke like a man in a dream.

"Yes; I am Giovanni Guasconti. You are Professor Pietro Baglioni. Now let me pass!"

"Not yet, not yet, Signor Giovanni Guasconti," said the professor, smiling, but at the same time scrutinizing the youth with an earnest glance. "What! Did I grow up side by side with your father? and shall his son pass me like a stranger in these old streets of Padua? Stand still, Signor Giovanni, for we must have a word or two before we part."

"Speedily, then, most worshipful professor, speedily," said Giovanni, with feverish impatience. "Does not your worship see that I am in haste?"

Now, while he was speaking there came a man in black along the street, stooping and moving feebly like a person in inferior health. His face was all overspread with a most sickly and sallow hue, but yet so pervaded with an expression of piercing and active intellect that an observer might easily have overlooked the merely physical attributes and have seen only this wonderful energy. As he passed, this person exchanged a cold and distant salutation with Baglioni, but fixed his eyes upon Giovanni with an intentness that seemed to bring out whatever was within him worthy of notice. Nevertheless, there was a peculiar quietness in the look, as if taking merely a speculative, not a human, interest in the young man.

"It is Dr. Rappaccini!" whispered the professor, when the stranger had passed. "Has he ever seen your face before?"

"Not that I know," answered Giovanni, starting at the name.

"He *has* seen you! he must have seen you!" said Baglioni hastily. "For some purpose or other, this man of science is making a study of you. I know that look of his! It is the same that coldly illuminates his face as he bends over a bird, a mouse, or a butterfly, which, in pursuance of some experiment, he has killed by the perfume of a flower; a look as deep as Nature itself, but without Nature's warmth of love. Signor Giovanni, I will stake my life upon it, you are the subject of one of Rappaccini's experiments."

"Will you make a fool of me?" cried Giovanni passionately. "*That,* signor professor, were an untoward experiment."

"Patience, patience!" replied the imperturbable professor. "I tell thee, my poor Giovanni, that Rappaccini has a scientific interest in thee. Thou hast fallen into fearful hands! And the Signora Beatrice, — what part does she act in this mystery?"

But Guasconti, finding Baglioni's pertinacity intolerable, here broke away, and was gone before the professor could again seize his arm. He looked after the young man intently and shook his head.

"This must not be," said Baglioni to himself. "The youth is the son of my old friend, and shall not come to any harm from which the arcana of medical science can preserve him. Besides, it is too insufferable an impertinence in Rappaccini, thus to snatch the lad out of my own hands, as I may say, and make use of him for his infernal experiments. This daughter of his! It shall be looked to. Perchance, most learned Rappaccini, I may foil you where you little dream of it!"

Meanwhile, Giovanni had pursued a circuitous route, and at length found himself at the door of his lodgings. As he crossed the threshold he was met by old Lisabetta, who smirked and smiled, and was evidently desirous to attract his attention; vainly, however, as the ebullition of his feelings had momentarily subsided into a cold and dull vacuity. He turned his eyes full upon the withered face that was puckering itself into a smile, but seemed to behold it not. The old dame, therefore, laid her grasp upon his cloak.

"Signor! signor!" whispered she, still with a smile over the whole breadth of her visage, so that it looked not unlike a grotesque carving in wood, darkened by centuries. "Listen, signor! There is a private entrance into the garden!"

"What do you say?" exclaimed Giovanni, turning quickly about, as if an inanimate thing should start into feverish life. "A private entrance into Dr. Rappaccini's garden?"

"Hush! hush! Not so loud!" whispered Lisabetta, putting her hand over his mouth. "Yes; into the worshipful doctor's garden, where you may see all this fine shrubbery. Many a young man in Padua would give gold to be admitted among those flowers."

Giovanni put a piece of gold into her hand.

"Show me the way," said he.

A surmise, probably excited by his conversation with Baglioni, crossed his mind, that this interposition of old Lisabetta might perchance be connected with the intrigue, whatever were its nature, in which the professor seemed to suppose that Dr. Rappaccini was involving him. But such a suspicion, though it disturbed Giovanni, was inadequate to restrain him. The instant that he was aware of the possibility of approaching Beatrice, it seemed an absolute necessity of his existence to do so. It mattered not whether she were angel or demon; he was irrevocably within her sphere, and must obey the law that whirled him onward, in ever-lessening circles, toward a result which he did not attempt to foreshadow; and yet, strange to say, there came across him a sudden doubt whether this intense interest on his part were not delusory; whether it were really of so deep and positive a nature as to justify him in now thrusting himself into an incalculable position; whether it were not merely the fantasy of a young man's brain, only slightly or not at all connected with his heart.

He paused, hesitated, turned half about, but again went on. His withered guide led him along several obscure passages, and finally undid a door, through which, as it was opened, there came the sight and sound of rustling leaves, with the broken sunshine glimmering among them. Giovanni stepped forth, and, forcing himself through the entanglement of a shrub that wreathed its tendrils over the hidden entrance, stood beneath his own window in the open area of Dr. Rappaccini's garden.

How often is it the case that, when impossibilities have come to pass and dreams have condensed their misty substance into tangible realities, we find ourselves calm, and even coldly self-possessed, amid circumstances which it would have been a delirium of joy or agony to anticipate! Fate delights to thwart us thus. Passion will choose his own time to rush upon the scene, and lingers sluggishly behind when an appropriate adjustment of events would seem to summon his appearance. So was it now with Giovanni. Day after day his pulses had throbbed with feverish blood at the improbable idea of an interview with Beatrice, and of standing with her, face to face, in this very garden, basking in the Oriental sunshine of her beauty, and snatching from her full gaze the mystery which he deemed the riddle of his own existence. But now there was a singular and untimely equanimity within his breast. He threw a glance around the garden to discover if Beatrice or her father were present, and, perceiving that he was alone, began a critical observation of the plants.

The aspect of one and all of them dissatisfied him; their gorgeousness seemed fierce, passionate, and even unnatural. There was hardly an individual shrub which a wanderer, straying by himself through a forest, would not have been startled to find growing wild, as if an unearthly face had glared at him out of the thicket. Several also would have shocked a delicate instinct by an appearance of artificialness indicating that there had been such commixture, and, as it were, adultery, of various vegetable species, that the production was no longer of God's making, but the monstrous offspring of man's depraved fancy, glowing with only an evil mockery of beauty. They were probably the result of experiment, which in one or two cases had succeeded in mingling plants individually lovely into a compound possessing the questionable and ominous character that distinguished the whole growth of the garden. In fine, Giovanni recognized but two or three plants in the collection, and those of a kind that he well knew to be poisonous. While busy with these contemplations he heard the rustling of a silken garment, and, turning, beheld Beatrice emerging from beneath the sculptured portal.

Giovanni had not considered with himself what should be his deportment; whether he should apologize for his intrusion into the garden, or assume that he was there with the privity at least, if not by the desire, of Dr. Rappaccini or his daughter; but Beatrice's manner placed him at his ease, although leaving him still in doubt by what agency he had gained admittance. She came lightly along the path and met him near the broken fountain. There was surprise in her face, but brightened by a simple and kind expression of pleasure.

"You are a connoisseur in flowers, signor," said Beatrice, with a smile, alluding to the bouquet which he had flung her from the window. "It is no marvel, therefore, if the sight of my father's rare collection has tempted you to take a nearer view. If he were here, he could tell you many strange and interesting facts as to the nature and habits of these shrubs; for he has spent a lifetime in such studies, and this garden is his world."

"And yourself, lady," observed Giovanni, "if fame says true, — you likewise are deeply skilled in the virtues indicated by these rich blossoms and these spicy perfumes. Would you deign to be my instructress, I should prove an apter scholar than if taught by Signor Rappaccini himself."

"Are there such idle rumors?" asked Beatrice, with the music of a pleasant laugh. "Do people say that I am skilled in my father's science of plants? What a jest is there! No; though I have grown up among these flowers, I know no more of them than their hues and perfume; and sometimes methinks I would fain rid myself of even that small knowledge. There are many flowers here, and those not the least brilliant, that shock and offend me when they meet my eye. But pray, signor, do not believe these stories about my science. Believe nothing of me save what you see with your own eyes."

"And must I believe all that I have seen with my own eyes?" asked Giovanni, pointedly, while the recollection of former scenes made him shrink. "No, signora; you demand too little of me. Bid me believe nothing save what comes from your own lips."

It would appear that Beatrice understood him. There came a deep flush to her cheek, but she looked full into Giovanni's eyes and responded to his gaze of uneasy suspicion with a queenlike haughtiness.

"I do so bid you, signor," she replied. "Forget whatever you may have fancied in regard to me. If true to the outward senses, still it may be false in its essence; but the words of Beatrice Rappaccini's lips are true from the depths of the heart outward. Those you may believe."

A fervor glowed in her whole aspect and beamed upon Giovanni's consciousness like the light of truth itself; but while she spoke there was a fragrance in the atmosphere around her, rich and delightful, though evanescent, yet which the young man, from an indefinable reluctance, scarcely dared to draw into his lungs. It might be the odor of the flowers. Could it be Beatrice's breath which thus embalmed her words with a strange richness, as if by steeping them in her heart? A faintness passed like a shadow over Giovanni and flitted away; he seemed to gaze through the beautiful girl's eyes into her transparent soul, and felt no more doubt or fear.

The tinge of passion that had colored Beatrice's manner vanished; she became gay, and appeared to derive a pure delight from her communion with the youth not unlike what the maiden of a lonely island might have felt conversing with a voyager from the civilized world. Evidently her experience of life had been confined within the limits of that garden. She talked now about matters as simple as the daylight or summer clouds, and now asked questions in reference to the city, or Giovanni's distant home, his friends, his mother, and his sisters — questions indicating such seclusion, and such lack of familiarity with modes and forms, that Giovanni responded as if to an infant. Her spirit gushed out before him like a fresh rill that was just catching its first glimpse of the sunlight and wondering at the reflections of earth and sky which were flung into its bosom. There came thoughts, too, from a deep source, and fantasies of gemlike brilliancy, as if diamonds and rubies sparkled upward among the bubbles of the fountain. Ever and anon there gleamed across the young man's mind a sense of wonder that he should be walking side by side with the being who had so wrought upon his imagination, whom he had idealized in such hues of terror, in whom he had positively witnessed such manifestations of dreadful attributes, — that he should be conversing with Beatrice like a brother, and should find her so human and so maidenlike. But such reflections were only momentary; the effect of her character was too real not to make itself familiar at once.

In this free intercourse they had strayed through the garden, and now, after many turns among its avenues, were come to the shattered fountain, beside which grew the magnificent shrub with its treasury of glowing blossoms. A fragrance was diffused from it which Giovanni recognized as identical with that which he had attributed to Beatrice's breath, but incomparably more powerful. As her eyes fell upon it, Giovanni beheld her press her hand to her bosom, as if her heart were throbbing suddenly and painfully.

"For the first time in my life," murmured she, addressing the shrub, "I had forgotten thee."

"I remember, signora," said Giovanni, "that you once promised to reward me with one of these living gems for the bouquet which I had the happy boldness to fling to your feet. Permit me now to pluck it as a memorial of this interview."

He made a step toward the shrub with extended hand; but Beatrice darted forward, uttering a shriek that went through his heart like a dagger. She caught his hand and drew it back with the whole force of her slender figure. Giovanni felt her touch thrilling through his fibres.

"Touch it not!" exclaimed she, in a voice of agony. "Not for thy life! It is fatal!"

Then, hiding her face, she fled from him and vanished beneath the sculptured portal. As Giovanni followed her with his eyes, he beheld the emaciated figure and pale intelligence of Dr. Rappaccini, who had been watching the scene, he knew not how long, within the shadow of the entrance.

No sooner was Guasconti alone in his chamber than the image

of Beatrice came back to his passionate musings, invested with
all the witchery that had been gathering around it ever since his
first glimpse of her, and now likewise imbued with a tender
warmth of girlish womanhood. She was human; her nature was
endowed with all gentle and feminine qualities; she was worthiest
to be worshipped; she was capable, surely, on her part, of the
height and heroism of love. Those tokens which he had hitherto
considered as proofs of a frightful peculiarity in her physical and
moral system were now either forgotten, or, by the subtle sophis-
try of passion transmuted into a golden crown of enchantment,
rendering Beatrice the more admirable by so much as she was
the more unique. Whatever had looked ugly was now beautiful;
or, if incapable of such a change, it stole away and hid itself
among those shapeless half ideas which throng the dim region
beyond the daylight of our perfect consciousness.

Thus did he spend the night, nor fell asleep until the dawn had
begun to awake the slumbering flowers in Dr. Rappaccini's garden, whither Giovanni's dreams doubtless led him. Up rose the
sun in his due season, and, flinging his beams upon the young
man's eyelids, awoke him to a sense of pain. When thoroughly
aroused, he became sensible of a burning and tingling agony in
his hand — in his right hand — the very hand which Beatrice had
grasped in her own when he was on the point of plucking one of
the gemlike flowers. On the back of that hand there was now a
purple print like that of four small fingers, and the likeness of a
slender thumb upon his wrist.

Oh, how stubbornly does love, — or even that cunning sem-
blance of love which flourishes in the imagination, but strikes
no depth of root into the heart, — how stubbornly does it hold
its faith until the moment comes when it is doomed to vanish into
thin mist! Giovanni wrapped a handkerchief about his hand and
wondered what evil thing had stung him, and soon forgot his pain
in a reverie of Beatrice.

After the first interview, a second was in the inevitable course
of what we call fate. A third; a fourth; and a meeting with
Beatrice in the garden was no longer an incident in Giovanni's
daily life, but the whole space in which he might be said to live;
for the anticipation and memory of that ecstatic hour made up
the remainder. Nor was it otherwise with the daughter of Rappaccini. She watched for the youth's appearance, and flew to his

side with confidence as unreserved as if they had been playmates from early infancy — as if they were such playmates still. If, by any unwonted chance, he failed to come at the appointed moment, she stood beneath the window and sent up the rich sweetness of her tones to float around him in his chamber and echo and reverberate throughout his heart: "Giovanni! Giovanni! Why tarriest thou? Come down!" and down he hastened into that Eden of poisonous flowers.

But, with all this intimate familiarity, there was still a reserve in Beatrice's demeanor, so rigidly and invariably sustained that the idea of infringing it scarcely occurred to his imagination. By all appreciable signs, they loved; they had looked love with eyes that conveyed the holy secret from the depths of one soul into the depths of the other, as if it were too sacred to be whispered by the way; they had even spoken love in those gushes of passion when their spirits darted forth in articulated breath like tongues of long-hidden flame; and yet there had been no seal of lips, no clasp of hands, nor any slightest caress such as love claims and hallows. He had never touched one of the gleaming ringlets of her hair; her garment — so marked was the physical barrier between them — had never been waved against him by a breeze. On the few occasions when Giovanni had seemed tempted to overstep the limit, Beatrice grew so sad, so stern, and withal wore such a look of desolate separation, shuddering at itself, that not a spoken word was requisite to repel him. At such times he was startled at the horrible suspicions that rose, monster-like, out of the caverns of his heart and stared him in the face; his love grew thin and faint as the morning mist; his doubts alone had substance. But, when Beatrice's face brightened again after the momentary shadow, she was transformed at once from the mysterious, questionable being whom he had watched with so much awe and horror; she was now the beautiful and unsophisticated girl whom he felt that his spirit knew with a certainty beyond all other knowledge.

A considerable time had now passed since Giovanni's last meeting with Baglioni. One morning, however, he was disagreeably surprised by a visit from the professor, whom he had scarcely thought of for whole weeks, and would willingly have forgotten still longer. Given up as he had long been to a pervading excitement, he could tolerate no companions except upon condition of their perfect sympathy with his present state of feeling. Such sympathy was not to be expected from Professor Baglioni.

The visitor chatted carelessly for a few moments about the gossip of the city and the university, and then took up another topic.

"I have been reading an old classic author lately," said he, "and met with a story that strangely interested me. Possibly you may remember it. It is of an Indian prince, who sent a beautiful woman as a present to Alexander the Great. She was as lovely as the dawn and gorgeous as the sunset; but what especially distinguished her was a certain rich perfume in her breath — richer than a garden of Persian roses. Alexander, as was natural to a youthful conqueror, fell in love at first sight with this magnificent stranger; but a certain sage physician, happening to be present, discovered a terrible secret in regard to her."

"And what was that?" asked Giovanni, turning his eyes downward to avoid those of the professor.

"That this lovely woman," continued Baglioni, with emphasis, "had been nourished with poisons from her birth upward, until her whole nature was so imbued with them that she herself had become the deadliest poison in existence. Poison was her element of life. With that rich perfume of her breath she blasted the very air. Her love would have been poison — her embrace death. Is not this a marvelous tale?"

"A childish fable," answered Giovanni, nervously starting from his chair. "I marvel how your worship finds time to read such nonsense among your graver studies."

"By the by," said the professor, looking uneasily about him, "what singular fragrance is this in your apartment? Is it the perfume of your gloves? It is faint, but delicious; and yet, after all, by no means agreeable. Were I to breathe it long, methinks it would make me ill. It is like the breath of a flower; but I see no flowers in the chamber."

"Nor are there any," replied Giovanni, who had turned pale as the professor spoke; "nor, I think, is there any fragrance except in your worship's imagination. Odors, being a sort of element combined of the sensual and the spiritual, are apt to deceive us in this manner. The recollection of a perfume, the bare idea of it, may easily be mistaken for a present reality."

"Ay; but my sober imagination does not often play such tricks," said Baglioni; "and, were I to fancy any kind of odor, it would be that of some vile apothecary drug wherewith my fingers are likely enough to be imbued. Our worshipful friend Rappaccini, as I have heard, tinctures his medicaments with odors richer than those of Araby. Doubtless, likewise, the fair and learned Signora Beatrice would minister to her patients with draughts as sweet as a maiden's breath; but woe to him that sips them!"

Giovanni's face evinced many contending emotions. The tone in which the professor alluded to the pure and lovely daughter of Rappaccini was a torture to his soul; and yet the intimation of a view of her character, opposite to his own, gave instantaneous distinctness to a thousand dim suspicions, which now grinned at him like so many demons. But he strove hard to quell them and to respond to Baglioni with a true lover's perfect faith.

"Signor professor," said he, "you were my father's friend; perchance, too, it is your purpose to act a friendly part toward his son. I would fain feel nothing toward you save respect and deference; but I pray you to observe, signor, that there is one subject on which we must not speak. You know not the Signora Beatrice. You cannot, therefore, estimate the wrong — the blasphemy, I may even say — that is offered to her character by a light or injurious word."

"Giovanni! my poor Giovanni!" answered the professor, with a calm expression of pity, "I know this wretched girl far better than yourself. You shall hear the truth in respect to the poisoner Rappaccini and his poisonous daughter; yes, poisonous as she is beautiful. Listen; for, even should you do violence to my gray hairs, it shall not silence me. That old fable of the Indian woman has become a truth by the deep and deadly science of Rappaccini and in the person of the lovely Beatrice."

Giovanni groaned and hid his face.

"Her father," continued Baglioni, "was not restrained by natural affection from offering up his child in this horrible manner as the victim of his insane zeal for science; for, let us do him justice, he is as true a man of science as ever distilled his own heart in an alembic. What, then, will be your fate? Beyond a doubt you are selected as the material of some new experiment. Perhaps the result is to be death; perhaps a fate more awful still. Rappaccini, with what he calls the interest of science before his eyes, will hesitate at nothing."

"It is a dream," muttered Giovanni to himself; "surely it is a dream."

"But," resumed the professor, "be of good cheer, son of my friend. It is not yet too late for the rescue. Possibly we may even succeed in bringing back this miserable child within the limits of ordinary nature, from which her father's madness has estranged her. Behold this little silver vase! It was wrought by the hands of the renowned Benvenuto Cellini, and is well worthy to be a love gift to the fairest dame in Italy. But its contents are invaluable. One little sip of this antidote would have rendered the most virulent poisons of the Borgias innocuous. Doubt not that it will be as efficacious against those of Rappaccini. Bestow the vase, and the precious liquid within it, on your Beatrice, and hopefully await the result."

Baglioni laid a small, exquisitely wrought silver vial on the table and withdrew, leaving what he had said to produce its effect upon the young man's mind.

"We will thwart Rappaccini yet," thought he, chuckling to himself, as he descended the stairs; "but, let us confess the truth of him, he is a wonderful man — a wonderful man indeed; a vile empiric, however, in his practice, and therefore not to be tolerated by those who respect the good old rules of the medical profession."

Throughout Giovanni's whole acquaintance with Beatrice, he had occasionally, as we have said, been haunted by dark surmises as to her character; yet so thoroughly had she made herself felt by him as a simple, natural, most affectionate, and guileless creature, that the image now held up by Professor Baglioni looked as strange and incredible as if it were not in accordance with his own original conception. True, there were ugly recollections connected with his first glimpses of the beautiful girl; he could not quite forget the bouquet that withered in her grasp, and the insect that perished amid the sunny air, by no ostensible agency save the fragrance of her breath. These incidents, however, dissolving in the pure light of her character, had no longer the efficacy of facts, but were acknowledged as mistaken fantasies, by whatever testimony of the senses they might appear to be substantiated. There is something truer and more real than what we can see with the eyes and touch with the finger. On such better evidence had Giovanni founded his confidence in Beatrice, though rather by the necessary force of her high attributes than by any deep and generous faith on his part. But now his spirit was incapable of sustaining itself at the height to which the early enthusiasm of passion had exalted it; he fell down, groveling among earthly doubts, and defiled therewith the pure whiteness of Beatrice's image. Not that he gave her up; he did but distrust. He resolved to institute some decisive test that should satisfy him, once for all, whether there were those dreadful peculiarities in her physical nature which could not be supposed to exist without some corresponding monstrosity of soul. His eyes, gazing down afar, might have deceived him as to the lizard, the insect, and the flowers; but if he could witness, at the distance of a few paces, the sudden blight of one fresh and healthful flower in Beatrice's hand, there would be room for no further question. With this idea he hastened to the florist's and purchased a bouquet that was still gemmed with the morning dew-drops.

It was now the customary hour of his daily interview with Beatrice. Before descending into the garden, Giovanni failed not to look at his figure in the mirror, — a vanity to be expected in a beautiful young man, yet, as displaying itself at that troubled and feverish moment, the token of a certain shallowness of feeling and insincerity of character. He did gaze, however, and said to himself that his features had never before possessed so rich a grace, nor his eyes such vivacity, nor his cheeks so warm a hue of superabundant life.

"At least," thought he, "her poison has not yet insinuated itself into my system. I am no flower to perish in her grasp."

With that thought he turned his eyes on the bouquet, which he had never once laid aside from his hand. A thrill of indefinable horror shot through his frame on perceiving that those dewy flowers were already beginning to droop; they wore the aspect of things that had been fresh and lovely yesterday. Giovanni grew white as marble, and stood motionless before the mirror, staring at his own reflection there as at the likeness of something frightful. He remembered Baglioni's remark about the fragrance that seemed to pervade the chamber. It must have been the poison in his breath! Then he shuddered — shuddered at himself. Recovering from his stupor, he began to watch with curious eye a spider that was busily at work hanging its web from the antique cornice of the apartment, crossing and recrossing the artful sys-

tem of interwoven lines — as vigorous and active a spider as ever
dangled from an old ceiling. Giovanni bent toward the insect,
and emitted a deep, long breath. The spider suddenly ceased its
toil; the web vibrated with a tremor originating in the body of
the small artisan. Again Giovanni sent forth a breath, deeper,
longer, and imbued with a venomous feeling out of his heart; he
knew not whether he were wicked or only desperate. The spider
made a convulsive gripe with his limbs and hung dead across the
window.

"Accursed! accursed!" muttered Giovanni, addressing himself.
"Hast thou grown so poisonous that this deadly insect perishes by
thy breath?"

At that moment a rich, sweet voice came floating up from the
garden.

"Giovanni! Giovanni! It is past the hour! Why tarriest thou?
Come down!"

"Yes," muttered Giovanni again. "She is the only being whom
my breath may not slay! Would that it might!"

He rushed down, and in an instant was standing before the
bright and loving eyes of Beatrice. A moment ago his wrath and
despair had been so fierce that he could have desired nothing so
much as to wither her by a glance; but with her actual presence
there came influences which had too real an existence to be at once
shaken off: recollections of the delicate and benign power of her
feminine nature, which had so often enveloped him in a religious
calm; recollections of many a holy and passionate outgush of her
heart, when the pure fountain had been unsealed from its depths
and made visible in its transparency to his mental eye; recollections which, had Giovanni known how to estimate them, would
have assured him that all this ugly mystery was but an earthly
illusion, and that, whatever mist of evil might seem to have
gathered over her, the real Beatrice was a heavenly angel. Incapable as he was of such high faith, still her presence had not
utterly lost its magic. Giovanni's rage was quelled into an aspect
of sullen insensibility. Beatrice, with a quick spiritual sense, immediately felt that there was a gulf of blackness between them
which neither he nor she could pass. They walked on together,
sad and silent, and came thus to the marble fountain and to its
pool of water on the ground, in the midst of which grew the
shrub that bore gem-like blossoms. Giovanni was affrighted at

the eager enjoyment — the appetite, as it were — with which he found himself inhaling the fragrance of the flowers.

"Beatrice," asked he, abruptly, "whence came this shrub?"

"My father created it," answered she, with simplicity.

"Created it! created it!" repeated Giovanni. "What mean you, Beatrice?"

"He is a man fearfully acquainted with the secrets of Nature," replied Beatrice; "and at the hour when I first drew breath this plant sprang from the soil, the offspring of his science, of his intellect, while I was but his earthly child. Approach it not!" continued she, observing with terror that Giovanni was drawing nearer to the shrub. "It has qualities that you little dream of. But I, dearest Giovanni, — I grew up and blossomed with the plant and was nourished with its breath. It was my sister, and I loved it with a human affection; for, alas! — hast thou not suspected it? — there was an awful doom."

Here Giovanni frowned so darkly upon her that Beatrice paused and trembled. But her faith in his tenderness reassured her, and made her blush that she had doubted for an instant.

"There was an awful doom," she continued, "the effect of my father's fatal love of science, which estranged me from all society of my kind. Until Heaven sent thee, dearest Giovanni, oh, how lonely was thy poor Beatrice!"

"Was it a hard doom?" asked Giovanni, fixing his eyes upon her.

"Only of late have I known how hard it was," answered she, tenderly. "Oh, yes; but my heart was torpid, and therefore quiet."

Giovanni's rage broke forth from his sullen gloom like a lightning-flash out of a dark cloud.

"Accursed one!" cried he, with venomous scorn and anger. "And, finding thy solitude wearisome, thou hast severed me likewise from all the warmth of life and enticed me into thy region of unspeakable horror!"

"Giovanni!" exclaimed Beatrice, turning her large bright eyes upon his face. The force of his words had not found its way into her mind; she was merely thunderstruck.

"Yes, poisonous thing!" repeated Giovanni, beside himself with passion. "Thou hast done it! Thou hast blasted me! Thou hast filled my veins with poison! Thou hast made me as hateful, as ugly, as loathsome and deadly a creature as thyself — a world's wonder of hideous monstrosity! Now, if our breath be happily as fatal to ourselves as to all others, let us join our lips in one kiss of unutterable hatred, and so die!"

"What has befallen me?" murmured Beatrice, with a low moan out of her heart. "Holy Virgin, pity me, a poor heart-broken child!"

"Thou, — dost thou pray?" cried Giovanni, still with the same fiendish scorn. "Thy very prayers, as they come from thy lips, taint the atmosphere with death. Yes; let us pray! Let us to church and dip our fingers in the holy water at the portal! They that come after us will perish as by a pestilence! Let us sign crosses in the air! It will be scattering curses abroad in the likeness of holy symbols!"

"Giovanni," said Beatrice calmly, for her grief was beyond passion, "why dost thou join thyself with me thus in those terrible words? I, it is true, am the horrible thing thou namest me. But thou, — what has thou to do, save with one other shudder at my hideous misery to go forth out of the garden and mingle with thy race, and forget that there ever crawled on earth such a monster as poor Beatrice?"

"Dost thou pretend ignorance?" asked Giovanni, scowling upon her. "Behold! this power have I gained from the pure daughter of Rappaccini."

There was a swarm of summer insects flitting through the air in search of the food promised by the flower odors of the fatal garden. They circled round Giovanni's head, and were evidently attracted toward him by the same influence which had drawn them for an instant within the sphere of several of the shrubs. He sent forth a breath among them, and smiled bitterly at Beatrice as at least a score of the insects fell dead upon the ground.

"I see it! I see it!" shrieked Beatrice. "It is my father's fatal science! No, no, Giovanni; it was not I! Never, never! I dreamed only to love thee and be with thee a little time, and so to let thee pass away, leaving but thine image in mine heart. For, Giovanni, believe it, though my body be nourished with poison, my spirit is God's creature, and craves love as its daily food. But my father, — he has united us in this fearful sympathy. Yes; spurn me, tread upon me, kill me! Oh, what is death after such words as thine? But it was not I. Not for a world of bliss would I have done it."

Giovanni's passion had exhausted itself in its outburst from his lips. There now came across him a sense, mournful, and not without tenderness, of the intimate and peculiar relationship between Beatrice and himself. They stood, as it were, in an utter solitude, which would be made none the less solitary by the densest throng of human life. Ought not, then, the desert of humanity around them to press this insulated pair closely together? If they should be cruel to one another, who was there to be kind to them? Besides, thought Giovanni, might there not still be a hope of his returning within the limits of ordinary nature, and leading Beatrice, the redeemed Beatrice, by the hand? Oh, weak, and selfish, and unworthy spirit, that could dream of an earthly union and earthly happiness as possible after such deep love had been so bitterly wronged as was Beatrice's love by Giovanni's blighting words! No, no; there could be no such hope. She must pass heavily, with that broken heart, across the borders of Time — she must bathe her hurts in some fount of paradise, and forget her grief in the light of immorality, and *there* be well.

But Giovanni did not know it.

"Dear Beatrice," said he, approaching her, while she shrank away as always at his approach, but now with a different impulse, "dearest Beatrice, our fate is not yet so desperate. Behold! there is a medicine, potent, as a wise physician has assured me, and almost divine in its efficacy. It is composed of ingredients the most opposite to those by which thy awful father has brought this calamity upon thee and me. It is distilled of blessed herbs. Shall we not quaff it together, and thus be purified from evil?"

"Give it me!" said Beatrice, extending her hand to receive the little silver vial which Giovanni took from his bosom. She added, with a peculiar emphasis, "I will drink; but do thou await the result."

She put Baglioni's antidote to her lips; and, at the same moment, the figure of Rappaccini emerged from the portal and came slowly toward the marble fountain. As he drew near, the pale man of science seemed to gaze with a triumphant expression at the beautiful youth and maiden, as might an artist who should spend his life in achieving a picture or a group of statuary and finally be satisfied with his success. He paused; his bent form grew erect with conscious power; he spread out his hand over them in the attitude of a father imploring a blessing upon his children; but those were the same hands that had thrown poison into the stream of their lives. Giovanni trembled. Beatrice shuddered nervously, and pressed her hand upon her heart.

"My daughter," said Rappaccini, "thou art no longer lonely in the world. Pluck one of those precious gems from thy sister shrub and bid thy bridegroom wear it in his bosom. It will not harm him now. My science and the sympathy between thee and him have so wrought within his system that he now stands apart from common men, as thou dost, daughter of my pride and triumph, from ordinary women. Pass on, then, through the world, most dear to another and dreadful to all besides!"

"My father," said Beatrice, feebly, — and still as she spoke she kept her hand upon her heart, — "wherefore didst thou inflict this miserable doom upon thy child?"

"Miserable!" exclaimed Rappaccini. "What mean you, foolish girl? Dost thou deem it misery to be endowed with marvelous gifts against which no power nor strength could avail an enemy — misery, to be able to quell the mightiest with a breath — misery, to be as terrible as thou art beautiful? Wouldst thou, then, have preferred the condition of a weak woman, exposed to all evil and capable of none?"

"I would fain have been loved, not feared," murmured Beatrice, sinking down upon the ground. "But now it matters not. I am going, father, where the evil which thou hast striven to mingle with my being will pass away like a dream — like the fragrance of these poisonous flowers, which will no longer taint my breath among the flowers of Eden. Farewall, Giovanni! Thy words of hatred are like lead within my heart; but they, too, will fall away as I ascend. Oh, was there not, from the first, more poison in thy nature than in mine?"

To Beatrice, — so radically had her earthly part been wrought upon by Rappaccini's skill, — as poison had been life, so the powerful antidote was death; and thus the poor victim of man's ingenuity and of thwarted nature, and of the fatality that attends all such efforts of perverted wisdom, perished there, at the feet of her father and Giovanni.

Just at that moment Professor Pietro Baglioni looked forth from the window, and called loudly, in a tone of triumph mixed with horror, to the thunder-stricken man of science.

"Rappaccini! Rappaccini! And is *this* the upshot of your experiment!"

Questions   1. Hawthorne is preoccupied with the problems of
sin and guilt; in many of his stories, as well as his novels, he is concerned with depicting the effect of sin upon an individual or a group.
Long before the term *psychology* was invented, he was in many ways
a psychologist interested in examining the hidden motives which impel
men and women to act as they do. What is the *sin* underlying "Rappaccini's Daughter"? What are the impulses or compulsions which
cause the major characters of this story to act as they do? Who, if one
exists, is the "villain" in this story?   2. Hawthorne apparently was
fascinated by the fantastic and the bizarre; in this respect "Rappaccini's
Daughter" is characteristic. Are you convinced by these elements? If
so, what means has the author employed to convince you?   3. What
is the theme of this story? In what ways is it similar to or different
from that of "Young Goodman Brown"? Is this a "moral" story? Do
you consider it more or less pessimistic than "Young Goodman Brown"?
4. Could this story have taken place in the setting of "Young Goodman
Brown"? Would any of the characters have been at home in the Salem
of "Young Goodman Brown"?   5. What are the dominant character
traits of each person in the story? Do you feel that these characters are
convincing human beings? Write a brief character sketch of each.
6. Joseph Conrad, in the Preface to *The Nigger of the Narcissus*, states:
"A work that aspires, however humbly, to the condition of art should
carry its justification in every line. And art itself may be defined as a
single-minded attempt to render the highest kind of justice to the
visible universe, by bringing to light the truth, manifold and one,
underlying its every aspect. It is an attempt to find in its forms, in its
colours, in its light, in its shadows, in the aspects of matter and in the
facts of life what of each is fundamental, what is enduring and essential — their one illuminating and convincing quality — the very truth
of their existence. The artist, then, like the thinker or the scientist,
seeks the truth and makes his appeal." In what ways, if any, is this
applicable to either of these stories by Hawthorne?

AMBROSE BIERCE

Chickamauga

ONE SUNNY autumn afternoon a child strayed away from its rude home in a small field and entered a forest unobserved. It was happy in a new sense of freedom from control, happy in the opportunity of exploration and adventure; for this child's spirit, in bodies of its ancestors, had for thousands of years been trained to memorable feats of discovery and conquest — victories in battles whose critical moments were centuries, whose victors' camps were cities of hewn stone. From the cradle of its race it had conquered its way through two continents and passing a great sea had penetrated a third, there to be born to war and dominion as a heritage.

The child was a boy aged about six years, the son of a poor planter. In his younger manhood the father had been a soldier, had fought against naked savages and followed the flag of his country into the capital of a civilized race to the far South. In the peaceful life of a planter the warrior-fire survived; once kindled, it is never extinguished. The man loved military books and pictures and the boy had understood enough to make himself a wooden sword, though even the eye of his father would hardly have known it for what it was. This weapon he now bore bravely, as became the son of an heroic race, and pausing now and again in the sunny space of the forest assumed, with some exaggeration, the postures of aggression and defense that he had been taught by the engraver's art. Made reckless by the ease with which he overcame invisible foes attempting to stay his advance, he committed the common enough military error of

77

pushing the pursuit to a dangerous extreme, until he found himself upon the margin of a wide but shallow brook, whose rapid waters barred his direct advance against the flying foe that had crossed with illogical ease. But the intrepid victor was not to be baffled; the spirit of the race which had passed the great sea burned unconquerable in that small breast and would not be denied. Finding a place where some bowlders in the bed of the stream lay but a step or a leap apart, he made his way across and fell again upon the rear-guard of his imaginary foe, putting all to the sword.

Now that the battle had been won, prudence required that he withdraw to his base of operations. Alas; like many a mightier conqueror, and like one, the mightiest, he could not

> curb the lust for war,
> Nor learn that tempted Fate will leave the loftiest star.

Advancing from the bank of the creek he suddenly found himself confronted with a new and more formidable enemy: in the path that he was following, sat, bolt upright, with ears erect and paws suspended before it, a rabbit! With a startled cry the child turned and fled, he knew not in what direction, calling with inarticulate cries for his mother, weeping, stumbling, his tender skin cruelly torn by brambles, his little heart beating hard with terror — breathless, blind with tears — lost in the forest! Then, for more than an hour, he wandered with erring feet through the tangled undergrowth, till at last, overcome by fatigue, he lay down in a narrow space between two rocks, within a few yards of the stream and still grasping his toy sword, no longer a weapon but a companion, sobbed himself to sleep. The wood birds sang merrily above his head; the squirrels, whisking their bravery of tail, ran barking from tree to tree, unconscious of the pity of it, and somewhere far away was a strange, muffled thunder, as if the partridges were drumming in celebration of nature's victory over the son of her immemorial enslavers. And back at the little plantation, where white men and black were hastily searching the fields and hedges in alarm, a mother's heart was breaking for her missing child.

Hours passed, and then the little sleeper rose to his feet. The chill of the evening was in his limbs, the fear of the gloom in his heart. But he had rested, and he no longer wept. With some blind instinct which impelled to action he struggled through the undergrowth about him and came to a more open ground — on his right the brook, to the left a gentle acclivity studded with infrequent trees; over all, the gathering gloom of twilight. A thin, ghostly mist rose along the water. It frightened and repelled him; instead of recrossing, in the direction whence he had come, he turned his back upon it, and went forward toward the dark inclosing wood. Suddenly he saw before him a strange moving object which he took to be some large animal — a dog, a pig — he could not name it; perhaps it was a bear. He had seen pictures of bears, but knew of nothing to their discredit and had vaguely wished to meet one. But something in form or movement of this object — something in the awkwardness of its approach — told him that it was not a bear, and curiosity was stayed by fear. He stood still and as it came slowly on gained courage every moment, for he saw that at least it had not the long, menacing ears of the rabbit. Possibly his impressionable mind was half conscious of something familiar in its shambling, awkward gait. Before it had approached near enough to resolve his doubts he saw that it was followed by another and another. To right and to left were many more; the whole open space about him was alive with them — all moving toward the brook.

They were men. They crept upon their hands and knees. They used their hands only, dragging their legs. They used their knees only, their arms hanging idle at their sides. They strove to rise to their feet, but fell prone in the attempt. They did nothing naturally, and nothing alike, save only to advance foot by foot in the same direction. Singly, in pairs and in little groups, they came on through the gloom, some halting now and again while others crept slowly past them, then resuming their movement. They came by dozens and by hundreds; as far on either hand as one could see in the deepening gloom they extended and the black wood behind them appeared to be inexhaustible. The very ground seemed in motion toward the creek. Occasionally one who had paused did not again go on, but lay motionless. He was dead. Some, pausing, made strange gestures with their hands, erected their arms and lowered them again, clasped their heads; spread their palms upward, as men are sometimes seen to do in public prayer.

Not all of this did the child note; it is what would have been noted by an elder observer; he saw little but that these were men, yet crept like babes. Being men, they were not terrible, though unfamiliarly clad. He moved among them freely, going from one to another and peering into their faces with childish curiosity. All their faces were singularly white and many were streaked and gouted with red. Something in this — something too, perhaps, in their grotesque attitudes and movements — reminded him of the painted clown whom he had seen last summer in the circus, and he laughed as he watched them. But on and ever on they crept, these maimed and bleeding men, as heedless as he of the dramatic contrast between his laughter and their own ghastly gravity. To him it was a merry spectacle. He had seen his father's negroes creep upon their hands and knees for his amusement — had ridden them so, "making believe" they were his horses. He now approached one of these crawling figures from behind and with an agile movement mounted it astride. The man sank upon his breast, recovered, flung the small boy fiercely to the ground as an unbroken colt might have done, then turned upon him a face that lacked a lower jaw — from the upper teeth to the throat was a great red gap fringed with hanging shreds of flesh and splinters of bone. The unnatural prominence of nose, the absence of chin, the fierce eyes, gave this man the appearance of a great bird of prey crimsoned in throat and breast by the blood of its quarry. The man rose to his knees, the child to his feet. The man shook his fist at the child; the child, terrified at last, ran to a tree near by, got upon the farther side of it and took a more serious view of the situation. And so the clumsy multitude dragged itself slowly and painfully along in hideous pantomime — moved forward down the slope like a swarm of great black beetles, with never a sound of going — in silence profound, absolute.

Instead of darkening, the haunted landscape began to brighten. Through the belt of trees beyond the brook shone a strange red light, the trunks and branches of the trees making a black lacework against it. It struck the creeping figures and gave them monstrous shadows, which caricatured their movements on the lit grass. It fell upon their faces, touching their whiteness with a ruddy tinge, accentuating the stains with which so many of them were freaked and maculated. It sparkled on buttons and bits of metal in their clothing. Instinctively the child turned toward the growing splendor and moved down the slope with his horrible companions; in a few moments had passed the foremost of the throng — not much of a feat, considering his advantages. He placed himself in the lead, his wooden sword still in hand, and solemnly directed the march, conforming his pace to theirs and occasionally turning as if to see that his forces did not straggle. Surely such a leader never before had such a following.

Scattered about upon the ground now slowly narrowing by the encroachment of this awful march to water, were certain articles to which, in the leader's mind, were coupled no significant associations; an occasional blanket, tightly rolled lengthwise, doubled and the ends bound together with a string; a heavy knapsack here, and there a broken rifle — such things, in short, as are found in the rear of retreating troops, the "spoor" of men flying from their hunters. Everywhere near the creek, which here had a margin of lowland, the earth was trodden into mud by the feet of men and horses. An observer of better experience in the use of his eyes would have noticed that these footprints pointed in both directions; the ground had been twice passed over — in advance and in retreat. A few hours before, these desperate, stricken men, with their more fortunate and now distant comrades, had penetrated the forest in thousands. Their successive battalions, breaking into swarms and re-forming in lines, had passed the child on every side — had almost trodden on him as he slept. The rustle and murmur of their march had not awakened him. Almost within a stone's throw of where he lay they had fought a battle; but all unheard by him were the roar of the musketry, the shock of the cannon, "the thunder of the captains and the shouting." He had slept through it all, grasping his little wooden sword with perhaps a tighter clutch in unconscious sympathy with his martial environment, but as heedless of the grandeur of the struggle as the dead who had died to make the glory.

The fire beyond the belt of woods on the farther side of the creek, reflected to earth from the canopy of its own smoke, was now suffusing the whole landscape. It transformed the sinuous line of mist to the vapor of gold. The water gleamed with dashes of red, and red, too, were many of the stones protruding above the surface. But that was blood; the less desperately wounded had stained them in crossing. On them, too, the child now crossed wtih eager steps; he was going to the fire. As he stood upon the farther bank he turned about to look at the companions of his march. The advance was arriving at the creek. The stronger had already drawn themselves to the brink and plunged their faces into the flood. Three or four who lay without motion appeared to have no heads. At this the child's eyes expanded with wonder; even his hospitable understanding could not accept a phenomenon implying such vitality as that. After slaking their thirst these men had not had the strength to back away from the water, nor to keep their heads above it. They were drowned. In rear of these, the open spaces of the forest showed the leader as many formless figures of his grim command as at first; but not nearly so many were in motion. He waved his cap for their encouragement and smilingly pointed with his weapon in the direction of the guiding light — a pillar of fire to this strange exodus.

Confident of the fidelity of his forces, he now entered the belt of woods, passed through it easily in the red illumination, climbed a fence, ran across a field, turning now and again to coquet with his responsive shadow, and so approached the blazing ruin of a dwelling. Desolation everywhere! In all the wide glare not a living thing was visible. He cared nothing for that; the spectacle pleased, and he danced with glee in imitation of the wavering flames. He ran about, collecting fuel, but every object that he found was too heavy for him to cast in from the distance to which the heat limited his approach. In despair he flung in his sword — a surrender to the superior forces of nature. His military career was at an end.

Shifting his position, his eyes fell upon some outbuildings which had an oddly familiar appearance, as if he had dreamed of them. He stood considering them with wonder, when suddenly the entire plantation, with its inclosing forest, seemed to turn as if upon a pivot. His little world swung half around; the points of the compass were reversed. He recognized the blazing building as his own home!

For a moment he stood stupefied by the power of the revelation, then ran with stumbling feet, making a half-circuit of the ruin. There, conspicuous in the light of the conflagration, lay the dead body of a woman — the white face turned upward, the hands thrown out and clutched full of grass, the clothing deranged, the long dark hair in tangles and full of clotted blood. The greater part of the forehead was torn away, and from the jagged hole the brain protruded, overflowing the temple, a frothy mass of gray, crowned with clusters of crimson bubbles — the work of a shell.

The child moved his little hands, making wild, uncertain gestures. He uttered a series of inarticulate and indescribable cries — something between the chattering of an ape and the gobbling of a turkey — a startling, soulless, unholy sound, the language of a devil. The child was a deaf mute.

Then he stood motionless, with quivering lips, looking down upon the wreck.

Ambrose Bierce (1842-1914?)   After a childhood of grinding poverty in Meigs County, Ohio, Ambrose Bierce enlisted in the Union Army shortly after the beginning of the Civil War and served for the duration. Twice wounded, he suffered a severe head-injury during the Battle of Kenesaw Mountain; years later his brother Albert attributed Bierce's black pessimism and unrelenting bitterness to this event. After the war Bierce became a prolific, controversial, and scathing journalist whom H. L. Mencken later called the keenest wit of America. His private life, like his fiction, was bleak and bitter; his marriage ended in disaster, and tragedy dogged the footsteps of his two sons. In 1913, a still-bitter Bierce left America for Mexico, and for a time was on the staff of the Mexican revolutionary leader, Pancho Villa. His death is shrouded in mystery.

Bierce's sardonic stories, first published as a volume originally entitled *Tales of Soldiers and Civilians*, in 1891, are a memorable combination of violence and horror. Life in Bierce's literary cosmos is a doomed charade; man is a helpless puppet; death is everywhere. Many of his stories depend heavily for effect on coincidence, and are sometimes weakened by an accumulation of horror or an unconvincing trick ending. At their best, however — as exampled in "Chickamauga" — they occupy a permanent, if limited, place in American literature.

The clarity of style and narrative simplicity of "Chickamauga" are unusual for the age in which the story was written. Even more impressive is the overwhelming effect of horror which is created. By the use of objective detail, Bierce produces the illusion of reality.

On the other hand, with such grotesque images as that of the child astride the back of the wounded soldier, or the painfully slow, deathly quiet group of wounded and maimed men crawling towards the water, Bierce achieves an almost surrealistic effect foreshadowing the work of Kafka. The final impression of "Chickamauga" is more that of a horrible fantasy than a realistic depiction of the aftermath of an actual battle.

In the Midst of Life (Original title, *Tales of Soldiers and Civilians*) in which "Chickamauga" appeared, is not at present available in any inexpensive edition.

Questions   1. Compare or contrast "Chickamauga" with other war stories in the text, such as Gascar's "The Horses" or Lagerkvist's "The Children's Campaign." In what ways are the techniques similar or dissimilar? In what ways are the final impressions similar or dissimilar?   2. What, if anything, does Bierce gain by making the child a deaf mute?   3. Do you feel that the final accumulation of horror at the end of the story adds to or detracts from the final artistic effect? 4. What means or devices does Bierce employ to create the illusion of reality?   5. Discuss the use and effect of contrast and paradox in "Chickamauga."   6. Bierce's stories have frequently been compared to those of Poe, although his friend George Sterling denounces such comparison as absurd. Judging from "Chickamauga," do you agree or disagree with Sterling?

HENRY JAMES

Brooksmith

WE are scattered now, the friends of the late Mr. Oliver Offord; but whenever we chance to meet I think we are conscious of a certain esoteric respect for each other. "Yes, you too have been in Arcadia," we seem not too grumpily to allow. When I pass the house in Mansfield Street I remember that Arcadia was there. I don't know who has it now, and don't want to know; it's enough to be so sure that if I should ring the bell there would be no such luck for me as that Brooksmith should open the door. Mr. Offord, the most agreeable, the most attaching of bachelors, was a retired diplomatist, living on his pension and on something of his own over and above; a good deal confined, by his infirmities, to his fireside and delighted to be found there any afternoon in the year, from five o'clock on, by such visitors as Brooksmith allowed to come up. Brooksmith was his butler and his most intimate friend, to whom we all stood, or I should say sat, in the same relation in which the subject of the sovereign finds himself to the prime minister. By having been for years, in foreign lands, the most delightful Englishman any one had ever known, Mr. Offord had in my opinion rendered signal service to his country. But I suppose he had been too much liked — liked even by those who didn't like *it* — so that as people of that sort never get titles or dotations for the horrid things they've *not* done, his principal reward was simply that we went to see him.

Oh we went perpetually, and it was not our fault if he was not overwhelmed with this particular honour. Any visitor who came once came again; to come merely once was a slight nobody, I'm

sure, had ever put upon him. His circle therefore was essentially
composed of habitués, who were habitués for each other as well
as for him, as those of a happy salon should be. I remember
vividly every element of the place, down to the intensely Lon-
donish look of the grey opposite houses, in the gap of the white
curtains of the high windows, and the exact spot where, on a
particular afternoon, I put down my tea-cup for Brooksmith,
lingering an instant, to gather it up as if he were plucking a
flower. Mr. Offord's drawing-room was indeed Brooksmith's garden, his pruned and tended human parterre, and if we all flourished there and grew well in our places it was largely owing to
his supervision.

Many persons have heard much, though most have doubtless
seen little, of the famous institution of the salon, and many are
born to the depression of knowing that this finest flower of social
life refuses to bloom where the English tongue is spoken. The
explanation is usually that our women have not the skill to cultivate it — the art to direct through a smiling land, between suggestive shores, a sinuous stream of talk. My affectionate, my
pious memory of Mr. Offord contradicts this induction only, I
fear, more insidiously to confirm it. The sallow and slightly
smoked drawing-room in which he spent so large a portion of the
last years of his life certainly deserved the distinguished name;
but on the other hand it couldn't be said at all to owe its stamp
to any intervention throwing into relief the fact that there was
no Mrs. Offord. The dear man had indeed, at the most, been
capable of one of those sacrifices to which women are deemed
peculiarly apt: he had recognised — under the influence, in some
degree, it is true, of physical infirmity — that if you wish people
to find you at home you must manage not to be out. He had in
short accepted the truth which many dabblers in the social art
are slow to learn, that you must really, as they say, take a line,
and that the only way as yet discovered of being at home is to
stay at home. Finally his own fireside had become a summary
of his habits. Why should he ever have left it? — since this
would have been leaving what was notoriously pleasantest in
London, the compact charmed cluster (thinning away indeed
into casual couples) round the fine old last-century chimney-
piece which, with the exception of the remarkable collection of
miniatures, was the best thing the place contained. Mr. Offord

wasn't rich; he had nothing but his pension and the use for life of the somewhat superannuated house.

When I'm reminded by some opposed discomfort of the present hour how perfectly we were all handled there, I ask myself once more what had been the secret of such perfection. One had taken it for granted at the time, for anything that is supremely good produces more acceptance than surprise. I felt we were all happy, but I didn't consider how our happiness was managed. And yet there were questions to be asked, questions that strike me as singularly obvious now that there's nobody to answer them. Mr. Offord had solved the insoluble; he had, without feminine help — save in the sense that ladies were dying to come to him and that he saved the lives of several — established a salon; but I might have guessed that there was a method in his madness, a law in his success. He hadn't hit it off by a mere fluke. There was an art in it all, and how was the art so hidden? Who indeed if it came to that was the occult artist? Launching this enquiry the other day I had already got hold of the tail of my reply. I was helped by the very wonder of some of the conditions that came back to me — those that used to seem as natural as sunshine in a fine climate.

How was it for instance that we never were a crowd, never either too many or too few, always the right people *with* the right people — there must really have been no wrong people at all — always coming and going, never sticking fast nor overstaying, yet never popping in or out with an indecorous familiarity? How was it that we all sat where we wanted and moved when we wanted and met whom we wanted and escaped whom we wanted; joining, according to the accident of inclination, the general circle or falling in with a single talker on a convenient sofa? Why were all the sofas so convenient, the accidents so happy, the talkers so ready, the listeners so willing, the subjects presented to you in a rotation as quickly foreordained as the courses at dinner? A dearth of topics would have been as unheard of as a lapse in the service. These speculations couldn't fail to lead me to the fundamental truth that Brooksmith had been somehow at the bottom of the mystery. If he hadn't established the salon at least he had carried it on. Brooksmith in short was the artist!

We felt this covertly at the time, without formulating it, and

were conscious, as an ordered and prosperous community, of his
evenhanded justice, all untainted with flunkeyism. He had none
of that vulgarity — his touch was infinitely fine. The delicacy
of it was clear to me on the first occasion my eyes rested, as they
were so often to rest again, on the domestic revealed, in the
turbid light of the street, by the opening of the house-door. I
saw on the spot that though he had plenty of school he carried
it without arrogance — he had remained articulate and human.
L'École Anglaise Mr. Offord used laughingly to call him when,
later on, it happened more than once that we had some conversation about him. But I remember accusing Mr. Offord of not
doing him quite ideal justice. That he wasn't one of the giants
of the school, however, was admitted by my old friend, who
really understood him perfectly and was devoted to him, as I
shall show; which doubtless poor Brooksmith had himself felt,
to his cost, when his value in the market was originally determined. The utility of his class in general is estimated by the
foot and the inch, and poor Brooksmith had only about five feet
three to put into circulation. He acknowledged the inadequacy
of this provision, and I'm sure was penetrated with the everlast-
ing fitness of the relation between service and stature. If *he* had
been Mr. Offord he certainly would have found Brooksmith wanting, and indeed the laxity of his employer on this score was one
of many things he had had to condone and to which he had at
last indulgently adapted himself.

I remember the old man's saying to me: "Oh my servants, if
they can live with me a fortnight they can live with me for ever.
But it's the first fortnight that tries 'em." It was in the first fortnight for instance that Brooksmith had had to learn that he was
exposed to being addressed as "my dear fellow" and "my poor
child." Strange and deep must such a probation have been to
him, and he doubtless emerged from it tempered and purified.
This was written to a certain extent in his appearance; in his
spare brisk little person, in his cloistered white face and extraor-
dinarily polished hair, which told of responsibility, looked as if
it were kept up to the same high standard as the plate; in his
small clear anxious eyes, even in the permitted, though not
exactly encouraged, tuft on his chin. "He thinks me rather mad,
but I've broken him in, and now he likes the place, he likes the
company," said the old man. I embraced this fully after I had be-

come aware that Brooksmith's main characteristic was a deep and shy refinement, though I remember I was rather puzzled when, on another occasion, Mr. Offord remarked: "What he likes is the talk — mingling in the conversation." I was conscious I had never seen Brooksmith permit himself this freedom, but I guessed in a moment that what Mr. Offord alluded to was a participation more intense than any speech could have represented — that of being perpetually present on a hundred legitimate pretexts, errands, necessities, and breathing the very atmosphere of criticism, the famous criticism of life. "Quite an education, sir, isn't it, sir?" he said to me one day at the foot of the stairs when he was letting me out; and I've always remembered the words and the tone as the first sign of the quickening drama of poor Brooksmith's fate. It was indeed an education, but to what was this sensitive young man of thirty-five, of the servile class, being educated?

Practically and inevitably, for the time, to companionship, to the perpetual, the even exaggerated reference and appeal of a person brought to dependence by his time of life and his infirmities and always addicted moreover — this was the exaggeration — to the art of giving you pleasure by letting you do things for him. There were certain things Mr. Offord was capable of pretending he liked you to do even when he didn't — this, I mean, if he thought *you* liked them. If it happened that you didn't either — which was rare, yet might be — of course there were cross-purposes; but Brooksmith was there to prevent their going very far. This was precisely the way he acted as moderator; he averted misunderstandings or cleared them up. He had been capable, strange as it may appear, of acquiring for this purpose an insight into the French tongue, which was often used at Mr. Offord's; for besides being habitual to most of the foreigners, and they were many, who haunted the place or arrived with letters — letters often requiring a little worried consideration, of which Brooksmith always had cognisance — it had really become the primary language of the master of the house. I don't know if all the *malentendus* were in French, but almost all the explanations were, and this didn't a bit prevent Brooksmith's following them. I know Mr. Offord used to read passages to him from Montaigne and Saint-Simon, for he read perpetually when alone — when *they* were alone, that is — and Brooksmith was always about. Perhaps you'll say no wonder Mr. Offord's butler regarded him as "rather mad." However, if I'm not sure what he thought about Montaigne I'm convinced he admired Saint-Simon. A certain feeling for letters must have rubbed off on him from the mere handling of his master's books, which he was always carrying to and fro and putting back in their places.

I often noticed that if an anecdote or a quotation, much more a lively discussion, was going forward, he would, if busy with the fire or the curtains, the lamp or the tea, find a pretext for remaining in the room till the point should be reached. If his purpose was to catch it you weren't discreet, you were in fact scarce human, to call him off, and I shall never forget a look, a hard stony stare — I caught it in its passage — which, one day when there were a good many people in the room, he fastened upon the footman who was helping him in the service and who, in an undertone, had asked him some irrelevant question. It was the only manifestation of harshness I ever observed on Brooksmith's part, and I at first wondered what was the matter. Then I became conscious that Mr. Offord was relating a very curious anecdote, never before perhaps made so public, and imparted to the narrator by an eye-witness of the fact, bearing on Lord Byron's life in Italy. Nothing would induce me to reproduce it here, but Brooksmith had been in danger of losing it. If I ever should venture to reproduce it I shall feel how much I lose in not having my fellow auditor to refer to.

The first day Mr. Offord's door was closed was therefore a dark date in contemporary history. It was raining hard and my umbrella was wet, but Brooksmith received it from me exactly as if this were a preliminary for going upstairs. I observed however that instead of putting it away he held it poised and trickling over the rug, and I then became aware that he was looking at me with deep acknowledging eyes — his air of universal responsibility. I immediately understood — there was scarce need of question and answer as they passed between us. When I took in that our good friend had given up as never before, though only for the occasion, I exclaimed dolefully: "What a difference it will make— and to how many people!"

"I shall be one of them, sir!" said Brooksmith; and that was the beginning of the end.

Mr. Offord came down again, but the spell was broken, the

great sign being that the conversation was for the first time not directed. It wandered and stumbled, a little frightened, like a lost child — it had let go the nurse's hand. "The worst of it is that now we shall talk about my health — *c'est la fin de tout*," Mr. Offord said when he reappeared; and then I recognised what a note of change that would be — for he had never tolerated anything so provincial. We "ran" to each other's health as little as to the daily weather. The talk became ours, in a word — not his; and as ours, even when *he* talked, it could only be inferior. In this form it was a distress to Brooksmith, whose attention now wandered from it altogether: he had so much closer a vision of his master's intimate conditions than our superficialities represented. There were better hours, and he was more in and out of the room, but I could see he was conscious of the decline, almost of the collapse, of our great institution. He seemed to wish to take counsel with me about it, to feel responsible for its going on in some form or other. When for the second period — the first had lasted several days — he had to tell me that his employer didn't receive, I half-expected to hear him say after a moment "Do you think I ought to, sir, in his place?" — as he might have asked me, with the return of autumn, if I thought he had better light the drawing-room fire.

He had a resigned philosophic sense of what his guests — our guests, as I came to regard them in our colloquies — would expect. His feeling was that he wouldn't absolutely have approved of himself as a substitute for Mr. Offord; but he was so saturated with the religion of habit that he would have made, for our friends, the necessary sacrifice to the divinity. He would take them on a little further and till they could look about them. I think I saw him also mentally confronted with the opportunity to deal — for once in his life — with some of his own dumb preferences, his limitations of sympathy, *weeding* a little in prospect and returning to a purer tradition. It was not unknown to me that he considered that toward the end of our host's career a certain laxity of selection had crept in.

At last it came to be the case that we all found the closed door more often than the open one; but even when it was closed Brooksmith managed a crack for me to squeeze through; so that practically I never turned away without having paid a visit. The difference simply came to be that the visit was to Brooksmith. It took place in the hall, at the familiar foot of the stairs, and we didn't sit down, at least Brooksmith didn't; moreover it was devoted wholly to one topic and always had the air of being already over — beginning, so to say, at the end. But it was always interesting — it always gave me something to think about. It's true that the subject of my meditation was ever the same — ever "It's all very well, but what *will* become of Brooksmith?" Even my private answer to this question left me still unsatisfied. No doubt Mr. Offord would provide for him, but *what* would he provide? — that was the great point. He couldn't provide society; and society had become a necessity of Brooksmith's nature. I must add that he never showed a symptom of what I may call sordid solicitude — anxiety on his own account. He was rather livid and intensely grave, as befitted a man before whose eyes the "shade of that which once was great" was passing away. He had the solemnity of a person winding up, under depressing circumstances, a long-established and celebrated business; he was a kind of social executor or liquidator. But his manner seemed to testify exclusively to the uncertainty of *our* future. I couldn't in those days have afforded it — I lived in two rooms in Jermyn Street and didn't "keep a man"; but even if my income had permitted I shouldn't have ventured to say to Brooksmith (emulating Mr. Offord) "My dear fellow, I'll take you on." The whole tone of our intercourse was so much more an implication that it was *I* who should now want a lift. Indeed there was a tacit assurance in Brooksmith's whole attitude that he should have me on his mind.

One of the most assiduous members of our circle had been Lady Kenyon, and I remember his telling me one day that her ladyship had in spite of her own infirmities, lately much aggravated, been in person to inquire. In answer to this I remarked that she would feel it more than any one. Brooksmith had a pause before saying in a certain tone — there's no reproducing some of his tones — "I'll go and see her." I went to see her myself and learned he had waited on her; but when I said to her, in the form of a joke but with a core of earnest, that when all was over some of us ought to combine, to club together, and set Brooksmith up on his own account, she replied a trifle disappointingly: "Do you mean in a public-house?" I looked at her in a way that I think Brooksmith himself would have approved, and then I answered: "Yes, the Offord Arms." What I had meant of course was that for the love of art itself we ought to look to it that such a peculiar faculty and so much acquired experience shouldn't be wasted. I really think that if we had caused a few black-edged cards to be struck off and circulated — "Mr. Brooksmith will continue to receive on the old premises from four to seven; business carried on as usual during the alterations" — the greater number of us would have rallied.

Several times he took me upstairs — always by his own proposal — and our dear old friend, in bed (in a curious flowered and brocaded casaque which made him, especially as his head was tied up in a handkerchief to match, look, to my imagination, like the dying Voltaire) held for ten minutes a sadly shrunken little salon. I felt indeed each time as if I were attending the last *coucher* of some social sovereign. He was royally whimsical about his sufferings and not at all concerned — quite as if the Constitution provided for the case — about his successor. He glided over *our* sufferings charmingly, and none of his jokes — it was a gallant abstention, some of them would have been so easy — were at our expense. Now and again, I confess, there was one at Brooksmith's, but so pathetically sociable as to make the excellent man look at me in a way that seemed to say: "Do exchange a glance with me, or I shan't be able to stand it." What he wasn't able to stand was not what Mr. Offord said about him, but what he wasn't able to say in return. His idea of conversation for himself was giving you the convenience of speaking to him; and when he went to "see" Lady Kenyon for instance it was to carry her the tribute of his receptive silence. Where would the speech of his betters have been if proper service had been a manifestation of sound? In that case the fundamental difference would have had to be shown by *their* dumbness, and many of them, poor things, were dumb enough without that provision. Brooksmith took an unfailing interest in the preservation of the fundamental difference; it was the thing he had most on his conscience.

What had become of it however when Mr. Offord passed away like any inferior person — was relegated to eternal stillness after the manner of a butler above-stairs? His aspect on the event — for the several successive days — may be imagined, and the multiplication by funereal observance of the things he didn't say. When everything was over — it was late the same day — I knocked at the door of the house of mourning as I so often had done before. I could never call on Mr. Offord again, but I had come literally to call on Brooksmith. I wanted to ask him if there was anything I could do for him, tainted with vagueness as this enquiry could only be. My presumptuous dream of taking him into my own service had died away: my service wasn't worth his being taken into. My offer could only be to help him to find another place, and yet there was an indelicacy, as it were, in taking for granted that his thoughts would immediately be fixed on another. I had a hope that he would be able to give his life a different form — though certainly not the form, the frequent result of such bereavements, of his setting up a little shop. That would have been dreadful; for I should have wished to forward any enterprise he might embark in, yet how could I have brought myself to go and pay him shillings and take back coppers over a counter? My visit then was simply an intended compliment. He took it as such, gratefully and with all the tact in the world. He knew I really couldn't help him and that I knew he knew I couldn't; but we discussed the situation — with a good deal of elegant generality — at the foot of the stairs, in the hall already dismantled, where I had so often discussed other situations with him. The executors were in possession, as was still more apparent when he made me pass for a few minutes into the dining-room, where various objects were muffled up for removal.

Two definite facts, however, he had to communicate; one being that he was to leave the house for ever that night (servants, for some mysterious reason, seem always to depart by night), and the other — he mentioned it only at the last and with hesitation — that he was already aware his late master had left him a legacy of eighty pounds. "I'm very glad," I said, and Brooksmith was of the same mind: "It was so like him to think of me." This was all that passed between us on the subject, and I know nothing of his judgement of Mr. Offord's memento. Eighty pounds are always eighty pounds, and no one has ever left *me* an equal sum; but, all the same, for Brooksmith, I was disappointed. I don't know what I had expected, but it was almost a shock. Eighty pounds might stock a small shop — a *very* small shop; but, I repeat, I couldn't bear to think of that. I asked my friend if he had been able to save a little, and he replied: "No, sir; I've had

to do things." I didn't enquire what things they might have
been; they were his own affair, and I took his word for them as
assentingly as if he had had the greatness of an ancient house
to keep up; especially as there was something in his manner that
seemed to convey a prospect of further sacrifice.

"I shall have to turn round a bit, sir — I shall have to look
about me," he said; and then he added indulgently, magnani-
mously: "If you should happen to hear of anything for me — "

I couldn't let him finish; this was, in its essence, too much in
the really grand manner. It would be a help to my getting him
off my mind to be able to pretend I *could* find the right place,
and that help he wished to give me, for it was doubtless painful
to him to see me in so false a position. I interposed with a few
words to the effect of how well aware I was that wherever he
should go, whatever he should do, he would miss our old friend
terribly — miss him even more than I should, having been with
him so much more. This led him to make the speech that has
remained with me as the very text of the whole episode.

"Oh sir, it's sad for *you*, very sad indeed, and for a great many
gentlemen and ladies; that it is, sir. But for me, sir, it is, if I may
say so, still graver even than that: it's just the loss of something
that was everything. For me, sir," he went on with rising tears,
"he was just *all*, if you know what I mean, sir. You have others,
sir, I dare say — not that I would have you understand me to
speak of them as in any way tantamount. But you have the pleasures of society, sir; if it's only in talking about him, sir, as I dare
say you do freely — for all his blest memory has to fear from it
— with gentlemen and ladies who have had the same honour.
That's not for me, sir, and I've to keep my associations to myself.
Mr. Offord was *my* society, and now, you see, I just haven't any.
You go back to conversation, sir, after all, and I go back to my
place," Brooksmith stammered, without exaggerated irony or
dramatic bitterness, but with a flat unstudied veracity and his
hand on the knob of the street-door. He turned it to let me out
and then he added: "I just go downstairs, sir, again, and I stay
there."

"My poor child," I replied in my emotion, quite as Mr. Offord
used to speak, "my dear fellow, leave it to me: *we'll* look after
you, we'll all do something for you."

"Ah if you could give me some one *like* him! But there ain't two such in the world," Brooksmith said as we parted.

He had given me his address — the place where he would be to be heard of. For a long time I had no occasion to make use of the information: he proved on trial so very difficult a case. The people who knew him and had known Mr. Offord didn't want to take him, and yet I couldn't bear to try to thrust him among strangers — strangers to his past when not to his present. I spoke to many of our old friends about him and found them all governed by the odd mixture of feelings of which I myself was conscious — as well as disposed, further, to entertain a suspicion that he was "spoiled," with which I then would have nothing to do. In plain terms a certain embarrassment, a sensible awkwardness when they thought of it, attached to the idea of using him as a menial: they had met him so often in society. Many of them would have asked him, and did ask him, or rather did ask me to ask him, to come and see them; but a mere visiting-list was not what I wanted for him. He was too short for people who were very particular; nevertheless I heard of an opening in a diplomatic household which led me to write him a note, though I was looking much less for something grand than for something human. Five days later I heard from him. The secretary's wife had decided, after keeping him waiting till then, that she couldn't take a servant out of a house in which there hadn't been a lady. The note had a P.S.: "It's a good job there wasn't, sir, such a lady as some."

A week later he came to see me and told me he was "suited," committed to some highly respectable people — they were something quit immense in the City — who lived on the Bayswater side of the Park. "I dare say it will be rather poor, sir," he admitted; "but I've seen the fireworks, haven't I, sir? — it can't be fireworks *every* night. After Mansfield Street there ain't much choice." There was a certain amount, however, it seemed; for the following year, calling one day on a country cousin, a lady of a certain age who was spending a fortnight in town with some friends of her own, a family unknown to me and resident in Chester Square, the door of the house was opened, to my surprise and gratification, by Brooksmith in person. When I came out I had some conversation with him from which I gathered that he had found the large City people too dull for endurance, and I guessed, though he didn't say it, that he had found them vulgar as well. I don't know what judgement he would have passed on his actual patrons if my relative hadn't been their friend; but in view of that connexion he abstained from comment.

None was necessary, however, for before the lady in question brought her visit to a close they honoured me with an invitation to dinner, which I accepted. There was a largeish party on the occasion, but I confess I thought of Brooksmith rather more than of the seated company. They required no depth of attention — they were all referable to usual irredeemable inevitable types. It was the world of cheerful commonplace and conscious gentility and prosperous density, a full-fed material insular world, a world of hideous florid plate and ponderous order and thin conversation. There wasn't a word said about Byron, or even about a minor bard then much in view. Nothing would have induced me to look at Brooksmith in the course of the repast, and I felt sure that not even my overturning the wine would have induced him to meet my eye. We were in intellectual sympathy — we felt, as regards each other, a degree of social responsibility. In short we had been in Arcadia together, and we had both come to *this!* No wonder we were ashamed to be confronted. When he had helped on my overcoat, as I was going away, we parted, for the first time since the earliest days of Mansfield Street, in silence. I thought he looked lean and wasted, and I guessed that his new place wasn't more "human" than his previous one. There was plenty of beef and beer, but there was no reciprocity. The question for him to have asked before accepting the position wouldn't have been "How many footmen are kept?" but "How much imagination?"

The next time I went to the house — I confess it wasn't very soon — I encountered his successor, a personage who evidently enjoyed the good fortune of never having quitted his natural level. Could any be higher? he seemed to ask — over the heads of three footmen and even of some visitors. He made me feel as if Brooksmith were dead; but I didn't dare to enquire — I couldn't have borne his "I haven't the least idea, sir." I dispatched a note to the address that worthy had given me after Mr. Offord's death, but I received no answer. Six months later however I was favoured with a visit from an elderly dreary

dingy person who introduced herself to me as Mr. Brooksmith's
aunt and from whom I learned that he was out of place and out
of health and had allowed her to come and say to me that if I
could spare half an hour to look in at him he would take it as a
rare honour.

I went the next day — his messenger had given me a new address — and found my friend lodged in a short sordid street in
Marylebone, one of those corners of London that wear the last
expression of sickly meanness. The room into which I was shown
was above the small establishment of a dyer and cleaner who had
inflated kid gloves and discoloured shawls in his shop-front.
There was a great deal of grimy infant life up and down the
place, and there was a hot moist smell within, as of the "boiling"
of dirty linen. Brooksmith sat with a blanket over his legs at a
clean little window where, from behind stiff bluish-white curtains, he could look across at a huckster's and a tinsmith's and a
small greasy public-house. He had passed through an illness
and was convalescent, and his mother, as well as his aunt, was
in attendance on him. I liked the nearer relative, who was
bland and intensely humble, but I had my doubts of the remoter,
whom I connected perhaps unjustly with the opposite public-
house — she seemed somehow greasy with the same grease —
and whose furtive eye followed every movement of my hand as
if to see if it weren't going into my pocket. It didn't take this
direction — I couldn't, unsolicited, put myself at that sort of
ease with Brooksmith. Several times the door of the room
opened and mysterious old women peeped in and shuffled back
again. I don't know who they were; poor Brooksmith seemed
encompassed with vague prying beery females.

He was vague himself, and evidently weak, and much embarrassed, and not an allusion was made between us to Mansfield Street. The vision of the salon of which he had been an
ornament hovered before me however, by contrast, sufficiently.
He assured me he was really getting better, and his mother
remarked that he would come round if he could only get his
spirits up. The aunt echoed this opinion, and I became more
sure that in her own case she knew where to go for such a
purpose. I'm afraid I was rather weak with my old friend, for
I neglected the opportunity, so exceptionally good, to rebuke
the levity which had led him to throw up honourable positions

— fine stiff steady berths in Bayswater and Belgravia, with morning prayers, as I knew, attached to one of them. Very likely his reasons had been profane and sentimental; he didn't want morning prayers, he wanted to be somebody's dear fellow; but I couldn't be the person to rebuke him. He shuffled these episodes out of sight — I saw he had no wish to discuss them. I noted further, strangely enough, that it would probably be a questionable pleasure for him to see me again: he doubted now even of my power to condone his aberrations. He didn't wish to have to explain; and his behaviour was likely in future to need explanation. When I bade him farewell he looked at me a moment with eyes that said everything: "How can I talk about those exquisite years in this place, before these people, with the old women poking their heads in? It was very good of you to come to see me; it wasn't my idea — *she* brought you. We've said everything; it's over; you'll lose all patience with me, and I'd rather you shouldn't see the rest." I sent him some money in a letter the next day, but I saw the rest only in the light of a barren sequel.

A whole year after my visit to him I became aware once, in dining out, that Brooksmith was one of the several servants who hovered behind our chairs. He hadn't opened the door of the house to me, nor had I recognised him in the array of retainers in the hall. This time I tried to catch his eye, but he never gave me a chance, and when he handed me a dish I could only be careful to thank him audibly. Indeed I partook of two *entrées* of which I had my doubts, subsequently converted into certainties, in order not to snub him. He looked well enough in health, but much older, and wore in an exceptionally marked degree the glazed and expressionless mask of the British domestic *de race*. I saw with dismay that if I hadn't known him I should have taken him, on the showing of his countenance, for an extravagant illustration of irresponsive servile gloom. I said to myself that he had become a reactionary, gone over to the Philistines, thrown himself into religion, the religion of his "place," like a foreign lady *sur le retour*. I divined moreover that he was only engaged for the evening — he had become a mere waiter, had joined the band of the white-waistcoated who "go out." There was something pathetic in this fact — it was a terrible vulgarisation of Brooksmith. It was the mercenary prose

of butlerhood; he had given up the struggle for the poetry. If
reciprocity was what he had missed where was the reciprocity
now? Only in the bottoms of the wine-glasses and the five
shillings — or whatever they get — clapped into his hand by the
permanent man. However, I supposed he had taken up a precarious branch of his profession because it after all sent him
less downstairs. His relations with London society were more
superficial, but they were of course more various. As I went
away on this occasion I looked out for him eagerly among the
four or five attendants whose perpendicular persons, fluting the
walls of London passages, are supposed to lubricate the process
of departure; but he was not on duty. I asked one of the others
if he were not in the house, and received the prompt answer:
"Just left, sir. Anything I can do for you, sir?" I wanted to say
"Please give him my kind regards"; but I abstained — I didn't
want to compromise him; and I never came across him again.

Often and often, in dining out, I looked for him, sometimes
accepting invitations on purpose to multiply the chances of my
meeting him. But always in vain; so that as I met many other
members of the casual class over and over again I at last adopted
the theory that he always procured a list of expected guests
beforehand and kept away from the banquets which he thus
learned I was to grace. At last I gave up hope, and one day at
the end of three years I received another visit from his aunt.
She was drearier and dingier, almost squalid, and she was in
great tribulation and want. Her sister, Mrs. Brooksmith, had
been dead a year, and three months later her nephew had disappeared. He had always looked after her a bit — since her
troubles; I never knew what her troubles had been — and now
she hadn't so much as a petticoat to pawn. She had also a niece,
to whom she had been everything before her troubles, but the
niece had treated her most shameful. These were details; the
great and romantic fact was Brooksmith's final evasion of his
fate. He had gone out to wait one evening as usual, in a white
waistcoat she had done up for him with her own hands — being
due at a large party up Kensington way. But he had never come
home again and had never arrived at the large party, nor at
any party that any one could make out. No trace of him had
come to light — no gleam of the white waistcoat had pierced the
obscurity of his doom. This news was a sharp shock to me, for

I had my ideas about his real destination. His aged relative had promptly, as she said, guessed the worst. Somehow and somewhere he had got out of the way altogether, and now I trust that, with characteristic deliberation, he is changing the plates of the immortal gods. As my depressing visitant also said, he never *had* got his spirits up. I was fortunately able to dismiss her with her own somewhat improved. But the dim ghost of poor Brooksmith is one of those that I see. He had indeed been spoiled.

Henry James (1843-1916) Shortly after his birth in New York City, Henry James and his older brother, William, were taken to Europe with their parents. Educated in England, Europe, and America, James took up permanent residence in London in 1876. He early displayed the passion for literature which was to dominate his life; when he was fourteen his father characterized him as a "devourer of libraries, and an immense writer of novels and dramas." Although today he is best known for his novels, James was always fascinated by short fiction, and he produced over a hundred stories, long and short, which constitute one of the major achievements in the history of the form.

High seriousness and preoccupation with technique characterize James's approach to short fiction. James believed that the fiction writer should strive for truth. The primary requisite of art, he said, is truth, speaking to the reader's heart. The short story writer, he believed, should seek for *balance*; he should avoid excess, sensationalism, and melodrama; he should concern himself directly and unequivocally with life, achieved in terms of individual human personalities. James brought to the short story a dignity and artistry lacking since the days of Hawthorne and Poe. His subsequent influence has been profound and pervasive; many of the significant achievements in modern fiction have been made by writers who think of Henry James as "The Master," and who find in his work and critical precepts a never-ending source of inspiration and information.

"Brooksmith," though one of James's less complex stories, is characteristic of much of the author's work, particularly in its perceptive characterization and in its disciplined technique. In addition, the theme — the failure of society to support the "artist" — is a favorite one with James. Around the unheroic figure of little Brooksmith, James has written a moving parable; the tragedy of Brooksmith, as a recent critic has commented, suggests the universal tragedy of the artist "who has been born into a world in which he can never be thoroughly at home."

Good introductions to James's work in this field are: *In the Cage and Other Tales* (ed. Morton Dauwen Zabel, Doubleday Anchor Book); *The Short Stories of Henry James* (ed. Clifton Fadiman, Modern Library); *Selected Short Stories* (ed. Quentin Anderson, Rinehart Edition).

Questions   1. "Yes, you too have been in Arcadia"; "In short we had been in Arcadia together, and we had both come to this!" What is the significance of these comments?   2. Discuss the significance of Brooksmith's remarks to the narrator: "For me, sir, he was just *all*, if you know what I mean, sir. . . . Mr. Offord was *my* society, and now, you see, I just haven't any. You go back to conversation, sir, after all, and I go back to my place."   3. Discuss the contrast between the Mansfield Street world of Mr. Offord and the Chester Square world where Brooksmith is employed after Mr. Offord's death. What bearing does this contrast (and what it suggests thematically) have on the eventual destruction of Brooksmith?   4. This story of the "terrible vulgarisation" of Brooksmith is a quiet study in mood and character, quite unlike any of the preceding stories in the text, which have contained a considerable amount of physical action. How would you contrast the mood or tone of this story with that of "The Fall of the House of Usher" or "Chickamauga"?   5. What characteristics do Mr. Offord, Brooksmith, and the narrator have in common? In what ways are they different? What element in the narrator's make-up is particularly responsive to Brooksmith?

ANTON CHEKHOV

The Runaway

IT WAS an endless affair. Pashka and his mother, drenched with rain, tramped mile after mile, first across stubble fields, then by soft woodland paths where yellow leaves stuck to his boots, and on and on till daybreak. After that he stood two hours in a dark entrance-hall, and waited for the doors to open. In the hall, of course, it was warmer and drier than outside; but even there the piercing wind carried the raindrops in. And as the hall slowly filled with patients, Pashka, wedging his way through the crowd, pressed his face against a sheepskin coat which smelt strongly of salted fish, and slumbered.

At last the bolt slipped, the door opened, and Pashka and his mother found themselves in the waiting-room. Yet another long delay! The patients sat on benches; no one stirred; no one opened his mouth. Pashka stared at the crowd, and likewise held his tongue, though he witnessed many ludicrous, inexplicable things. But once when a boy hopped into the room on one leg, he nudged his mother's side, grinned in his sleeve, and exclaimed —

"Look, mother — a sparrow!"

"Don't talk, child, don't talk!"

At a little window appeared the *feldscher's* sleepy face. "Come and give your names."

THE RUNAWAY From *The Short Stories of Anton Chekhov,* Modern Library Edition, published by Random House, Inc.

The waiting patients, among them the funny, hopping boy, crowded round the window. Of each the *feldscher* asked name and patronymic, age, village, dates of illness, and other questions. From his mother's answer, Pashka learnt that his name was Pavl Galaktionoff, that he was seven years old, and that he had been ill since Easter.

When the names were entered there was another short delay; and then through the waiting-room walked the doctor, in white apron, with a towel on his shoulder. As he passed the hopping boy, he shrugged his shoulders, and said in a sing-song voice —

"You're a donkey! Now aren't you a donkey? I told you Monday, and you come on Friday! Don't worry yourself so far as I'm concerned, but if you're not careful, fool, you'll lose your leg!"

The hopping boy blinked, grimaced piteously as if asking for alms, and began —

"Ivan Nikolaitch, be so kind . . ."

"None of your Ivan Nikolaitch!" said the doctor teasingly. "I told you Monday — you should obey! You're a donkey, that's all."

The reception began. The doctor sat in his room, and called for the patients in turn. Now and then from the room came shrill exclamations, the sobs of children, and the doctor's angry exclamations —

"Don't howl. I won't murder you! Sit quiet!"

At last came Pashka's turn. "Pavl Galaktionoff!" cried the doctor. Pashka's mother at first seemed dazed, as if the summons were unexpected; but she recovered herself, took Pashka's hand, and led him into the doctor's room. The doctor sat on a table, and tapped mechanically with a mallet a thick book.

"What is the matter?" he asked, without looking at his visitors.

"My boy has a boil, *batiushka*, on his elbow," answered Pashka's mother; and her expression implied that she herself was suffering from Pashka's boil.

"Take off his clothes!"

Pashka, panting, untied his neckerchief, rubbed his nose on his sleeve, and began to unbutton his coat.

"Woman! have you come to pay me a visit?" said the doctor irritably. "Why don't you hurry? Are you the only one waiting?"

Pashka hurriedly threw his coat on the floor, and, with his

mother's help, took off his shirt. The doctor looked at him absent-mindedly, and slapped him on the bare stomach.

"Serious, brother Pashka," he exclaimed. "You have outgrown your corporation!" When he had said this, he sighed, and added, "Show me your elbow!"

Pashka took fright at a bowl of blood-tinged water, looked at the doctor's apron, and began to cry.

"For shame!" said the doctor mockingly. "He's big enough to get married, yet he begins to howl. For shame!"

Pashka tried to stop his tears. He looked at his mother, and his expression said, "Don't tell them at home that I cried at the hospital."

The doctor examined the elbow, pinched it, sighed, smacked his lips, and again felt the elbow.

"You ought to be whipped, woman!" he said. "Why didn't you bring him sooner? His arm is nearly gone! Look at him, idiot, can't you see that the joint is diseased?"

"It is you who know best, *batiushka!*" said Pashka's mother.

"*Batiushka!* the lad's arm is rotting off, and you with your *batiushka!* What sort of a workman will he make without arms? You'll have to nurse him all his life! If you've got a pimple on your nose you run off here for treatment, but you let your own child rot for six months! You people are all the same!"

He lighted a cigarette. While it burned away he scolded Pashka's mother, hummed a tune, shook his head rhythmically, and thought something out. Naked Pashka stood before him, listened to the tune, and watched the smoke. When the cigarette went out the doctor started, and said in a low voice —

"Listen, woman! Ointments and mixtures are no use in this case; you must leave him here."

"If it must be so, *batiushka,* so be it."

"We must have an operation. . . . And you, Pashka, you must stay," said the doctor, patting his shoulder. "We will let mother go, but you, brother, you will stay with me. It is not bad here, brother! I have raspberry bushes. You and I, Pashka, as soon as we get better, will go and catch thrushes, and I will show you a fox. We shall pay visits together. Eh? Will you stay? And mother will come for you to-morrow."

Pashka looked questioningly at his mother.

"You must stay, child," she said.

"Of course he'll stay," said the doctor merrily. "There is nothing to argue about! I'll show him a live fox. We'll drive to the fair and buy sugar-candy. Marya Denisovna, take him upstairs!"

The doctor was certainly a merry, talkative man; and Pashka was attracted, all the more because he had never been at a fair, and wanted to see a live fox. But his mother? He thought the problem out, and decided to ask the doctor to let his mother remain with him; but before he could open his mouth the nurse was leading him upstairs. With mouth wide open, he looked around. The stairs, the floors, the door-posts, all were painted a beautiful yellow; and everywhere there was a tempting smell of fast-butter. Everywhere hung lamps, everywhere lay carpets; and brass water-taps projected from every wall. But most of all Pashka was pleased by his bed with its grey, shaggy counterpane. He felt the pillows and the counterpane, and came to the conclusion that the doctor had a very nice house.

It was a little ward with only three cots. The first was vacant, the second Pashka's; and on the third sat a very old man with sour eyes, who coughed without cease, and spat into a bowl. From his bed Pashka could see through the open door part of another ward with two beds; on one lay a thin, very pallid man with a caoutchouc bladder on his head. A peasant, arms apart, with bandaged head, looking very like an old woman, sat on the other.

Having set Pashka on his bed, the nurse left him. She returned immediately with an armful of clothes. "These are for you," she said to him. "Put them on."

Pashka took off his old clothes, and, not without pleasure, arrayed himself in his new garments. After donning a shirt, a pair of trousers, and a grey dressing-gown, he looked at himself complacently, and thought how he would like to walk down the village street in his new clothes. Imagination painted his mother sending him to the kitchen garden by the river, to pluck cabbage leaves for the pig, while the village boys and girls stood round him and gaped enviously at his dressing-gown.

When next the nurse returned she brought two tin bowls, two spoons, and two slices of bread. She gave one bowl to the old man, and the other to Pashka. "Eat!" she said.

When Pashka examined the bowl he found it full of greasy soup with a piece of meat at the bottom; and again he reasoned that the doctor lived comfortably, and was not half as angry as he seemed. He dallied over the soup, licked the spoon after each mouthful, and when nothing remained but the meat, cast a side-long glance at the old man, and felt envy. With a sigh, he began the meat, trying to make it last as long as possible. But his efforts were in vain; the meat vanished speedily. There remained only the bread. Bread without condiment is tasteless food, but there was no remedy; after weighing the problem he ate the bread also. And just as he had finished it the nurse arrived with two more bowls. This time the bowls contained roast beef and potatoes.

"Where is your bread?" she asked. Pashka did not answer, but distended his cheeks and puffed out the air.

"You've gobbled it up?" said the nurse reproachfully. "What will you eat your meat with?" She left him, and returned with more bread. Never in his life had Pashka eaten roast beef, and, trying it now, he found it very tasty. But it disappeared in a few seconds; and again only the bread was left, a bigger slice than the first. The old man, having finished his dinner, hid his bread in a drawer; and Pashka resolved to do the same, but after a moment's hesitation, he ate it up.

After dinner he set out to explore. In the next ward he found four men, in addition to those he had seen from his bed. Only one drew his attention. This was a tall, skeleton peasant, morose and hairy-faced, who sat on his bed, shook his head incessantly, and waved his arms pendulum-wise. Pashka could not tear his eyes away. At first the peasant's measured pendulum movements seemed droll, and made for the amusement of onlookers; but when Pashka looked at the peasant's face, he understood that this meant intolerable pain, and he felt sorry. In the third ward were two men with dark-red faces — red as if plastered with clay. They sat up motionless in bed, and, with their strange faces and nearly hidden features, resembled heathen gods.

"Auntie, why are they like that?" he asked the nurse.

"They are small-pox patients, laddie."

When Pashka returned to his own room he sat on his bed, and waited for the doctor to come and catch thrushes or drive to the fair. But the doctor tarried. At the door of the next ward the *feldscher* stood for a moment. He bent over the patient with the icebag, and cried —

"Mikhailo!"

But sleeping Mikhailo did not hear. The *feldscher* waved his hand, and went away. While waiting for the doctor, Pashka looked at his neighbour. The old man continued to cough, and spit into the bowl, and his cough was drawn-out and wheezy. But one thing pleased Pashka intensely. When the old man, having coughed, inhaled a breath, something whistled in his chest, and sang in different notes.

"Grandfather, what is that whistling in your inside?" asked Pashka.

The old man did not answer. Pashka waited a minute, and began again.

"Grandfather, where is the fox?"

"What fox?"

"The live one."

"Where should it be? In the wood, of course."

The hours slipped by, but no doctor came. At last the nurse brought Pashka's tea, and scolded him for having eaten the bread; the *feldscher* returned and tried to awaken Mikhailo; the lamps were lighted; but still no doctor. It was already too late to drive to the fair or catch thrushes. Pashka stretched himself on his bed and began to think. He thought of the doctor's promised sugar-candy, of his mother's face and voice, of the darkness in the cabin at home, of querulous Yegorovna. And he suddenly felt tedium and grief. But remembering that his mother would come in the morning, he smiled, and fell asleep.

He was awakened by a noise. Men walked in the adjoining ward and spoke in whispers. The dim gleam of nightlights and lamps showed three figures moving near Mikhailo's bed.

"Shall we take him on the mattress, or as he is?" asked one.

"As he is. There's no room for the mattress, *Akh*, he's dead at a bad hour, heaven rest his soul!"

Then — one of the figures taking Mikhailo's shoulders, another his feet — they lifted him and the folds of his dressing-gown hung limply in the air. The third — it was the woman-like peasant — crossed himself; and all three, shuffling their feet, tripping in the folds of the dressing-gown, went out of the ward.

The sleeping man's chest whistled, and sang in different notes. Pashka heard it, looked in fright at the black windows, and jumped out of bed in panic.

"Mother!" he screamed.

And, without awaiting an answer, he rushed into the adjoining ward. The lamps and nightlights barely banished the gloom; the patients, agitated by Mikhailo's death, were sitting up in their beds. Grim, dishevelled, haunted by shades, they looked like giants; they seemed to increase in size; and far away in a dark corner sat a peasant nodding his head and swinging his pendulous hands. Without seeing the door, Pashka tore through the small-pox ward into the corridor, thence into an endless chamber full of long-haired monsters with ancient faces. He flew through the women's ward, again reached the corridor, recognised the balustrade, and rushed downstairs. And there, finding himself in the waiting-room where he had sat that morning, he looked wildly for the door.

The latch rattled, a cold wind blew, and Pashka, stumbling, sped into the yard, in his head a single thought: to flee, to flee! He did not know the road, but felt that it was enough to run without cease and that he would soon be at home with his mother. The moon shone through the clouds of an overcast sky. Pashka ran straight ahead, dashed round a shed into the shrubbery, stood a second in doubt, then rushed back to the hospital and ran around it. But there he stopped in indecision, for suddenly before his eyes rose the white crosses of a graveyard.

"Mother!" he screamed, and turned back again.

And at last, as he dashed past the black, menacing building he saw a lighted window.

In the darkness, the bright red patch breathed terror. But Pashka, mad with panic, unknowing whither to flee, turned towards it with relief. Beside the window were steps and a hall door with a white notice-board. Pashka rushed up the steps, and looked through the window. A sharp, breathless joy suddenly seized him. For there in the window at a table sat the merry, talkative doctor with a book in his hands. Pashka laughed with joy; he tried to cry out; but some irresistible force suppressed his breath, and struck him on the legs, and he staggered and fell senseless on the steps.

When he came to himself it was quite light; and the sing-song voice that had promised the fair, the thrushes, and the live fox whispered in his ear —

"You're a donkey, Pashka! Now aren't you a donkey? You ought to be whipped. . . ."

Anton Chekhov (1860-1904)   The third of six children of an Orthodox Russian grocer whose father had been a serf, Anton Chekhov entered the University of Moscow in 1879 as a medical student. To support himself and the family of his bankrupt father, he became a free-lance writer while studying medicine. When he was graduated in 1884, he had become fairly well known as a contributor to periodicals. Except for a brief period thereafter, he never practiced medicine regularly; if medicine, he once remarked, was his wife, literature was his mistress. In spite of persistent ill health, he remained an indefatigable worker, and by the time of his death he had written scores of stories, and several novels and plays, some of which are still not available in English translations.

The extreme simplicity of "The Runaway" is characteristic of Chekhov. The story is written in straightforward chronological method, with no flashbacks and no probings of a character's mind. Characters, incidents, and setting are directly revealed through unadorned dialogue and action. Chekhov is a realist who tried to depict things as he saw them; his profound interest in human beings, however, is Christian rather than scientific, and sets him somewhat apart from the Continental naturalists of his time.

A story like "The Runaway" suggests more than it actually says. Without editorializing, Chekhov creates characters and situations which by implication condemn evils in his society. Written in a period of great social unrest and revolution, Chekhov's stories are concerned with archetypal, universal experiences; Pashka of "The Runaway," for example, though specifically a product of late-nineteenth-century Russia, is kin to all lonely, unloved, and frightened "little people" of all times and places.

Good recent selections of Chekhov's stories include: *Peasants and Other Stories* (ed. Edmund Wilson, Doubleday Anchor Book); *The Short Stories of Anton Chekhov* (ed. Robert Linscott, Modern Library); *The Unknown Chekhov* (ed. Avrahm Yarmolinsky, Noonday Press).

Questions   1. Write brief character sketches of each of the three major people of this story (Pashka, his mother, the doctor). Do you think the strong contrasts in character types here are effective? What means does Chekhov employ to make the reader sympathize with

Pashka? Will Pashka ever "go to a fair," ever "see a live fox," as the doctor says? When the doctor tells of things they will do, "You and I, Pashka, as soon as we get better," does he mean what he says? Is the doctor really "not half as angry as he seems"?   2. Examine the marked change in tone of this story, from the simple, realistic opening sections involving Pashka and his mother, to the nightmarish later scenes when Pashka awakens at night in the "hospital." What is the purpose of this contrast? What does it achieve in terms of the overall effectiveness and emotional appeal of the story?   3. From whose point of view is this story narrated? Are there any shifts in point of view?

O. HENRY

Mammon
and the Archer

OLD Anthony Rockwall, retired manufacturer and proprietor of
Rockwall's Eureka Soap, looked out the library window of his
Fifth Avenue mansion and grinned. His neighbour to the right
— the aristocratic clubman, G. Van Schuylight Suffolk-Jones —
came out to his waiting motor-car, wrinkling a contumelious
nostril, as usual, at the Italian renaissance sculpture of the soap
palace's front elevation.

"Stuck-up old statuette of nothing doing!" commented the ex-
Soap King. "The Eden Musee'll get that old frozen Nesselrode
yet if he don't watch out. I'll have this house painted red, white,
and blue next summer and see if that'll make his Dutch nose turn
up any higher."

And then Anthony Rockwall, who never cared for bells, went
to the door of his library and shouted "Mike!" in the same voice
that had once chipped off pieces of the welkin on the Kansas
prairies.

"Tell my son," said Anthony to the answering menial, "to come
in here before he leaves the house."

When young Rockwall entered the library the old man laid
aside his newspaper, looked at him with a kindly grimness on his

MAMMON AND THE ARCHER From *The Four Million,* by O. Henry. Copyright by Doubleday & Company, Inc. Reprinted by permission.

big, smooth, ruddy countenance, rumpled his mop of white hair
with one hand and rattled the keys in his pocket with the other.

"Richard," said Anthony Rockwall, "what do you pay for the
soap that you use?"

Richard, only six months home from college, was startled a
little. He had not yet taken the measure of this sire of his, who
was as full of unexpectednesses as a girl at her first party.

"Six dollars a dozen, I think, dad."

"And your clothes?"

"I suppose about sixty dollars, as a rule."

"You're a gentleman," said Anthony, decidedly. "I've heard of
these young bloods spending $24 a dozen for soap, and going
over the hundred mark for clothes. You've got as much money
to waste as any of 'em, and yet you stick to what's decent and
moderate. Now I use the old Eureka — not only for sentiment,
but it's the purest soap made. Whenever you pay more than 10
cents a cake for soap you buy bad perfume and labels. But 50
cents is doing very well for a young man in your generation,
position, and condition. As I said, you're a gentleman. They say
it takes three generations to make one. They're off. Money'll do
it as slick as soap grease. It's made you one. By hokey! it's almost made one of me. I'm nearly as impolite and disagreeable
and ill-mannered as these two old Knickerbocker gents on each
side of me that can't sleep of nights because I bought in between
'em."

"There are some things that money can't accomplish," remarked
young Rockwall, rather gloomily.

"Now, don't say that," said old Anthony, shocked. "I bet my
money on money every time. I've been through the encyclopedia
down to Y looking for something you can't buy with it; and I
expect to have to take up the appendix next week. I'm for money
against the field. Tell me something money won't buy."

"For one thing," answered Richard, rankling a little, "it won't
buy one into the exclusive circles of society."

"Oho! won't it?" thundered the champion of the root of evil.
"You tell me where your exclusive circles would be if the first
Astor hadn't had the money to pay for his steerage passage
over?"

Richard sighed.

"And that's what I was coming to," said the old man, less

boisterously. "That's why I asked you to come in. There's something going wrong with you, boy. I've been noticing it for two weeks. Out with it. I guess I could lay my hands on eleven millions within twenty-four hours, besides the real estate. If it's your liver, there's the *Rambler* down in the bay, coaled, and ready to steam down to the Bahamas in two days."

"Not a bad guess, dad; you haven't missed it far."

"Ah," said Anthony, keenly; "what's her name?"

Richard began to walk up and down the library floor. There was enough comradeship and sympathy in this crude old father of his to draw his confidence.

"Why don't you ask her?" demanded old Anthony. "She'll jump at you. You've got the money and the looks, and you're a decent boy. Your hands are clean. You've got no Eureka soap on 'em. You've been to college, but she'll overlook that."

"I haven't had a chance,' said Richard.

"Make one," said Anthony. "Take her for a walk in the park, or a straw ride, or walk home with her from church. Chance! Pshaw!"

"You don't know the social mill, dad. She's part of the stream that turns it. Every hour and minute of her time is arranged for days in advance. I must have that girl, dad, or this town is a blackjack swamp forevermore. And I can't write it — I can't do that."

"Tut!" said the old man. "Do you mean to tell me that with all the money I've got you can't get an hour or two of a girl's time for yourself?"

"I've a put it off too late. She's going to sail for Europe at noon day after to-morrow for a two years' stay. I'm to see her alone to-morrow evening for a few minutes. She's at Larchmont now at her aunt's. I can't go there. But I'm allowed to meet her with a cab at the Grand Central Station to-morrow evening at the 8.30 train. We drive down Broadway to Wallack's at a gallop, where her mother and a box party will be waiting for us in the lobby. Do you think she would listen to a declaration from me during that six or eight minutes under those circumstances? No. And what chance would I have in the theatre or afterward? None. No, dad, this is one tangle that your money can't unravel. We can't buy one minute of time with cash; if we could, rich people would live longer. There's no hope of getting a talk with Miss Lantry before she sails."

"All right, Richard, my boy," said old Anthony, cheerfully. "You may run along down to your club now. I'm glad it ain't your liver. But don't forget to burn a few punk sticks in the joss house to the great god Mazuma from time to time. You say money won't buy time? Well, of course, you can't order eternity wrapped up and delivered at your residence for a price, but I've seen Father Time get pretty bad stone bruises on his heels when he walked through the gold diggings."

That night came Aunt Ellen, gentle, sentimental, wrinkled, sighing, oppressed by wealth, in to brother Anthony at his evening paper, and began discourse on the subject of lovers' woes.

"He told me all about it," said brother Anthony, yawning. "I told him my bank account was at his service. And then he began to knock money. Said money couldn't help. Said the rules of society couldn't be bucked for a yard by a team of ten-million-aires."

"Oh, Anthony," sighed Aunt Ellen, "I wish you would not think so much of money. Wealth is nothing where a true affection is concerned. Love is all-powerful. If he only had spoken earlier! She could not have refused our Richard. But now I fear it is too late. He will have no opportunity to address her. All your gold cannot bring happiness to your son."

At eight o'clock the next evening Aunt Ellen took a quaint old gold ring from a moth-eaten case and gave it to Richard.

"Wear it to-night, nephew," she begged. "Your mother gave it to me. Good luck in love she said it brought. She asked me to give it to you when you had found the one you loved."

Young Rockwall took the ring reverently and tried it on his smallest finger. It slipped as far as the second joint and stopped. He took it off and stuffed it into his vest pocket, after the manner of man. And then he 'phoned for his cab.

At the station he captured Miss Lantry out of the gadding mob at eight thirty-two.

"We mustn't keep mamma and the others waiting," said she.

"To Wallack's Theatre as fast as you can drive!" said Richard loyally.

They whirled up Forty-second to Broadway, and then down

the white-starred lane that leads from the soft meadows of sunset to the rocky hills of morning.

At Thirty-fourth Street young Richard quickly thrust up the trap and ordered the cabman to stop.

"I've dropped a ring," he apologised, as he climbed out. "It was my mother's, and I'd hate to lose it. I won't detain you a minute — I saw where it fell."

In less than a minute he was back in the cab with the ring.

But within that minute a crosstown car had stopped directly in front of the cab. The cabman tried to pass to the left, but a heavy express wagon cut him off. He tried the right, and had to back away from a furniture van that had no business to be there. He tried to back out, but dropped his reins and swore dutifully. He was blockaded in a tangled mess of vehicles and horses.

One of those street blockades had occurred that sometimes tie up commerce and movement quite suddenly in the big city.

"Why don't you drive on?" said Miss Lantry, impatiently. "We'll be late."

Richard stood up in the cab and looked around. He saw a congested flood of wagons, trucks, cabs, vans and street cars filling the vast space where Broadway, Sixth Avenue and Thirty-fourth Street cross one another as a twenty-six inch maiden fills her twenty-two inch girdle. And still from all the cross streets they were hurrying and rattling toward the converging point at full speed, and hurling themselves into the struggling mass, locking wheels and adding their drivers' imprecations to the clamour. The entire traffic of Manhattan seemed to have jammed itself around them. The oldest New Yorker among the thousands of spectators that lined the sidewalks had not witnessed a street blockade of the proportions of this one.

"I'm very sorry," said Richard, as he resumed his seat, "but it looks as if we are stuck. They won't get this jumble loosened up in an hour. It was my fault. If I hadn't dropped the ring we —"

"Let me see the ring," said Miss Lantry. "Now that it can't be helped, I don't care. I think theatres are stupid, anyway."

At 11 o'clock that night somebody tapped lightly on Anthony Rockwall's door.

"Come in," shouted Anthony, who was in a red dressing-gown, reading a book of piratical adventures.

Somebody was Aunt Ellen, looking like a grey-haired angel that had been left on earth by mistake.

"They're engaged, Anthony," she said, softly. "She has promised to marry our Richard. On their way to the theatre there was a street blockade, and it was two hours before their cab could get out of it.

"And oh, brother Anthony, don't ever boast of the power of money again. A little emblem of true love — a little ring that symbolised unending and unmercenary affection — was the cause of our Richard finding his happiness. He dropped it in the street, and got out to recover it. And before they could continue the blockade occurred. He spoke to his love and won her there while the cab was hemmed in. Money is dross compared with true love, Anthony."

"All right," said old Anthony. "I'm glad the boy has got what he wanted. I told him I wouldn't spare any expense in the matter if — "

"But, brother Anthony, what good could your money have done?"

"Sister," said Anthony Rockwall. "I've got my pirate in a devil of a scrape. His ship has just been scuttled, and he's too good a judge of the value of money to let drown. I wish you would let me go on with this chapter."

The story should end here. I wish it would as heartily as you who read it wish it did. But we must go to the botttom of the well for the truth.

The next day a person with red hands and a blue polka-dot necktie, who called himself Kelly, called at Anthony Rockwall's house, and was at once received in the library.

"Well," said Anthony, reaching for his cheque-book, "it was a good bilin' of soap. Let's see — you had $5,000 in cash."

"I paid out $300 more of my own," said Kelly. "I had to go a little above the estimate. I got the express wagons and cabs mostly for $5; but the trucks and two-horse teams mostly raised me to $10. The motormen wanted $10, and some of the loaded teams $20. The cops struck me hardest — $50 I paid two, and the rest $20 and $25. But didn't it work beautiful, Mr. Rockwall? I'm glad William A. Brady wasn't onto that little outdoor vehicle mob scene. I wouldn't want William to break his heart with jealousy. And never a rehearsal, either! The boys was on time to the fraction of a second. It was two hours before a snake could get below Greeley's statue."

"Thirteen hundred — there you are, Kelly," said Anthony, tearing off a check. "Your thousand, and the $300 you were out. You don't despise money, do you, Kelly?"

"Me?" said Kelly. "I can lick the man that invented poverty."

Anthony called Kelly when he was at the door.

"You didn't notice," said he, "anywhere in the tie-up, a kind of a fat boy without any clothes on shooting arrows around with a bow, did you?"

"Why, no," said Kelly, mystified. "I didn't. If he was like you say, maybe the cops pinched him before I got there."

"I thought the little rascal wouldn't be on hand," chuckled Anthony. "Good-by, Kelly."

O. Henry (William Sydney Porter) (1862-1910)　　Probably the most prolific and widely read writer in the history of the short story, William Sydney Porter was born in Greensboro, North Carolina. After working briefly in his uncle's drug store, he wandered to Texas where he worked as a ranch hand, as a reporter for a Houston paper, and as a teller in an Austin bank. Accused of embezzlement, he fled the country in 1896, but returned from Honduras to attend his dying wife. After her death he stood trial and was convicted; it was while serving a three-year term in the Columbus, Ohio, penitantiary that he began writing fiction. On his release he went to New York, there to become popular and famous under the pseudonym said to have been derived from the name of a guard at the penitentiary. By the time of his death, apparently hastened by alcoholism, O. Henry had published hundreds of stories. Most of these originally appeared in magazines and newspapers; in book form they totaled fifteen volumes.

Unlike most of the stories in this anthology, the typical O. Henry story depends almost entirely for its effect upon plot; the high seriousness of James, the moral depth of Hawthorne, the artistry of Crane or Joyce are conspicuously absent from his fiction. Like the characters of "Mammon and the Archer," O. Henry's people bear small resemblance to human beings as they actually exist; rather, they are deftly manipulated caricatures. O. Henry's stories are usually little more than mechanically plotted anecdotes which rely on surprise endings; their effect depends on the withholding of important information from the reader until the last possible moment. Almost every commercial writer since O. Henry's day has imitated the many tricks, devices, and gimmicks which O. Henry so skillfully utilized; few, however, have succeeded in capturing the freshness, the ingenuity, and the swiftness of pace which make O. Henry's best pieces far superior to the rather shoddy formularized products of his imitators.

Convenient one-volume selections from O. Henry's more than 600 stories are *The Best Short Stories of O. Henry* (ed. Bennett A. Cerf and Van H. Cartmell, Modern Library); *The Pocket Book of O. Henry Stories* (ed. Harry Hansen, Pocket Books).

Questions   In what ways is Old Anthony Rockwall the typical rich man of television, the movies, and the mass circulation magazines? In what ways, if any, does he differ from this stereotyped figure? What do you think of the character of Richard? Would you say he is at all representative of the young college graduate of today?   2. Are there any evidences of "social consciousness" in this story? If so, are they intended to be taken seriously?   3. In what ways does this story remind you of the "short short" stories in today's popular magazines? In what ways is it different?   4. What is your opinion of such comments as "The story should end here. I wish it would as heartily as you who read it wish it would. But we must go to the bottom of the well for the truth." What is the purpose of such a passage?   5. Are you convinced by the ending of the story? Do you think the author intended that you *should* be convinced? Are you convinced by the character of Kelly, by his actions, or by his reaction to the question concerning a "kind of a fat boy without any clothes on shooting arrows around with a bow"?   6. Recent collectors of an anthology of O. Henry's stories have said that "Mammon and the Archer" is a "gem" of its kind — "mellow, humorous, ironic, ingenious, and shot through with . . . 'human interest.'" Do you agree or disagree?

STEPHEN CRANE

The
Open Boat

*A Tale intended to be after the fact. Being the Experi-
ence of Four Men from the Sunk Steamer "Commodore"*

I

NONE OF THEM knew the color of the sky. Their eyes glanced
level, and were fastened upon the waves that swept toward them.
These waves were of the hue of slate, save for the tops, which
were of foaming white, and all of the men knew the colors of
the sea. The horizon narrowed and widened, and dipped and
rose, and at all times its edge was jagged with waves that seemed
thrust up in points like rocks.

Many a man ought to have a bath-tub larger than the boat
which here rode upon the sea. These waves were most wrong-
fully and barbarously abrupt and tall, and each froth-top was a
problem in small boat navigation.

The cook squatted in the bottom and looked with both eyes
at the six inches of gunwale which separated him from the ocean.
His sleeves were rolled over his fat forearms, and the two flaps
of his unbuttoned vest dangled as he bent to bail out the boat.
Often he said: "Gawd! That was a narrow clip." As he remarked it he invariably gazed eastward over the broken sea.

The oiler, steering with one of the two oars in the boat, sometimes raised himself suddenly to keep clear of water that swirled

120

in over the stern. It was a thin little oar and it seemed often ready to snap.

The correspondent, pulling at the other oar, watched the waves and wondered why he was there.

The injured captain, lying in the bow, was at this time buried in that profound dejection and indifference which comes, temporarily at least, to even the bravest and most enduring when, willy nilly, the firm fails, the army loses, the ship goes down. The mind of the master of a vessel is rooted deep in the timbers of her, though he command for a day or a decade, and this captain had on him the stern impression of a scene in the grays of dawn of seven turned faces, and later a stump of a top-mast with a white ball on it that slashed to and fro at the waves, went low and lower, and down. Thereafter there was something strange in his voice. Although steady, it was deep with mourning, and of a quality beyond oration or tears.

"Keep 'er a little more south, Billie," said he.

"'A little more south,' sir," said the oiler in the stern.

A seat in this boat was not unlike a seat upon a bucking broncho, and, by the same token, a broncho is not much smaller. The craft pranced and reared, and plunged like an animal. As each wave came, and she rose for it, she seemed like a horse making at a fence outrageously high. The manner of her scramble over these walls of water is a mystic thing, and, moreover, at the top of them were ordinarily these problems in white water, the foam racing down from the summit of each wave, requiring a new leap, and a leap from the air. Then, after scornfully bumping a crest, she would slide, and race, and splash down a long incline, and arrive bobbing and nodding in front of the next menace.

A singular disadvantage of the sea lies in the fact that after successfully surmounting one wave you discover that there is another behind it just as important and just as nervously anxious to do something effective in the way of swamping boats. In a ten-foot dingey one can get an idea of the resources of the sea in the line of waves that is not probable to the average experience which is never at sea in a dingey. As each slaty wall of water approached, it shut all else from the view of the men in the boat, and it was not difficult to imagine that this particular wave was the final outburst of the ocean, the last effort of the grim water. There was a terrible grace in the move of the waves, and they came in silence, save for the snarling of the crests.

In the wan light, the faces of the men must have been gray. Their eyes must have glinted in strange ways as they gazed steadily astern. Viewed from a balcony, the whole thing would doubtless have been weirdly picturesque. But the men in the boat had no time to see it, and if they had had leisure there were other things to occupy their minds. The sun swung steadily up the sky, and they knew it was broad day because the color of the sea changed from slate to emerald-green, streaked with amber lights, and the foam was like tumbling snow. The process of the breaking day was unknown to them. They were aware only of this effect upon the color of the waves that rolled toward them.

In disjointed sentences the cook and the correspondent argued as to the difference between a life-saving station and a house of refuge. The cook had said: "There's a house of refuge just north of the Mosquito Inlet Light, and as soon as they see us, they'll come off in their boat and pick us up."

"As soon as who see us?" said the correspondent.

"The crew," said the cook.

"Houses of refuge don't have crews," said the correspondent. "As I understand them, they are only places where clothes and grub are stored for the benefit of shipwrecked people. They don't carry crews."

"Oh, yes, they do," said the cook.

"No, they don't," said the correspondent.

"Well, we're not there yet, anyhow," said the oiler, in the stern.

"Well," said the cook, "perhaps it's not a house of refuge that I'm thinking of as being near Mosquito Inlet Light. Perhaps it's a life-saving station."

"We're not there yet," said the oiler, in the stern.

II

As the boat bounced from the top of each wave, the wind tore through the hair of the hatless men, and as the craft plopped her stern down again the spray slashed past them. The crest of each of these waves was a hill, from the top of which the men surveyed, for a moment, a broad tumultuous expanse, shining and wind-riven. It was probably splendid. It was probably glorious, this play of the free sea, wild with lights of emerald and white and amber.

"Bully good thing it's an on-shore wind," said the cook. "If not, where would we be? Wouldn't have a show."

"That's right," said the correspondent.

The busy oiler nodded his assent.

Then the captain, in the bow, chuckled in a way that expressed humor, contempt, tragedy, all in one. "Do you think we've got much of a show now, boys?" said he.

Whereupon the three were silent, save for a trifle of hemming and hawing. To express any particular optimism at this time they felt to be childish and stupid, but they all doubtless possessed this sense of the situation in their mind. A young man thinks doggedly at such times. On the other hand, the ethics of their condition was decidedly against any open suggestion of hopelessness. So they were silent.

"Oh, well," said the captain, soothing his children, "we'll get ashore all right."

But there was that in his tone which made them think, so the oiler quoth: "Yes! If this wind holds!"

The cook was bailing: "Yes! If we don't catch hell in the surf."

Canton flannel gulls flew near and far. Sometimes they sat down on the sea, near patches of brown seaweed that rolled over the waves with a movement like carpets on a line in a gale. The birds sat comfortably in groups, and they were envied by some in the dingey, for the wrath of the sea was no more to them than it was to a covey of prairie chickens a thousand miles inland. Often they came very close and stared at the men with black bead-like eyes. At these times they were uncanny and sinister in their unblinking scrutiny, and the men hooted angrily at them, telling them to be gone. One came, and evidently decided to alight on the top of the captain's head. The bird flew parallel to the boat and did not circle, but made short sidelong jumps in the air in chicken-fashion. His black eyes were wistfully fixed upon the captain's head. "Ugly brute," said the oiler to the bird. "You look as if you were made with a jack-knife." The cook and the correspondent swore darkly at the creature. The captain naturally wished to knock it away with the end of the heavy painter; but he did not dare do it, because anything resembling an emphatic gesture would have capsized this freighted boat, and so with his open hand, the captain gently and carefully waved the gull away. After it had been discouraged from the pursuit the captain breathed easier on account of his hair, and others breathed easier because the bird struck their minds at this time as being somehow gruesome and ominous.

In the meantime the oiler and the correspondent rowed. And also they rowed.

They sat together in the same seat, and each rowed an oar. Then the oiler took both oars; then the correspondent took both oars; then the oiler; then the correspondent. They rowed and they rowed. The very ticklish part of the business was when the time came for the reclining one in the stern to take his turn at the oars. By the very last star of truth, it is easier to steal eggs from under a hen than it was to change seats in the dingey. First the man in the stern slid his hand along the thwart and moved with care, as if he were of Sèvres. Then the man in the rowing seat slid his hand along the other thwart. It was all done with the most extraordinary care. As the two sidled past each other, the whole party kept watchful eyes on the coming wave, and the captain cried: "Look out now! Steady there!"

The brown mats of seaweed that appeared from time to time were like islands, bits of earth. They were travelling, apparently, neither one way nor the other. They were, to all intents, stationary. They informed the men in the boat that it was making progress slowly toward the land.

The captain, rearing cautiously in the bow, after the dingey soared on a great swell, said that he had seen the lighthouse at Mosquito Inlet. Presently the cook remarked that he had seen it. The correspondent was at the oars then, and for some reason he too wished to look at the lighthouse, but his back was toward the far shore and the waves were important, and for some time he could not seize an opportunity to turn his head. But at last there came a wave more gentle than the others, and when at the crest of it he swiftly scoured the western horizon.

"See it?" said the captain.

"No," said the correspondent slowly. "I didn't see anything."

"Look again," said the captain. He pointed. "It's exactly in that direction."

At the top of another wave, the correspondent did as he was

bid, and this time his eyes chanced on a small still thing on the edge of the swaying horizon. It was precisely like the point of a pin. It took an anxious eye to find a lighthouse so tiny.

"Think we'll make it, captain?"

"If this wind holds and the boat don't swamp, we can't do much else," said the captain.

The little boat, lifted by each towering sea, and splashed viciously by the crests, made progress that in the absence of seaweed was not apparent to those in her. She seemed just a wee thing wallowing, miraculously top up, at the mercy of five oceans. Occasionally, a great spread of water, like white flames, swarmed into her.

"Bail her, cook," said the captain serenely.

"All right, captain," said the cheerful cook.

III

It would be difficult to describe the subtle brotherhood of men that was here established on the seas. No one said that it was so. No one mentioned it. But it dwelt in the boat, and each man felt it warm him. They were a captain, an oiler, a cook, and a correspondent, and they were friends, friends in a more curiously iron-bound degree than may be common. The hurt captain, lying against the water-jar in the bow, spoke always in a low voice and calmly, but he could never command a more ready and swiftly obedient crew than the motley three of the dingey. It was more than a mere recognition of what was best for the common safety. There was surely in it a quality that was personal and heartfelt. And after this devotion to the commander of the boat there was this comradeship that the correspondent, for instance, who had been taught to be cynical of men, knew even at the time was the best experience of his life. But no one said that it was so. No one mentioned it.

"I wish we had a sail," remarked the captain. "We might try my overcoat on the end of an oar and give you two boys a chance to rest." So the cook and the correspondent held the mast and spread wide the overcoat. The oiler steered, and the little boat made good way with her new rig. Sometimes the oiler had to scull sharply to keep a sea from breaking into the boat, but otherwise sailing was a success.

Meanwhile the lighthouse had been growing slowly larger. It

had now almost assumed color, and appeared like a little gray
shadow on the sky. The man at the oars could not be prevented
from turning his head rather often to try for a glimpse of this
little gray shadow.

At last, from the top of each wave the men in the tossing boat
could see land. Even as the lighthouse was an upright shadow on
the sky, this land seemed but a long black shadow on the sea. It
certainly was thinner than paper. "We must be about opposite
New Smyrna," said the cook, who had coasted this shore often in
schooners. "Captain, by the way, I believe they abandoned that
life-saving station there about a year ago."

"Did they?" said the captain.

The wind slowly died away. The cook and the correspondent
were not now obliged to slave in order to hold high the oar. But
the waves continued their old impetuous swooping at the dingey,
and the little craft, no longer under way, struggled woundily over
them. The oiler or the correspondent took the oars again.

Shipwrecks are apropos of nothing. If men could only train for
them and have them occur when the men had reached pink condition, there would be less drowning at sea. Of the four in the
dingey none had slept any time worth mentioning for two days
and two nights previous to embarking in the dingey, and in the
excitement of clambering about the deck of a foundering ship
they had also forgotten to eat heartily.

For these reasons, and for others, neither the oiler nor the correspondent was fond of rowing at this time. The correspondent
wondered ingenuously how in the name of all that was sane could
there be people who thought it amusing to row a boat. It was
not an amusement; it was a diabolical punishment, and even a
genius of mental aberrations could never conclude that it was
anything but a horror to the muscles and a crime against the
back. He mentioned to the boat in general how the amusement of
rowing struck him, and the weary-faced oiler smiled in full sympathy. Previously to the foundering, by the way, the oiler had
worked double-watch in the engine-room of the ship.

"Take her easy, now, boys," said the captain. "Don't spend
yourselves. If we have to run a surf you'll need all your strength,
because we'll sure have to swim for it. Take your time."

Slowly the land arose from the sea. From a black line it became a line of black and a line of white, trees and sand. Finally,

the captain said that he could make out a house on the shore. "That's the house of refuge, sure," said the cook. "They'll see us before long, and come out after us."

The distant lighthouse reared high. "The keeper ought to be able to make us out now, if he's looking through a glass," said the captain. "He'll notify the life-saving people."

"None of those other boats could have got ashore to give word of the wreck," said the oiler, in a low voice. "Else the life-boat would be out hunting us."

Slowly and beautifully the land loomed out of the sea. The wind came again. It had veered from the north-east to the south-east. Finally, a new sound struck the ears of the men in the boat. It was the low thunder of the surf on the shore. "We'll never be able to make the lighthouse now," said the captain. "Swing her head a little more north, Billie."

"'A little more north,' sir," said the oiler.

Whereupon the little boat turned her nose once more down the wind, and all but the oarsman watched the shore grow. Under the influence of this expansion doubt and direful apprehension was leaving the minds of the men. The management of the boat was still most absorbing, but it could not prevent a quiet cheerfulness. In an hour, perhaps, they would be ashore.

Their backbones had become thoroughly used to balancing in the boat, and they now rode this wild colt of a dingey like circus men. The correspondent thought that he had been drenched to the skin, but happening to feel in the top pocket of his coat, he found therein eight cigars. Four of them were soaked with sea-water; four were perfectly scatheless. After a search, somebody produced three dry matches, and thereupon the four waifs rode in their little boat, and with an assurance of an impending rescue shining in their eyes, puffed at the big cigars and judged well and ill of all men. Everybody took a drink of water.

IV

"Cook," remarked the captain, "there don't seem to be any signs of life about your house of refuge."

"No," replied the cook. "Funny they don't see us!"

A broad stretch of lowly coast lay before the eyes of the men. It was of low dunes topped with dark vegetation. The roar of the surf was plain, and sometimes they could see the white lip of a wave as it spun up the beach. A tiny house was blocked out black upon the sky. Southward, the slim lighthouse lifted its little gray length.

Tide, wind, and waves were swinging the dingey northward. "Funny they don't see us," said the men.

The surf's roar was here dulled, but its tone was, nevertheless, thunderous and mighty. As the boat swam over the great rollers, the men sat listening to this roar. "We'll swamp sure," said everybody.

It is fair to say here that there was not a life-saving station within twenty miles in either direction, but the men did not know this fact, and in consequence they made dark and opprobrious remarks concerning the eyesight of the nation's life-savers. Four scowling men sat in the dingey and surpassed records in the invention of epithets.

"Funny they don't see us."

The light-heartedness of a former time had completely faded. To their sharpened minds it was easy to conjure pictures of all kinds of incompetency and blindness and, indeed, cowardice. There was the shore of the populous land, and it was bitter and bitter to them that from it came no sign.

"Well," said the captain, ultimately, "I suppose we'll have to make a try for ourselves. If we stay out here too long, we'll none of us have strength left to swim after the boat swamps."

And so the oiler, who was at the oars, turned the boat straight for the shore. There was a sudden tightening of muscles. There was some thinking.

"If we don't all get ashore — " said the captain. "If we don't all get ashore, I suppose you fellows know where to send news of my finish?"

They then briefly exchanged some addresses and admonitions. As for the reflections of the men, there was a great deal of rage in them. Perchance they might be formulated thus: "If I am going to be drowned — if I am going to be drowned — if I am going to be drowned, why, in the name of the seven mad gods who rule the sea, was I allowed to come thus far and contemplate sand and trees? Was I brought here merely to have my nose dragged away as I was about to nibble the sacred cheese of life? It is preposterous. If this old ninny-woman, Fate, cannot do better than this, she should be deprived of the management of men's fortunes.

She is an old hen who knows not her intention. If she has decided to drown me, why did she not do it in the beginning and save me all this trouble? The whole affair is absurd. . . . But no, she cannot mean to drown me. She dare not drown me. She cannot drown me. Not after all this work." Afterward the man might have had an impulse to shake his fist at the clouds: "Just you drown me, now, and then hear what I call you!"

The billows that came at this time were more formidable. They seemed always just about to break and roll over the little boat in a turmoil of foam. There was a preparatory and long growl in the speech of them. No mind unused to the sea would have concluded that the dingey could ascend these sheer heights in time. The shore was still afar. The oiler was a wily surfman. "Boys," he said swiftly, "she won't live three minutes more, and we're too far out to swim. Shall I take her to sea again, captain?"

"Yes! Go ahead!" said the captain.

This oiler, by a series of quick miracles, and fast and steady oarsmanship, turned the boat in the middle of the surf and took her safely to sea again.

There was a considerable silence as the boat bumped over the furrowed sea to deeper water. Then somebody in gloom spoke. "Well, anyhow, they must have seen us from the shore by now."

The gulls went in slanting flight up the wind toward the gray desolate east. A squall, marked by dingy clouds, and clouds brick-red, like smoke from a burning building, appeared from the south-east.

"What do you think of those life-saving people? Ain't they peaches?"

"Funny they haven't seen us."

"Maybe they think we're out here for sport! Maybe they think we're fishin'. Maybe they think we're damned fools."

It was a long afternoon. A changed tide tried to force them southward, but wind and wave said northward. Far ahead, where coastline, sea, and sky formed their mighty angle, there were little dots which seemed to indicate a city on the shore.

"St. Augustine?"

The captain shook his head. "Too near Mosquito Inlet."

And the oiler rowed, and then the correspondent rowed. Then the oiler rowed. It was a weary business. The human back can become the seat of more aches and pains than are registered in books for the composite anatomy of a regiment. It is a limited area, but it can become the theater of innumerable muscular conflicts, tangles, wrenches, knots, and other comforts.

"Did you ever like to row, Billie?" asked the correspondent.

"No," said the oiler. "Hang it!"

When one exchanged the rowing-seat for a place in the bottom of the boat, he suffered a bodily depression that caused him to be careless of everything save an obligation to wiggle one finger. There was cold sea-water swashing to and fro in the boat, and he lay in it. His head, pillowed on a thwart, was within an inch of the swirl of a wave crest, and sometimes a particularly obstreperous sea came in-board and drenched him once more. But these matters did not annoy him. It is almost certain that if the boat had capsized he would have tumbled comfortably out upon the ocean as if he felt sure that it was a great soft mattress.

"Look! There's a man on the shore!"

"Where?"

"There! See 'im? See 'im?"

"Yes, sure! He's walking along."

"Now he's stopped. Look! He's facing us!"

"He's waving at us!"

"So he is! By thunder!"

"Ah, now we're all right! Now we're all right! There'll be a boat out here for us in half an hour."

"He's going on. He's running. He's going up to that house there."

The remote beach seemed lower than the sea, and it required a searching glance to discern the little black figure. The captain saw a floating stick and they rowed to it. A bath-towel was by some weird chance in the boat, and tying this on the stick, the captain waved it. The oarsman did not dare turn his head, so he was obliged to ask questions.

"What's he doing now?"

"He's standing still again. He's looking. I think. . . . There he goes again. Toward the house. . . . Now he's stopped again."

"Is he waving at us?"

"No, not now! he was, though."

"Look! There comes another man!"

"He's running."

"Look at him go, would you."

"Why, he's on a bicycle. Now he's met the other man. They're both waving at us. Look!"

"There comes something up the beach."

"What the devil is that thing?"

"Why, it looks like a boat."

"Why, certainly it's a boat."

"No, it's on wheels."

"Yes, so it is. Well, that must be the life-boat. They drag them along shore on a wagon."

"That's the life-boat, sure."

"No, by —, it's — it's an omnibus."

"I tell you it's a life-boat."

"It is not! It's an omnibus. I can see it plain. See? One of these big hotel omnibuses."

"By thunder, you're right. It's an omnibus, sure as fate. What do you suppose they are doing with an omnibus? Maybe they are going around collecting the life-crew, hey?"

"That's it, likely. Look! There's a fellow waving a little black flag. He's standing on the steps of the omnibus. There come those other two fellows. Now they're all talking together. Look at the fellow with the flag. Maybe he ain't waving it."

"That ain't a flag, is it? That's his coat. Why, certainly, that's his coat."

"So it is. It's his coat. He's taken it off and is waving it around his head. But would you look at him swing it."

"Oh, say, there isn't any life-saving station there. That's just a winter resort hotel omnibus that has brought over some of the boarders to see us drown."

"What's that idiot with the coat mean? What's he signaling, anyhow?"

"It looks as if he were trying to tell us to go north. There must be a life-saving station up there."

"No! He thinks we're fishing. Just giving us a merry hand. See? Ah, there, Willie."

"Well, I wish I could make something out of those signals. What do you suppose he means?"

"He don't mean anything. He's just playing."

"Well, if he'd just signal us to try the surf again, or to go to sea and wait, or go north, or go south, or go to hell — there would be some reason in it. But look at him. He just stands there and keeps his coat revolving like a wheel. The ass!"

"There come more people."

"Now there's quite a mob. Look! Isn't that a boat?"

"Where? Oh, I see where you mean. No, that's no boat."

"That fellow is still waving his coat."

"He must think we like to see him do that. Why don't he quit it? It don't mean anything."

"I don't know. I think he is trying to make us go north. It must be that there's a life-saving station there somewhere."

"Say, he ain't tired yet. Look at 'im wave."

"Wonder how long he can keep that up. He's been revolving his coat ever since he caught sight of us. He's an idiot. Why aren't they getting men to bring a boat out? A fishing boat — one of those big yawls — could come out here all right. Why don't he do something?"

"Oh, it's all right, now."

"They'll have a boat out here for us in less than no time, now that they've seen us."

A faint yellow tone came into the sky over the low land. The shadows on the sea slowly deepened. The wind bore coldness with it, and the men began to shiver.

"Holy smoke!" said one, allowing his voice to express his impious mood, "if we keep on monkeying out here! If we've got to flounder out here all night!"

"Oh, we'll never have to stay here all night! Don't you worry. They've seen us now, and it won't be long before they'll come chasing out after us."

The shore grew dusky. The man waving a coat blended gradually into this gloom, and it swallowed in the same manner the omnibus and the group of people. The spray, when it dashed uproariously over the side, made the voyagers shrink and swear like men who were being branded.

"I'd like to catch the chump who waved the coat. I feel like soaking him one, just for luck."

"Why? What did he do?"

"Oh, nothing, but then he seemed so damned cheerful."

In the meantime the oiler rowed, and then the correspondent rowed, and then the oiler rowed. Gray-faced and bowed forward, they mechanically, turn by turn, plied the leaden oars. The form of the lighthouse had vanished from the southern horizon, but finally a pale star appeared, just lifting from the sea. The streaked saffron in the west passed before the all-merging darkness, and the sea to the east was black. The land had vanished, and was expressed only by the low and drear thunder of the surf.

"If I am going to be drowned — if I am going to be drowned — if I am going to be drowned, why, in the name of the seven mad gods who rule the sea, was I allowed to come thus far and contemplate sand and trees? Was I brought here merely to have my nose dragged away as I was about to nibble the sacred cheese of life?"

The patient captain, drooped over the water-jar, was sometimes obliged to speak to the oarsman.

"Keep her head up! Keep her head up!"

"'Keep her head up,' sir." The voices were weary and low.

This was surely a quiet evening. All save the oarsman lay heavily and listlessly in the boat's bottom. As for him, his eyes were just capable of noting the tall black waves that swept forward in a most sinister silence, save for an occasional subdued growl of a crest.

The cook's head was on a thwart, and he looked without interest at the water under his nose. He was deep in other scenes. Finally he spoke. "Billie," he murmured, dreamfully, "what kind of pie do you like best?"

v

"Pie," said the oiler and the correspondent, agitatedly. "Don't talk about those things, blast you!"

"Well," said the cook, "I was just thinking about ham sandwiches, and — ".

A night on the sea in an open boat is a long night. As darkness settled finally, the shine of the light, lifting from the sea in the south, changed to full gold. On the northern horizon a new light appeared, a small bluish gleam on the edge of the waters. These two lights were the furniture of the world. Otherwise there was nothing but waves.

Two men huddled in the stern, and distances were so magnificent in the dingey that the rower was enabled to keep his feet partly warmed by thrusting them under his companions. Their legs indeed extended far under the rowing-seat until they touched the feet of the captain forward. Sometimes, despite the efforts of the tired oarsman, a wave came piling into the boat, an icy wave of the night, and the chilling water soaked them anew. They would twist their bodies for a moment and groan, and sleep the dead sleep once more, while the water in the boat gurgled about them as the craft rocked.

The plan of the oiler and the correspondent was for one to row until he lost the ability, and then arouse the other from his sea-water couch in the bottom of the boat.

The oiler plied the oars until his head drooped forward, and the overpowering sleep blinded him. And he rowed yet afterward. Then he touched a man in the bottom of the boat, and called his name. "Will you spell me for a little while?" he said, meekly.

"Sure, Billie," said the correspondent, awakening and dragging himself to a sitting position. They exchanged places carefully, and the oiler, cuddling down in the sea-water at the cook's side, seemed to go to sleep instantly.

The particular violence of the sea had ceased. The waves came without snarling. The obligation of the man at the oars was to keep the boat headed so that the tilt of the rollers would not capsize her, and to preserve her from filling when the crests rushed past. The black waves were silent and hard to be seen in the darkness. Often one was almost upon the boat before the oarsman was aware.

In a low voice the correspondent addressed the captain. He was not sure that the captain was awake, although this iron man seemed to be always awake. "Captain, shall I keep her making for that light north, sir?"

The same steady voice answered him. "Yes. Keep it about two points off the port bow."

The cook had tied a life-belt around himself in order to get even the warmth which this clumsy cork contrivance could donate, and he seemed almost stove-like when a rower, whose teeth invariably chattered wildly as soon as he ceased his labor, dropped down to sleep.

The correspondent, as he rowed, looked down at the two men sleeping underfoot. The cook's arm was around the oiler's shoulders, and, with their fragmentary clothing and haggard faces, they were the babes of the sea, a grotesque rendering of the old babes in the wood.

Later he must have grown stupid at his work, for suddenly there was a growling of water, and a crest came with a roar and a swash into the boat, and it was a wonder that it did not set the cook afloat in his life-belt. The cook continued to sleep, but the oiler sat up, blinking his eyes and shaking with the new cold.

"Oh, I'm awful sorry, Billie," said the correspondent, contritely.

"That's all right, old boy," said the oiler, and lay down again and was asleep.

Presently it seemed that even the captain dozed, and the correspondent thought that he was the one man afloat on all the oceans. The wind had a voice as it came over the waves, and it was sadder than the end.

There was a long, loud swishing astern of the boat, and a gleaming trail of phosphorescence, like blue flame, was furrowed on the black waters. It might have been made by a monstrous knife.

Then there came a stillness, while the correspondent breathed with the open mouth and looked at the sea.

Suddenly there was another swish and another long flash of bluish light, and this time it was alongside the boat, and might almost have been reached with an oar. The correspondent saw an enormous fin speed like a shadow through the water, hurling the crystalline spray and leaving the long glowing trail.

The correspondent looked over his shoulder at the captain. His face was hidden, and he seemed to be asleep. He looked at the babes of the sea. They certainly were asleep. So, being bereft of sympathy, he leaned a little way to one side and swore softly into the sea.

But the thing did not then leave the vicinity of the boat. Ahead or astern, on one side or the other, at intervals long or short, fled the long sparkling streak, and there was to be heard the whiroo of the dark fin. The speed and power of the thing was greatly to be admired. It cut the water like a gigantic and keen projectile.

The presence of this biding thing did not affect the man with the same horror that it would if he had been a picnicker. He simply looked at the sea dully and swore in an undertone.

Nevertheless, it is true that he did not wish to be alone. He wished one of his companions to awaken by chance and keep him company with it. But the captain hung motionless over the water-jar, and the oiler and the cook in the bottom of the boat were plunged in slumber.

VI

"If I am going to be drowned — if I am going to be drowned — if I am going to be drowned, why, in the name of the seven mad gods who rule the sea, was I allowed to come thus far and contemplate sand and trees?"

During this dismal night, it may be remarked that a man would conclude that it was really the intention of the seven mad gods to drown him, despite the abominable injustice of it. For it was certainly an abominable injustice to drown a man who had worked so hard, so hard. The man felt it would be a crime most unnatural. Other people had drowned at sea since galleys swarmed with painted sails, but still —

When it occurs to a man that nature does not regard him as important, and that she feels she would not maim the universe by disposing of him, he at first wishes to throw bricks at the temple, and he hates deeply the fact that there are no bricks and no temples. Any visible expression of nature would surely be pelleted with his jeers.

Then, if there be no tangible thing to hoot he feels, perhaps, the desire to confront a personification and indulge in pleas, bowed to one knee, and with hands supplicant, saying: "Yes, but I love myself."

A high cold star on a winter's night is the word he feels that she says to him. Thereafter he knows the pathos of his situation.

The men in the dingey had not discussed these matters, but each had, no doubt, reflected upon them in silence and according to his mind. There was seldom any expression upon their faces save the general one of complete weariness. Speech was devoted to the business of the boat.

To chime the notes of his emotion, a verse mysteriously entered the correspondent's head. He had even forgotten that he had forgotten this verse, but it suddenly was in his mind.

"A soldier of the Legion lay dying in Algiers,
There was lack of woman's nursing, there was dearth of woman's tears;
But a comrade stood beside him, and he took that comrade's hand,
And he said: 'I shall never see my own, my native land.'"

In his childhood, the correspondent had been made acquainted with the fact that a soldier of the Legion lay dying in Algiers, but he had never regarded the fact as important. Myriads of his school-fellows had informed him of the soldier's plight, but the dinning had naturally ended by making him perfectly indifferent. He had never considered it his affair that a soldier of the Legion lay dying in Algiers, nor had it appeared to him as a matter for sorrow. It was less to him than the breaking of a pencil's point.

Now, however, it quaintly came to him as a human, living thing. It was no longer merely a picture of a few throes in the breast of a poet, meanwhile drinking tea and warming his feet at the grate; it was an actuality — stern, mournful, and fine.

The correspondent plainly saw the soldier. He lay on the sand with his feet out straight and still. While his pale left hand was upon his chest in an attempt to thwart the going of his life, the blood came between his fingers. In the far Algerian distance, a city of low square forms was set against a sky that was faint with the last sunset hues. The correspondent, plying the oars and dreaming of the slow and slower movements of the lips of the soldier, was moved by a profound and perfectly impersonal comprehension. He was sorry for the soldier of the Legion who lay dying in Algiers.

The thing which had followed the boat and waited had evidently grown bored at the delay. There was no longer to be ~shark~ heard the slash of the cut water, and there was no longer the flame of the long trail. The light in the north still glimmered, but it was apparently no nearer to the boat. Sometimes the boom of the surf rang in the correspondent's ears, and he turned the craft seaward then and rowed harder. Southward, someone had evidently built a watch-fire on the beach. It was too low and too far to be seen, but it made a shimmering, roseate reflection upon the bluff back of it, and this could be discerned from the boat. The wind came stronger, and sometimes a wave suddenly raged out like a mountain-cat, and there was to be seen the sheen and sparkle of a broken crest.

The captain, in the bow, moved on his water-jar and sat erect. "Pretty long night," he observed to the correspondent. He looked at the shore. "Those life-saving people take their time."

"Did you see that shark playing around?"

"Yes, I saw him. He was a big fellow, all right."

"Wish I had known you were awake."

Later the correspondent spoke into the bottom of the boat.

"Billie!" There was a slow and gradual disentanglement. "Billie, will you spell me?"

"Sure," said the oiler.

As soon as the correspondent touched the cold comfortable sea-water in the bottom of the boat, and had huddled close to the cook's life-belt he was deep in sleep, despite the fact that his teeth played all the popular airs. This sleep was so good to him that it was but a moment before he heard a voice call his name in a tone that demonstrated the last stages of exhaustion. "Will you spell me?"

"Sure, Billie."

The light in the north had mysteriously vanished, but the correspondent took his course from the wide-awake captain.

Later in the night they took the boat farther out to sea, and the captain directed the cook to take one oar at the stern and keep the boat facing the seas. He was to call out if he should hear the thunder of the surf. This plan enabled the oiler and the correspondent to get respite together. "We'll give those boys a chance to get into shape again," said the captain. They curled down and, after a few preliminary chatterings and trembles, slept once more the dead sleep. Neither knew they had bequeathed to the cook the company of another shark, or perhaps the same shark.

As the boat caroused on the waves, spray occasionally bumped over the side and gave them a fresh soaking, but this had no power to break their repose. The ominous slash of the wind and the water affected them as it would have affected mummies.

"Boys," said the cook, with the notes of every reluctance in his voice, "she's drifted in pretty close. I guess one of you had better take her to sea again." The correspondent, aroused, heard the crash of the toppled crests.

As he was rowing, the captain gave him some whisky-and-water, and this steadied the chills out of him. "If I ever get ashore and anybody shows me even a photograph of an oar —"

At last there was a short conversation.

"Billie . . . Billie, will you spell me?"

"Sure," said the oiler.

VII

When the correspondent again opened his eyes, the sea and the sky were each of the gray hue of the dawning. Later, carmine and gold was painted upon the waters. The morning appeared finally, in its splendor, with a sky of pure blue, and the sunlight flamed on the tips of the waves.

On the distant dunes were set many little black cottages, and a tall white windmill reared above them. No man, nor dog, nor bicycle appeared on the beach. The cottages might have formed a deserted village.

The voyagers scanned the shore. A conference was held in the boat. "Well," said the captain, "if no help is coming, we might better try a run through the surf right away. If we stay out here much longer we will be too weak to do anything for ourselves at all." The others silently acquiesced in this reasoning. The boat was headed for the beach. The correspondent wondered if none ever ascended the tall wind-tower, and if then they never looked seaward. This tower was a giant, standing with its back to the plight of the ants. It represented in a degree, to the correspondent, the serenity of nature amid the struggles of the individual — nature in the wind, and nature in the vision of men. She did not seem cruel to him then, nor beneficent, nor treacherous, nor wise. But she was indifferent, flatly indifferent. It is, perhaps, plausible that a man in this situation, impressed with the unconcern of the universe, should see the innumerable flaws of his life, and have them taste wickedly in his mind and wish for another chance. A distinction between right and wrong seems absurdly clear to him, then, in this new ignorance of the grave-edge, and he understands that if he were given another opportunity he would mend his conduct and his words, and be better and brighter during an introduction or at a tea.

"Now, boys," said the captain, "she is going to swamp sure. All we can do is to work her in as far as possible, and then when she swamps, pile out and scramble for the beach. Keep cool now, and don't jump until she swamps sure."

The oiler took the oars. Over his shoulders he scanned the surf. "Captain," he said, "I think I'd better bring her about, and keep her head-on to the seas and back her in."

"All right, Billie," said the captain. "Back her in." The oiler swung the boat then and, seated in the stern, the cook and the correspondent were obliged to look over their shoulders to contemplate the lonely and indifferent shore.

The monstrous in-shore rollers heaved the boat high until the men were again enabled to see the white sheets of water scudding up the slanted beach. "We won't get in very close," said the captain. Each time a man could wrest his attention from the rollers, he turned his glance toward the shore, and in the expression of the eyes during this contemplation there was a singular quality. The correspondent, observing the others, knew that they were not afraid, but the full meaning of their glances was shrouded.

As for himself, he was too tired to grapple fundamentally with the fact. He tried to coerce his mind into thinking of it, but the mind was dominated at this time by the muscles, and the muscles said they did not care. It merely occurred to him that if he should drown it would be a shame.

There were no hurried words, no pallor, no plain agitation. The men simply looked at the shore. "Now, remember to get well clear of the boat when you jump," said the captain.

Seaward the crest of a roller suddenly fell with a thunderous crash, and the long white comber came roaring down upon the boat.

"Steady now," said the captain. The men were silent. They turned their eyes from the shore to the comber and waited. The boat slid up the incline, leaped at the furious top, bounced over it, and swung down the long back of the waves. Some water had been shipped and the cook bailed it out.

But the next crest crashed also. The tumbling, boiling flood of white water caught the boat and whirled it almost perpendicular. Water swarmed in from all sides. The correspondent had his hands on the gunwale at this time, and when the water entered at that place he swiftly withdrew his fingers, as if he objected to wetting them.

The little boat, drunken with this weight of water, reeled and snuggled deeper into the sea.

"Bail her out, cook! Bail her out," said the captain.

"All right, captain," said the cook.

"Now, boys, the next one will do for us, sure," said the oiler. "Mind to jump clear of the boat."

The third wave moved forward, huge, furious, implacable. It fairly swallowed the dingey, and almost simultaneously the men tumbled into the sea. A piece of life-belt had lain in the bottom of the boat, and as the correspondent went overboard he held this to his chest with his left hand.

The January water was icy, and he reflected immediately that it was colder than he had expected to find it off the coast of Florida. This appeared to his dazed mind as a fact important enough to be noted at the time. The coldness of the water was sad; it was tragic. This fact was somehow so mixed and confused with his opinion of his own situation that it seemed almost a proper reason for tears. The water was cold.

When he came to the surface he was conscious of little but the noisy water. Afterward he saw his companions in the sea. The oiler was ahead in the race. He was swimming strongly and rapidly. Off to the correspondent's left, the cook's great white and corked back bulged out of the water, and in the rear the captain was hanging with his one good hand to the keel of the overturned dingey.

There is a certain immovable quality to a shore, and the correspondent wondered at it amid the confusion of the sea.

It seemed also very attractive, but the correspondent knew that it was a long journey, and he paddled leisurely. The piece of life-preserver lay under him, and sometimes he whirled down the incline of a wave as if he were on a hand-sled.

But finally he arrived at a place in the sea where travel was beset with difficulty. He did not pause swimming to inquire what manner of current had caught him, but there his progress ceased. The shore was set before him like a bit of scenery on a stage, and he looked at it and understood with his eyes each detail of it.

As the cook passed, much farther to the left, the captain was calling to him, "Turn over on your back, cook! Turn over on your back and use the oar."

"All right, sir." The cook turned on his back, and, paddling with an oar, went ahead as if he were a canoe.

Presently the boat also passed to the left of the correspondent with the captain clinging with one hand to the keel. He would have appeared like a man raising himself to look over a board fence, if it were not for the extraordinary gymnastics of the boat.

The correspondent marvelled that the captain could still hold to it.

They passed on, nearer to shore — the oiler, the cook, the captain — and following them went the water-jar, bouncing gaily over the seas.

The correspondent remained in the grip of this strange new enemy — a current. The shore, with its white slope of sand and its green bluff, topped with little silent cottages, was spread like a picture before him. It was very near to him then, but he was impressed as one who in a gallery looks at a scene from Brittany or Algiers.

He thought: "I am going to drown? Can it be possible? Can it be possible? Can it be possible?" Perhaps an individual must consider his own death to be the final phenomenon of nature.

But later a wave perhaps whirled him out of this small deadly current, for he found suddenly that he could again make progress toward the shore. Later still, he was aware that the captain, clinging with one hand to the keel of the dingey, had his face turned away from the shore and toward him, and was calling his name. "Come to the boat! Come to the boat!"

In his struggle to reach the captain and the boat, he reflected that when one gets properly wearied, drowning must really be a comfortable arrangement, a cessation of hostilities accompanied by a large degree of relief, and he was glad of it, for the main thing in his mind for some moments had been horror of the temporary agony. He did not wish to be hurt.

Presently he saw a man running along the shore. He was undressing with most remarkable speed. Coat, trousers, shirt, everything flew magically off him.

"Come to the boat," called the captain.

"All right, captain." As the correspondent paddled, he saw the captain let himself down to bottom and leave the boat. Then the correspondent performed his one little marvel of the voyage. A large wave caught him and flung him with ease and supreme speed completely over the boat and far beyond it. It struck him even then as an event in gymnastics, and a true miracle of the sea. An overturned boat in the surf is not a plaything to a swimming man.

The correspondent arrived in water that reached only to his waist, but his condition did not enable him to stand for more than a moment. Each wave knocked him into a heap, and the under-tow pulled at him.

Then he saw the man who had been running and undressing, and undressing and running, come bounding into the water. He dragged ashore the cook, and then waded toward the captain, but the captain waved him away, and sent him to the correspondent. He was naked, naked as a tree in winter, but a halo was about his head, and he shone like a saint. He gave a strong pull, and a long drag, and a bully heave at the correspondent's hand. The correspondent, schooled in the minor formulae, said: "Thanks, old man." But suddenly the man cried: "What's that?" He pointed a swift finger. The correspondent said: "Go."

In the shallows, face downward, lay the oiler. His forehead touched sand that was periodically, between each wave, clear of the sea.

The correspondent did not know all that transpired afterward. When he achieved safe ground he fell, striking the sand with each particular part of his body. It was as if he had dropped from a roof, but the thud was grateful to him.

It seems that instantly the beach was populated with men, with blankets, clothes, and flasks, and women with coffee-pots and all the remedies sacred to their minds. The welcome of the land to the men from the sea was warm and generous, but a still and dripping shape was carried slowly up the beach, and the land's welcome for it could only be the different and sinister hospitality of the grave.

When it came night, the white waves paced to and fro in the moonlight, and the wind brought the sound of the great sea's voice to the men on shore, and they felt that they could then be interpreters.

Stephen Crane (1871-1900) Stephen Crane, the fourteenth child of a Methodist minister, was born in Newark, New Jersey. Through writing he helped finance two years at Lafayette College and Syracuse University, and he subsequently became a successful journalist and traveling correspondent as well as a fiction writer. *Maggie,* his first novel, published in 1892, was based on his observations while living on New York's Bowery; *The Red Badge of Courage*

(1895), a psychological reconstruction of a boy's war experience, established his international reputation; *The Little Regiment* (1896), was his first collection of short stories. Like Chekhov's, Crane's life was darkened by almost constant ill health; he died of tuberculosis, at the age of twenty-eight, in the Black Forest of Germany.

Although Crane is frequently spoken of as one of the pioneer American realists, his emphasis on style, imagery, and tone, his tendency to view life subjectively through the eyes of his characters, and his effective use of symbols give much of his work a romantic, almost mythic, rather than realistic quality. If read on one level, "The Open Boat" is a moving and effective example of realistic writing; Crane knew from actual experience the ordeal of shipwreck, and communicates it vividly to the reader. But he is doing much more than writing a factually accurate amount of shipwreck and its aftermath. By the use of specfic details — such as the wind-tower and the ants — he forces a more than literal interpretation upon the reader; these thematic and symbolic elements in the story are skilfully incorporated within the framework of incident, setting, and character, and are a logical outgrowth of these narrative elements.

Crane, like Hawthorne, could not resist the impulse to underscore, as it were, the thematic qualities of this tale. By means of the correspondent (Crane himself, or his alter ego), the author suggests that nature is neither cruel, "nor beneficent, nor treacherous, nor wise. But she was indifferent, flatly indifferent." What then remains? Crane's implications are inescapable. Even though man is defeated by combat, he is enriched by it. Struggle, the author suggests, is important in itself. Through it, man matures, is initiated by ritual into a kind of brotherhood; through it, man establishes kinship with men.

A good selection from Crane's short stories is: *Stephen Crane: Stories and Tales* (ed. Robert W. Stallman, Vintage).

Questions   1. Compare or contrast the occupants of the boat. Which, in your opinion, is the most individualized character? Which is the least individualized? How does Crane individualize these characters?   2. When does the correspondent realize that the "subtle brotherhood" which the sea establishes is "the best experience of his life"? Is this the key to the "meaning of the story"? If so, how do you explain the seeming paradox of the oiler's death?   3. Do you consider this an essentially pessimistic story, or the reverse?   4. List the details by means of which Crane establishes the illusion of reality. (The story actually grew out of the sinking of the S. S. *Commodore* en route to Cuba in 1896. Crane survived to report the event factually for an American newspaper before transmuting the experience into "The Open Boat"). 5. Discuss some of the details or symbols by means of which Crane suggests the thematic implications of the story (for example, the verses about the dying soldier in Algiers). 6. Notice the contrasts throughout the story (between the men themselves, between the men and the land-dwellers, between the survivors and the dead man). What other contrasts occur in the story?

WALTER DE LA MARE

The Riddle

So THESE seven children, Ann, and Matilda, James, William and
Henry, Harriet and Dorothea, came to live with their grandmother. The house in which their grandmother had lived since
her childhood was built in the time of the Georges. It was not a
pretty house, but roomy, substantial, and square; and an elm tree
outstretched its branches almost to the windows.

When the children were come out of the cab (five sitting inside and two beside the driver), they were shown into their
grandmother's presence. They stood in a little black group before the old lady, seated in her bow-window. And she asked
them each their names, and repeated each name in her kind,
quavering voice. Then to one she gave a work-box, to William a
jack-knife, to Dorothea a painted ball; to each a present according to age. And she kissed all her grandchildren to the youngest.

"My dears," she said, "I wish to see all of you bright and gay
in my house. I am an old woman, so that I cannot romp with
you; but Ann must look to you, and Mrs. Fenn too. And every
morning and every evening you must all come in to see your
granny; and bring me smiling faces, that call back to my mind
my own son Harry. But all the rest of the day, when school is
done, you shall do just as you please, my dears. And there is
only one thing, just one, I would have you remember. In the

THE RIDDLE Reprinted from *The Collected Tales of Walter de la Mare*,
by permission of Alfred A. Knopf, Inc. Copyright 1923, 1950, by Walter
de la Mare.

large spare bedroom that looks out on the slate roof there stands in the corner an old oak chest; ay, older than I, my dears, a great deal older; older than my grandmother. Play anywhere else in the house, but not there." She spoke kindly to them all, smiling at them; but she was very aged, and her eyes seemed to see nothing of this world.

And the seven children, though at first they were gloomy and strange, soon began to be happy and at home in the great house. There was much to interest and amuse them there; all was new to them. Twice every day, morning and evening, they came in to see their grandmother, who every day seemed more feeble; and she spoke pleasantly to them of her mother, and her childhood, but never forgetting to visit her store of sugar-plums. And so the weeks passed by.

It was evening twilight when Henry went upstairs from the nursery by himself to look at the oak chest. He pressed his fingers into the carved fruit and flowers, and spoke to the dark-smiling heads at the corners; and then, with a glance over his shoulder, he opened the lid and looked in. But the chest concealed no treasure, neither gold nor baubles, nor was there anything to alarm the eye. The chest was empty, except that it was lined with silk of old-rose, seeming darker in the dusk, and smelling sweet of pot-pourri. And while Henry was looking in, he heard the softened laughter and the clinking of the cups downstairs in the nursery; and out at the window he saw the day darkening. These things brought strangely to his memory his mother, who in her glimmering white dress used to read to him in the dusk; and he climbed in the chest; and the lid closed gently down over him.

When the other six children were tired with their playing, they filed into their grandmother's room as usual for her goodnight and her sugar-plums. She looked out between the candles at them as if she were unsure of something in her thoughts. The next day Ann told her grandmother that Henry was not anywhere to be found.

"Dearie me, child. Then he must have gone away for a time," said the old lady. She paused. "But remember all of you, do not meddle with the oak chest."

But Matilda could not forget her brother Henry, finding no pleasure in playing without him. So she would loiter in the house thinking where he might be. And she carried her wood doll in her bare arms, singing under her breath all she could make up about him. And when in a bright morning she peeped in on the chest, so sweet-scented and secret it seemed that she took her doll with her into it — just as Henry himself had done.

So Ann, and James, and William, Harriet and Dorothea were left at home to play together. "Some day maybe they will come back to you, my dears," said their grandmother, "or maybe you will go to them. Heed my warning as best you may."

Now Harriet and William were friends together, pretending to be sweethearts; while James and Dorothea liked wild games of hunting, and fishing, and battles.

On a silent afternoon in October Harriet and William were talking softly together, looking out over the slate roof at the green fields, and they heard the squeak and frisking of a mouse behind them in the room. They went together and searched for the small, dark hole from whence it had come out. But finding no hole, they began to finger the carving of the chest, and to give names to the dark-smelling heads, just as Henry had done. "I know! Let's pretend you are Sleeping Beauty, Harriet," said William, "and I'll be the Prince that squeezes through the thorns and comes in." Harriet looked gently and strangely at her brother; but she got into the box and lay down, pretending to be asleep; and on tiptoe William leaned over, and seeing how big was the chest he stepped in to kiss the Sleeping Beauty and to wake her from her quiet sleep. Slowly the carved lid turned on its noiseless hinges. And only the clatter of James and Dorothea came in sometimes to recall Ann from her book.

But their old grandmother was very feeble, and her sight dim, and her hearing extremely difficult.

Snow was falling through the still air upon the roof; and Dorothea was a fish in the oak chest, and James stood over the hole in the ice, brandishing a walking-stick for a harpoon, pretending to be an Esquimau. Dorothea's face was red, and her wild eyes sparkled through her tousled hair. And James had a crooked scratch upon his cheek. "You must struggle, Dorothea, and then I shall swim back and drag you out. Be quick now!" He shouted with laughter as he was drawn into the open chest. And the lid closed softly and gently down as before.

Ann, left to herself, was too old to care overmuch for sugar-plums, but she would go solitary to bid her grandmother good-night; and the old lady looked wistfully at her over her spectacles. "Well, my dear," she said with trembling head; and she squeezed Ann's fingers between her own knuckled finger and thumb. "What lonely old people we are, to be sure!" Ann kissed her grandmother's soft, loose cheek. She left the old lady sitting in her easy chair, her hands upon her knees, and her head turned sidelong towards her.

When Ann was gone to bed she used to sit reading her book by candlelight. She drew up her knees under the sheets, resting her book upon them. Her story was about fairies and gnomes, and the gently-flowing moonlight of the narrative seemed to illumine the white pages, and she could hear in fancy fairy voices, so silent was the great many-roomed house, and so mellifluent were the words of the story. Presently she put out her candle, and, with a confused babel of voices close to her ear, and faint swift pictures before her eyes, she fell asleep.

And in the dead of night she arose out of bed in dream, and with eyes wide open yet seeing nothing of reality, moved silently through the vacant house. Past the room where her grandmother was snoring in brief, heavy slumber, she stepped light and surely, and down the wide staircase. And Vega the far-shining stood over against the window above the slate roof. Ann walked in the strange room as if she were being guided by the hand towards the oak chest. There, just as if she was dreaming it was her bed, she laid herself down in the old rose silk, in the fragrant place. But it was so dark in the room that the movement of the lid was indistinguishable.

Through the long day, the grandmother sat in her bow-window. Her lips were pursed, and she looked with dim, inquisitive scrutiny upon the street where people passed to and fro, and vehicles rolled by. At evening she climbed the stair and stood in the doorway of the large spare bedroom. The ascent had shortened her breath. Her magnifying spectacles rested upon her nose. Leaning her hand on the doorpost she peered in towards the glimming square of window in the quiet gloom. But she could not see far, because her sight was dim and the light of day feeble. Nor could she detect the faint fragrance, as of autumnal leaves. But in her mind was a tangled skein of memories — laughter and tears, and little children now old-fashioned,

and the advent of friends, and long farewells. And gossiping
fitfully, inarticulately, with herself, the old lady went down
again to her window-seat.

Walter de la Mare (1873-1956)   Born at Charlton, Kent, England, Walter de la Mare was educated at St. Paul's Cathedral Choir
School. For many years he was a statistician with the Anglo-American
Oil Company; he was "rescued" from this position by a small pension
from the Asquith government which made it possible for him to con-
centrate on his imaginative, highly individualistic art. He was at first
known primarily as a poet — his first book, *Poems of Childhood,* was
published in 1902 — and he continued to write poetry throughout his
long lifetime. He is also a distinguished writer of fiction who produced six volumes of short stories and four longer works including the
incomparable *Memoirs of a Midget.*

Although many of de la Mare's stories are firmly rooted in the *real,*
his favorite fictional world is one of fantasy, dreams, and the supernatural. He was fascinated, as a recent critic has aptly stated, by the
"twilight side of life." To try to force a "literal" meaning on a story
like "The Riddle" is short-sighted; de la Mare's indirect, implica-
tional method eludes realistic analysis. De la Mare, like William
Blake, created his own heaven and hell; he is concerned with the
contemplation of universal truths and the enigma of the human soul.
These truths he often approaches through fantasy and dreams, and he
frequently suggests them through daring images and unusual symbols.

Some readers interpret "The Riddle" as de la Mare's variation on
the theme of the forbidden fruit or Pandora's Box; some, as a life-
death fantasy. Still others may read the story as a lonely old woman's
recollection of the past when life was richer and fuller in a home filled
with the laughing presence of children. Mr. de la Mare himself, when
asked if the children in the story died, replied yes, he did mean that
they had died. When asked if he had meant to make the grandmother
a somewhat sinister figure, he was less direct and stated that she
wasn't meant to be any more sinister than she appeared to be. Perhaps
the ultimate "clue" to the story lies in the final paragraph: "in her
mind was a tangled skein of memories — laughter and tears, and
little children now old-fashioned, and the advent of friends, and long
farewells."

An excellent introduction to de la Mare's short fiction is *The Collected Tales of Walter de la Mare,* with an appreciative commentary
by Edward Wagenknecht (Knopf).

Questions   1. What is the purpose of the opening sentence of the story, with its echoes of nursery tales, fairy stories, and the like? 2. What, if anything, is the significance of the fact that there are *seven* children?   3. Do you agree with some critics that there is something "sinister" about the grandmother?   4. Would the story be more effective had the author individualized the children more fully? Compare or contrast the children.   5. What are some of the symbols in this story? Compare or contrast de la Mare's use of symbols with Hawthorne's.

SHERWOOD ANDERSON

Adventure

ALICE HINDMAN, a woman of twenty-seven when George Willard was a mere boy, had lived in Winesburg all her life. She clerked in Winney's Dry Goods Store and lived with her mother who had married a second husband.

Alice's step-father was a carriage-painter, and given to drink. His story is an odd one. It will be worth telling some day.

At twenty-seven Alice was tall and somewhat slight. Her head was large and overshadowed her body. Her shoulders were a little stooped and her hair and eyes brown. She was very quiet but beneath a placid exterior a continual ferment went on.

When she was a girl of sixteen and before she began to work in the store, Alice had an affair with a young man. The young man, named Ned Currie, was older than Alice. He, like George Willard, was employed on the *Winesburg Eagle* and for a long time he went to see Alice almost every evening. Together the two walked under the trees through the streets of the town and talked of what they would do with their lives. Alice was then a very pretty girl and Ned Currie took her into his arms and kissed her. He became excited and said things he did not intend to say and Alice, betrayed by her desire to have something beautiful come into her rather narrow life, also grew excited. She also talked. The outer crust of her life, all of her natural diffidence

ADVENTURE From *Winesburg, Ohio* by Sherwood Anderson. Copyright 1919 by B. W. Huebsch, 1947 by Eleanor Copenhaver Anderson. Reprinted by permission of The Viking Press, Inc.

and reserve, was torn away and she gave herself over to the emotions of love. When, late in the fall of her sixteenth year, Ned Currie went away to Cleveland where he hoped to get a place on a city newspaper and rise in the world, she wanted to go with him. With a trembling voice she told him what was in her mind. "I will work and you can work," she said. "I do not want to harness you to a needless expense that will prevent your making progress. Don't marry me now. We will get along without that and we can be together. Even though we live in the same house no one will say anything. In the city we will be unknown and people will pay no attention to us."

Ned Currie was puzzled by the determination and abandon of his sweetheart and was also deeply touched. He had wanted the girl to become his mistress but changed his mind. He wanted to protect and care for her. "You don't know what you're talking about," he said sharply; "you may be sure I'll let you do no such thing. As soon as I get a good job I'll come back. For the present you'll have to stay here. It's the only thing we can do."

On the evening before he left Winesburg to take up his new life in the city, Ned Currie went to call on Alice. They walked about through the streets for an hour and then got a rig from Wesley Moyer's livery and went for a drive in the country. The moon came up and they found themselves unable to talk. In his sadness the young man forgot the resolutions he had made regarding his conduct with the girl.

They got out of the buggy at a place where a long meadow ran down to the bank of Wine Creek and there in the dim light became lovers. When at midnight they returned to town they were both glad. It did not seem to them that anything that could happen in the future could blot out the wonder and beauty of the thing that had happened. "Now we will have to stick to each other, whatever happens we will have to do that," Ned Currie said as he left the girl at her father's door.

The young newspaper man did not succeed in getting a place on a Cleveland paper and went west to Chicago. For a time he was lonely and wrote to Alice almost every day. Then he was caught up by the life of the city; he began to make friends and found new interests in life. In Chicago he boarded at a house where there were several women. One of them attracted his attention and he forgot Alice in Winesburg. At the end of a year he had stopped writing letters, and only once in a long time, when he was lonely or when he went into one of the city parks and saw the moon shining on the grass as it had shone that night on the meadow by Wine Creek, did he think of her at all.

In Winesburg the girl who had been loved grew to be a woman. When she was twenty-two years old her father, who owned a harness repair shop, died suddenly. The harness maker was an old soldier, and after a few months his wife received a widow's pension. She used the first money she got to buy a loom and became a weaver of carpets, and Alice got a place in Winney's store. For a number of years nothing could have induced her to believe that Ned Currie would not in the end return to her.

She was glad to be employed because the daily round of toil in the store made the time of waiting seem less long and un-interesting. She began to save money, thinking that when she had saved two or three hundred dollars she would follow her lover to the city and try if her presence would not win back his affections.

Alice did not blame Ned Currie for what had happened in the moonlight in the field, but felt that she could never marry an-other man. To her the thought of giving to another what she still felt could belong only to Ned seemed monstrous. When other young men tried to attract her attention she would have nothing to do with them. "I am his wife and shall remain his wife whether he comes back or not," she whispered to herself, and for all of her willingness to support herself could not have understood the growing modern idea of a woman's owning herself and giving and taking for her own ends in life.

Alice worked in the dry goods store from eight in the morning until six at night and on three evenings a week went back to the store to stay from seven until nine. As time passed and she be-came more and more lonely she began to practice the devices common to lonely people. When at night she went upstairs into her own room she knelt on the floor to pray and in her prayers whispered things she wanted to say to her lover. She became attached to inanimate objects, and because it was her own, could not bear to have anyone touch the furniture of her room. The trick of saving money, begun for a purpose, was carried on after the scheme of going to the city to find Ned Currie had been given up. It became a fixed habit, and when she needed new clothes she did not get them. Sometimes on rainy afternoons in the store she got out her bank book and, letting it lie open before her, spent hours dreaming impossible dreams of saving money enough so that the interest would support both herself and her future husband.

"Ned always liked to travel about," she thought. "I'll give him the chance. Some day when we are married and I can save both his money and my own, we will be rich. Then we can travel together all over the world."

In the dry goods store weeks ran into months and months into years as Alice waited and dreamed of her lover's return. Her employer, a grey old man with false teeth and a thin grey mustache that drooped down over his mouth, was not given to conversation, and sometimes, on rainy days and in the winter when a storm raged in Main Street, long hours passed when no customers came in. Alice arranged and rearranged the stock. She stood near the front window where she could look down the deserted street and thought of the evenings when she had walked with Ned Currie and of what he had said, "We will have to stick to each other now." The words echoed and re-echoed through the mind of the maturing woman. Tears came into her eyes. Sometimes when her employer had gone out and she was alone in the store she put her head on the counter and wept. "Oh, Ned, I am waiting," she whispered over and over, and all the time the creeping fear that he would never come back grew stronger within her.

In the spring when the rains have passed and before the long hot days of summer have come, the country about Winesburg is delightful. The town lies in the midst of open fields, but beyond the fields are pleasant patches of woodlands. In the wooded places are many little cloistered nooks, quiet places where lovers go to sit on Sunday afternoons. Through the trees they look out across the fields and see farmers at work about the barns or people driving up and down on the roads. In the town bells ring and occasionally a train passes, looking like a toy thing in the distance.

For several years after Ned Currie went away, Alice did not go into the wood with other young people on Sunday, but one day, after he had been gone for two or three years and when her loneliness seemed unbearable, she put on her best dress and set out. Finding a little sheltered place from which she could see the

town and a long stretch of the fields, she sat down. Fear of age
and ineffectuality took possession of her. She could not sit still,
and arose. As she stood looking out over the land something,
perhaps the thought of never-ceasing life as it expresses itself in
the flow of the seasons, fixed her mind on the passing years.
With a shiver of dread, she realized that for her the beauty and
freshness of youth had passed. For the first time she felt that
she had been cheated. She did not blame Ned Currie and did
not know what to blame. Sadness swept over her. Dropping to
her knees, she tried to pray, but instead of prayers words of protest came to her lips. "It is not going to come to me. I will never
find happiness. Why do I tell myself lies?" she cried, and an odd
sense of relief came with this, her first bold attempt to face the
fear that had become a part of her everyday life.

In the year when Alice Hindman became twenty-five two
things happened to disturb the dull uneventfulness of her days.
Her mother married Bush Milton, the carriage painter of Winesburg, and she herself became a member of the Winesburg
Methodist Church. Alice joined the church because she had become frightened by the loneliness of her position in life. Her
mother's second marriage had emphasized her isolation. "I am
becoming old and queer. If Ned comes he will not want me. In
the city where he is living men are perpetually young. There is
so much going on that they do not have time to grow old," she
told herself with a grim little smile, and went resolutely about
the business of becoming acquainted with people. Every Thurs-
day evening when the store had closed she went to a prayer
meeting in the basement of the church and on Sunday evening
attended a meeting of an organization called The Epworth
League.

When Will Hurley, a middle-aged man who clerked in a drug
store and who also belonged to the church, offered to walk home
with her she did not protest. "Of course I will not let him make
a practice of being with me, but if he comes to see me once in a
long time there can be no harm in that," she told herself, still
determined in her loyalty to Ned Currie.

Without realizing what was happening, Alice was trying feebly
at first, but with growing determination, to get a new hold upon
life. Beside the drug clerk she walked in silence, but sometimes
in the darkness as they went stolidly along she put out her hand

and touched softly the folds of his coat. When he left her at the gate before her mother's house she did not go indoors, but stood for a moment by the door. She wanted to call to the drug clerk, to ask him to sit with her in the darkness on the porch before the house, but was afraid he would not understand. "It is not him that I want," she told herself; "I want to avoid being so much alone. If I am not careful I will grow unaccustomed to being with people."

.   .   .   .

During the early fall of her twenty-seventh year a passionate restlessness took possession of Alice. She could not bear to be in the company of the drug clerk, and when, in the evening, he came to walk with her she sent him away. Her mind became intensely active and when, weary from the long hours of standing behind the counter in the store, she went home and crawled into bed, she could not sleep. With staring eyes she looked into the darkness. Her imagination, like a child awakened from long sleep, played about the room. Deep within her there was something that would not be cheated by phantasies and that demanded some definite answer from life.

Alice took a pillow into her arms and held it tightly against her breasts. Getting out of bed, she arranged a blanket so that in the darkness it looked like a form lying between the sheets and, kneeling beside the bed, she caressed it, whispering words over and over, like a refrain. "Why doesn't something happen? Why am I left here alone?" she muttered. Although she sometimes thought of Ned Currie, she no longer depended on him. Her desire had grown vague. She did not want Ned Currie or any other man. She wanted to be loved, to have something answer the call that was growing louder and louder within her.

And then one night when it rained Alice had an adventure. It frightened and confused her. She had come home from the store at nine and found the house empty. Bush Milton had gone off to town and her mother to the house of a neighbor. Alice went upstairs to her room and undressed in the darkness. For a moment she stood by the window hearing the rain beat against the glass and then a strange desire took possession of her. Without stopping to think of what she intended to do, she ran downstairs through the dark house and out into the rain. As she stood on the little grass plot before the house and felt the cold rain on her body a mad desire to run naked through the streets took possession of her.

She thought that the rain would have some creative and wonderful effect on her body. Not for years had she felt so full of youth and courage. She wanted to leap and run, to cry out, to find some other lonely human and embrace him. On the brick sidewalk before the house a man stumbled homeward. Alice started to run. A wild, desperate mood took possession of her. "What do I care who it is. He is alone, and I will go to him," she thought; and then without stopping to consider the possible result of her madness, called softly. "Wait!" she cried. "Don't go away. Whoever you are, you must wait."

The man on the sidewalk stopped and stood listening. He was an old man and somewhat deaf. Putting his hand to his mouth, he shouted: "What? What say?" he called.

Alice dropped to the ground and lay trembling. She was so frightened at the thought of what she had done that when the man had gone on his way she did not dare get to her feet, but crawled on hands and knees through the grass to the house. When she got to her own room she bolted the door and drew her dressing table across the doorway. Her body shook as with a chill and her hands trembled so that she had difficulty getting into her nightdress. When she got into bed she buried her face in the pillow and wept broken-heartedly. "What is the matter with me? I will do something dreadful if I am not careful," she thought, and turning her face to the wall, began trying to force herself to face gravely the fact that many people must live and die alone, even in Winesburg.

Sherwood Anderson (1876-1941)   Born in Camden, Ohio, Sherwood Anderson served in Cuba during the Spanish-American War, returned to Ohio to marry and become manager of a paint factory, and then fled both job and family to fulfill his artistic ambitions. In Chicago he met and was encouraged by Theodore Dreiser and Carl Sandburg; in Paris and New Orleans he knew Ezra Pound, Gertrude Stein, and the young Hemingway and Faulkner. *Windy McPherson's Son,* his first novel, was published when he was forty. This was followed by other novels, poems, semi-fictional or autobiographical works, and collections of short stories, of which *Winesburg, Ohio: A Group*

of Tales of Ohio Small-Town Life (1919) is the most distinguished. For some years prior to his death (in Panama, ironically enough, from complications caused by a sliver of toothpick swallowed at a cocktail party) Anderson was a newspaper editor in Marion, Virginia.

The stories in *Winesburg* are narrated with simplicity, directness, and economy, as Anderson probes beneath the surface of the insignificant but not unworthy men and women of Winesburg to depict their innermost tensions, fears, and conflicts. These stories, which in less skilful or less compassionate hands might have been merely a drab series of clinical studies, are illuminated by the presence of "something fine" in the author's unhappy, unfulfilled people. Alice Hindman of "Adventure" is characteristic: she possesses many admirable qualities, not the least of which is the fortitude which enables her to "face bravely the fact that many people must live and die alone, even in Winesburg."

Winesburg, Ohio is available in several inexpensive editions including those of the Modern Library and the New American Library.

Questions   **1.** In "The Book of the Grotesque," which is a kind of prologue to *Winesburg, Ohio,* Anderson says that when the world was young, there were many thoughts but "no such thing as a truth." Man himself made "the truths"; when an individual "took one of the truths to himself, called it his truth, and tried to live his life by it, he became a grotesque and the truth he embraced became a falsehood." According to this definition, is Alice Hindman a "grotesque"? If so, what are the factors or events which turned her into a "grotesque"? **2.** Alice's story, like many of the *Winesburg* pieces, is a study of loneliness, isolation, and frustration. These subjects or themes are among the most prevalent in twentieth-century literature. What authors that you have read are concerned with these or similar ideas?   **3.** How does Anderson handle the problem of time in this story, the facts of which cover some eleven years in Alice Hindman's life? Compare with the time element in a story such as "Chicamauga."   **4.** Examine the dialogue of this story. Is it used primarily as a narrative device to advance the story, or as a means of characterizing Alice and the other people? Compare or contrast it with the dialogue of other stories in this book.   **5.** Anderson dedicated *Winesburg* to his mother, whose observations on life, he says, first awoke in him "the hunger to see beneath the surface of lives." Does this dedicatory statement have any significance in connection with "Adventure"?

A. E. COPPARD

Arabesque — The Mouse

In the main street amongst tall establishments of mart and worship was a high narrow house pressed between a coffee factory and a bootmaker's. It had four flights of long dim echoing stairs, and at the top, in a room that was full of the smell of dried apples and mice, a man in the middle age of life had sat reading Russian novels until he thought he was mad. Late was the hour, the night outside black and freezing, the pavements below empty and undistinguishable when he closed his book and sat motionless in front of the glowing but flameless fire. He felt he was very tired, yet he could not rest. He stared at a picture on the wall until he wanted to cry; it was a colour-print by Utamaro of a suckling child caressing its mother's breasts as she sits in front of a blackbound mirror. Very chaste and decorative it was, in spite of its curious anatomy. The man gazed, empty of sight though not of mind, until the sighing of the gas-jet maddened him. He got up, put out the light, and sat down again in the darkness trying to compose his mind before the comfort of the fire. And he was just about to begin a conversation with himself when a mouse crept from a hole in the skirting near the fireplace and scurried into the fender. The man had the crude dislike for

ARABESQUE — THE MOUSE   Reprinted from *The Collected Tales of A. E. Coppard,* by permission of Alfred A. Knopf, Inc. Copyright 1929, 1948, by A. E. Coppard.

such sly nocturnal things, but this mouse was so small and bright, its antics so pretty, that he drew his feet carefully from the fender and sat watching it almost with amusement. The mouse moved along the shadows of the fender, out upon the hearth, and sat before the glow, rubbing its head, ears, and tiny belly with its paws as if it were bathing itself with the warmth, until, sharp and sudden, the fire sank, an ember fell, and the mouse flashed into its hole.

The man reached forward to the mantel-piece and put his hand upon a pocket lamp. Turning on the beam, he opened the door of a cupboard beside the fireplace. Upon one of the shelves there was a small trap baited with cheese, a trap made with a wire spring, one of those that smashed down to break the back of ingenuous and unwary mice.

"Mean — so mean," he mused, "to appeal to the hunger of any living thing just in order to destroy it."

He picked up the empty trap as if to throw it in the fire.

"I suppose I had better leave it though — the place swarms with them." He still hesitated. "I hope that little beastie won't go and do anything foolish." He put the trap back quite carefully, closed the door of the cupboard, sat down again and extinguished the lamp.

Was there anyone else in the world so squeamish and foolish about such things! Even his mother, mother so bright and beautiful, even she had laughed at his childish horrors. He recalled how once in his childhood, not long after his sister Yosine was born, a friendly neighbour had sent him home with a bundle of dead larks tied by the feet "for supper." The pitiful inanimity of the birds had brought a gush of tears; he had run weeping home and into the kitchen, and there he had found the strange thing doing. It was dusk; his mother was kneeling before the fire. He dropped the larks.

"Mother!" he exclaimed softly.

She looked at his tearful face.

"What's the matter, Filip?" she asked, smiling too at his astonishment.

"Mother! What are you doing?"

Her bodice was open and she was squeezing her breasts; long thin streams of milk spurted into the fire with a plunging noise.

"Weaning your little sister," laughed Mother. She took his

inquisitive face and pressed it against the delicate warmth of her bosom, and he forgot the dead birds behind him.

"Let me do it, Mother," he cried, and doing so he discovered the throb of the heart in his mother's breast. Wonderful it was for him to experience it, although she could not explain it to him.

"Why does it do that?"

"If it did not beat, little son, I should die and the Holy Father would take me from you."

"God?"

She nodded. He put his hand upon his own breast. "Oh, feel it, Mother!" he cried. Mother unbuttoned his little coat and felt the gentle *tick tick* with her warm palm.

"Beautiful!" she said.

"Is it a good one?"

She kissed his smiling lips. "It is good if it beats truly. Let it always beat truly, Filip; let it always beat truly."

There was the echo of a sigh in her voice, and he had divined some grief, for he was very wise. He kissed her bosom in his tiny ecstasy and whispered soothingly: "Little mother! little mother!" In such joys he forgot his horror of the dead larks; indeed he helped Mother to pluck them and spit them for supper.

It was a black day that succeeded, and full of tragedy for the child. A great bay horse with a tawny mane had knocked down his mother in the lane, and a heavy cart had passed over her, crushing both her hands. She was borne away moaning with anguish to the surgeon who cut off the two hands. She died in the night. For years the child's dreams were filled with the horror of the stumps of arms, bleeding unendingly. Yet he had never seen them, for he was sleeping when she died.

While this old woe was come vividly before him he again became aware of the mouse. His nerves stretched upon him in repulsion, but he soon relaxed to a tolerant interest, for it was really a most engaging little mouse. It moved with curious staccato scurries, stopping to rub its head or flicker with its ears; they seemed almost transparent ears. It spied a red cinder and skipped innocently up to it . . . sniffing . . . sniffing . . . until it jumped back scorched. It would crouch as a cat does, blinking in the warmth, or scamper madly as if dancing, and then roll upon its side rubbing its head with those pliant paws. The melancholy man watched it until it came at last to rest and squatted meditatively upon its haunches, hunched up, looking curiously wise, a pennyworth of philosophy; then once more the coals sank with a rattle and again the mouse was gone.

The man sat on before the fire and his mind filled again with unaccountable sadness. He had grown into manhood with a burning generosity of spirit and rifts of rebellion in him that proved too exacting for his fellows and seemed mere wantonness to men of casual rectitudes. "Justice and Sin," he would cry, "Property and Virtue — incompatibilities! There can be no sin in a world of justice, no property in a world of virtue!" With an engaging extravagance and a certain clear-eyed honesty of mind he had put his two and two together and seemed then to rejoice, as in some topsy-turvy dream, in having rendered unto Cæsar, as you might say, the things that were due to Napoleon! But this kind of thing could not pass unexpiated in a world of men having an infinite regard for Property and a pride in their traditions of Virtue and Justice. They could indeed forgive him his sins, but they could not forgive him his compassions. So he had to go seek for more melodious-minded men and fair unambiguous women. But rebuffs can deal more deadly blows than daggers; he became timid — a timidity not of fear but of pride — and grew with the years into misanthropy, susceptible to trivial griefs and despairs, a vessel of emotion that emptied as easily as it filled, until he came at last to know that his griefs were half deliberate, his despairs half unreal, and to live but for beauty — which is tranquility — to put her wooing hand upon him.

Now, while the mouse hunts in the cupboard, one fair recollection stirs in the man's mind — of Cassia and the harmony of their only meeting. Cassia who had such rich red hair, and eyes, yes, her eyes were full of starry inquiry like the eyes of mice. It was so long ago that he had forgotten how he came to be in it, that unaccustomed orbit of vain vivid things — a village festival, all oranges and houp-la. He could not remember how he came to be there, but at night, in the court hall, he had danced with Cassia — fair and unambiguous indeed! — who had come like the wind from among the roses and swept into his heart.

"It is easy to guess," he had said to her, "what you like most in the world."

She laughed. "To dance? Yes, and you . . . ?"

"To find a friend."

"I know, I know," she cried, caressing him with recognitions. "Ah, at times I quite love my friends — until I begin to wonder how much they hate me!"

He had loved at once that cool pale face, the abundance of her hair as light as the autumn's clustered bronze, her lilac dress and all the sweetness about her like a bush of lilies. How they had laughed at the two old peasants whom they had overheard gabbling of trifles like sickness and appetite!

"There's a lot of nature in a parsnip," said one, a fat person of the kind that swells grossly when stung by a bee, "a lot of nature when it's young, but when it's old it's like everything else."

"True it is."

"And I'm very fond of vegetables, yes, and I'm very fond of bread."

"Come out with me," whispered Cassia to Filip, and they walked out in the blackness of midnight into what must have been a garden.

"Cool it is here," she said, "and quiet, but too dark even to see your face — can you see mine?"

"The moon will not rise until after dawn," said he, "it will be white in the sky when the starlings whistle in your chimney."

They walked silently and warily about until they felt the chill of the air. A dull echo of the music came to them through the walls, then stopped, and they heard the bark of a fox away in the woods.

"You are cold," he whispered, touching her bare neck with timid fingers. "Quite, quite cold," drawing his hand tenderly over the curves of her chin and face. "Let us go in," he said, moving with discretion from the rapture he desired.

"We will come out again," said Cassia.

But within the room the ball was just at an end, the musicians were packing up their instruments and the dancers were flocking out and homewards, or to the buffet which was on a platform at one end of the room. The two old peasants were there, munching hugely.

"I tell you," said one of them, "there's nothing in the world for it but the grease of an owl's liver. That's it, that's it! Take something on your stomach now, just to offset the chill of the dawn!"

Filip and Cassia were beside them, but there were so many people crowding the platform that Filip had to jump down. He stood then looking up adoringly at Cassia, who had pulled a purple cloak about her.

"For Filip, Filip, Filip," she said, pushing the last bite of her sandwich into his mouth and pressing upon him her glass of Loupiac. Quickly he drank it with a great gesture, and flinging the glass to the wall, took Cassia into his arms, shouting: "I'll carry you home, the whole way home, yes, I'll carry you!"

"Put me down!" she cried, beating his head and pulling his ear, as they passed among the departing dancers. "Put me down, you wild thing!"

Dark, dark was the lane outside, and the night an obsidian net, into which he walked carrying the girl. But her arms were looped around him; she discovered paths for him, clinging more tightly as he staggered against a wall, stumbled upon a gulley, or when her sweet hair was caught in the boughs of a little lime tree.

"Do not loose me, Filip, will you? Do not loose me," Cassia said, putting her lips against his temple.

His brain seemed bursting, his heart rocked within him, but he adored the rich grace of her limbs against his breast. "Here it is," she murmured, and he carried her into a path that led to her home in a little lawned garden where the smell of ripe apples upon the branches and the heavy lustre of roses stole upon the air. Roses and apples! Roses and apples! He carried her right into the porch before she slid down and stood close to him with her hands still upon his shoulders. He could breathe happily at the release, standing silent and looking round at the sky sprayed with wondrous stars but without a moon.

"You are stronger than I thought you, stronger than you look; you are really very strong," she whispered, nodding her head to him. Opening the buttons of his coat, she put her palm against his breast.

"Oh, how your heart does beat! Does it beat truly — and for whom?"

He had seized her wrists in a little fury of love, crying: "Little mother, little mother!"

"What are you saying?" asked the girl; but before he could continue there came a footstep sounding behind the door, and the clack of a bolt. . . .

What was that? Was that really a bolt or was it . . . was it

. . . the snap of the trap? The man sat up in his room intently listening, with nerves quivering again, waiting for the trap to kill the little philosopher. When he felt it was all over he reached guardedly in the darkness for the lantern, turned on the beam, and opened the door of the cupboard. Focussing the light upon the trap, he was amazed to see the mouse sitting on its haunches before it, uncaught. Its head was bowed, but its bead-like eyes were full of brightness, and it sat blinking, it did not flee.

"Shoosh!" said the man, but the mouse did not move. "Why doesn't it go? Shoosh!" he said again, and suddenly the reason of the mouse's strange behavior was made clear. The trap had not caught it completely, but it had broken off both its forefeet, and the thing crouched there holding out its two bleeding stumps humanly, too stricken to stir.

Horror flooded the man, and conquering his repugnance he plucked the mouse up quickly by the neck. Immediately the thing fastened its teeth in his finger; the touch was no more than the slight prick of a pin. The man's impulse then exhausted itself. What should he do with it? He put his hand behind him, he dared not look, but there was nothing to be done except kill it at once, quickly, quickly. Oh, how should he do it? He bent towards the fire as if to drop the mouse into its quenching glow; but he paused and shuddered, he would hear its cries, he would have to listen. Should he crush it with finger and thumb? A glance towards the window decided him. He opened the sash with one hand and flung the wounded mouse far into the dark street. Closing the window with a crash, he sank into a chair, limp with pity too deep for tears.

So he sat for two minutes, five minutes, ten minutes. Anxiety and shame filled him with heat. He opened the window again, and the freezing air poured in and cooled him. Seizing his lantern, he ran down the echoing stairs, into the dark empty street, searching long and vainly for the little philosopher until he had to desist and return to his room, shivering, frozen to his very bones.

When he had recovered some warmth he took the trap from its shelf. The two feet dropped into his hand; he cast them into the fire. Then he once more set the trap and put it back carefully into the cupboard.

A(lfred) E(dgar) Coppard (1878-1957)   A. E. Coppard was
born at Folkestone, England. At the age of nine he went to London,
worked at various odd jobs, later became a clerk, and finally deserted
business to devote himself to writing poetry and short fiction. Between
1921 and 1938 he wrote approximately two hundred short stories
which were published in such individual collections as *Adam and Eve
and Pinch Me, Fishmonger's Fiddle,* and *Silver Circus.* For years
Mr. Coppard has been deeply respected by writers and critics on
both sides the Atlantic, but he has never won the popular acclaim his
rich talents merit.

Coppard is a painstaking craftsman who has never bowed to contemporary trends, fashions, or fads. His short fiction is characterized
by variety, vitality, and artistry; it includes realistic stories like "The
Higgler," "Ninepenny Flute," and "A Little Boy Lost"; ghost stories
and tales of the supernatural; tone-poems like "The Fair Young Wil-
lowy Tree"; and tales of fantasy and whimsy like "Silver Circus" and
"Arabesque — The Mouse." Regardless of subject matter, mood, and
technique, almost all of Coppard's work is of extremely high caliber
and bears his unmistakable mark.

The method of "Arabesque — The Mouse" is elliptical and implica-
tional rather than straightforward and matter-of-fact. That is, what
the author does *not* say or does *not* include in the story is often as significant as what he *does* say or include. The relationship between
Filip and his mother, for example, is suggested rather than overtly
stated. Similarly, the influence of the mother upon the son is never
underscored, but is left to the individual reader to interpret. Only a
very unperceptive reader, however, can ignore its implications in the
climactic scene between Filip and Cassia, or in the image of the
maimed mouse.

Thirty-eight of Coppard's stories, selected and given a brief pre-
fatory comment by the author himself, are available in *The Collected
Tales of A. E. Coppard* (Knopf).

Questions   1. Compare or contrast "Arabesque — The Mouse"
with de la Mare's "The Riddle." In what ways are the overall effects
similar?   2. What significance do you attach to the "colour-print of
Utamaro" at the beginning of the story? to the bundle of dead larks?
to the amputation of the mother's hands?   3. Many of Coppard's
stories are peopled by non-exceptional English characters in an imme-

diately recognizable English setting. Is this true of "Arabesque — The
Mouse"?   4. We are told that Filip has been "reading Russian
novels until he thought he was mad." Do *you* think he is mad?
5. Contrast, always an important element in fiction, plays a particularly important part in this story. What are some of the dramatic
contrasts here, and what is their effect on the reader?   6. Notice
Coppard's treatment of time, and his use of flashbacks in this story.
Does this "juggling of chronology" add to the effect of the story? Is
it necessary to the final success of the story? Could the story, for
example, have been effectively written in the straight chronological
fashion of "The Fall of the House of Usher" or "The Open Boat"?

JAMES JOYCE

Araby

NORTH RICHMOND STREET, being blind, was a quiet street except at the hour when the Christian Brothers' School set the boys free. An uninhabited house of two storeys stood at the blind end, detached from its neighbours in a square ground. The other houses of the street, conscious of decent lives within them, gazed at one another with brown imperturbable faces.

The former tenant of our house, a priest, had died in the back drawing-room. Air, musty from having been long enclosed, hung in all the rooms, and the waste room behind the kitchen was littered with old useless papers. Among these I found a few paper-covered books, the pages of which were curled and damp: *The Abbot*, by Walter Scott, *The Devout Communicant* and *The Memoirs of Vidocq*. I like the last best because its leaves were yellow. The wild garden behind the house contained a central apple-tree and a few straggling bushes under one of which I found the late tenant's rusty bicycle-pump. He had been a very charitable priest; in his will he had left all his money to institutions and the furniture of his house to his sister.

When the short days of winter came dusk fell before we had well eaten our dinners. When we met in the street the houses had grown sombre. The space of sky above us was the colour of everchanging violet and towards it the lamps of the street lifted their feeble lanterns. The cold air stung us and we played till our bodies glowed. Our shouts echoed in the silent street. The career of our play brought us through the dark muddy lanes behind the houses where we ran the gauntlet of the rough tribes from the cottages, to the back doors of the dark dripping gardens where odours arose from the ashpits, to the dark odorous stables where a coachman smoothed and combed the horse or shook music from the buckled harness. When we returned to the street light from the kitchen windows had filled the areas. If my uncle was seen turning the corner we hid in the shadow until we had seen him safely housed. Or if Mangan's sister came out on the doorstep to call her brother in to his tea we watched her from our shadow peer up and down the street. We waited to see whether she would remain or go in and, if she remained, we left our shadow and walked up to Mangan's steps resignedly. She was waiting for us, her figure defined by the light from the half-opened door. Her brother always teased her before he obeyed and I stood by the railings looking at her. Her dress swung as she moved her body and the soft rope of her hair tossed from side to side.

Every morning I lay on the floor in the front parlour watching her door. The blind was pulled down to within an inch of the sash so that I could not be seen. When she came out on the door-step my heart leaped. I ran to the hall, seized my books and followed her. I kept her brown figure always in my eye and, when we came near the point at which our ways diverged, I quickened my pace and passed her. This happened morning after morning. I had never spoken to her, except for a few casual words, and yet her name was like a summons to all my foolish blood.

Her image accompanied me even in places the most hostile to romance. On Saturday evenings when my aunt went marketing I had to go to carry some of the parcels. We walked through the flaring streets, jostled by drunken men and bargaining women, amid the curses of labourers, the shrill litanies of shop-boys who stood on guard by the barrels of pigs' cheeks, the nasal chanting of street-singers, who sang a *come-all-you* about O'Donovan Rossa, or a ballad about the troubles in our native land. These noises converged in a single sensation of life for me: I imagined that I bore my chalice safely through a throng of foes. Her name sprang to my lips at moments in strange prayers and praises which I myself did not understand. My eyes were often full of tears (I could not tell why) and at times a flood from my heart seemed to pour itself out into my bosom. I thought little of the future. I did not know whether I would ever speak to her or not or, if I spoke to her, how I could tell her of my confused adoration. But my body was like a harp and her words and gestures were like fingers running upon the wires.

One evening I went into the back drawing-room in which the priest had died. It was a dark rainy evening and there was no sound in the house. Through one of the broken panes I heard the rain impinge upon the earth, the fine incessant needles of water playing in the sodden beds. Some distant lamp or lighted window gleamed below me. I was thankful that I could see so little. All my senses seemed to desire to veil themselves and, feeling that I was about to slip from them, I pressed the palms of my hands together until they trembled, murmuring: *"O love! O love!"* many times.

At last she spoke to me. When she addressed the first words to me I was so confused that I did not know what to answer. She asked me was I going to *Araby*. I forgot whether I answered yes or no. It would be a splendid bazaar, she said she would love to go.

"And why can't you?" I asked.

While she spoke she turned a silver bracelet round and round her wrist. She could not go, she said, because there would be a retreat that week in her convent. Her brother and two other boys were fighting for their caps and I was alone at the railings. She held one of the spikes, bowing her head towards me. The light from the lamp opposite our door caught the white curve of her neck, lit up her hair that rested there and, falling, lit up the hand upon the railing. It fell over one side of her dress and caught the white border of a petticoat, just visible as she stood at ease.

"It's well for you," she said.

"If I go," I said, "I will bring you something."

What innumerable follies laid waste my waking and sleeping thoughts after that evening! I wished to annihilate the tedious intervening days. I chafed against the work of school. At night in my bedroom and by day in the classroom her image came between me and the page I strove to read. The syllables of the

word *Araby* were called to me through the silence in which my
soul luxuriated and cast an Eastern enchantment over me. I
asked for leave to go to the bazaar on Saturday night. My aunt
was surprised and hoped it was not some Freemason affair. I
answered few questions in class. I watched my master's face pass
from amiability to sternness; he hoped I was not beginning to
idle. I could not call my wandering thoughts together. I had
hardly any patience with the serious work of life which, now
that it stood between me and my desire, seemed to me child's
play, ugly monotonous child's play.

On Saturday morning I reminded my uncle that I wished to
go to the bazaar in the evening. He was fussing at the hallstand,
looking for the hat-brush, and answered me curtly:

"Yes, boy, I know."

As he was in the hall I could not go into the front parlour and
lie at the window. I left the house in bad humour and walked
slowly towards the school. The air was pitilessly raw and already
my heart misgave me.

When I came home to dinner my uncle had not yet been home.
Still it was early. I sat staring at the clock for some time and,
when its ticking began to irritate me, I left the room. I mounted
the staircase and gained the upper part of the house. The high
cold empty gloomy rooms liberated me and I went from room
to room singing. From the front window I saw my companions
playing below in the street. Their cries reached me weakened
and indistinct and, leaning my forehead against the cool glass,
I looked over at the dark house where she lived. I may have
stood there for an hour, seeing nothing but the brown-clad figure
cast by my imagination, touched discreetly by the lamplight at
the curved neck, at the hand upon the railings and at the border
below the dress.

When I came downstairs again I found Mrs. Mercer sitting
at the fire. She was an old garrulous woman, a pawnbroker's
widow, who collected used stamps for some pious purpose. I had
to endure the gossip of the tea-table. The meal was prolonged
beyond an hour and still my uncle did not come. Mrs. Mercer
stood up to go; she was sorry she couldn't wait any longer, but
it was after eight o'clock and she did not like to be out late, as
the night air was bad for her. When she had gone I began to
walk up and down the room, clenching my fists. My aunt said:

"I'm afraid you may put off your bazaar for this night of Our Lord."

At nine o'clock I heard my uncle's latchkey in the halldoor. I heard him talking to himself and heard the hallstand rocking when it had received the weight of his overcoat. I could interpret these signs. When he was midway through his dinner I asked him to give me the money to go to the bazaar. He had forgotten.

"The people are in bed and after their first sleep now," he said. I did not smile. My aunt said to him energetically:

"Can't you give him the money and let him go? You've kept him late enough as it is."

My uncle said he was very sorry he had forgotten. He said he believed in the old saying: "All work and no play makes Jack a dull boy." He asked me where I was going and, when I had told him a second time he asked me did I know *The Arab's Farewell to his Steed*. When I left the kitchen he was about to recite the opening lines of the piece to my aunt.

I held a florin tightly in my hand as I strode down Buckingham Street towards the station. The sight of the streets thronged with buyers and glaring with gas recalled to me the purpose of my journey. I took my seat in a third-class carriage of a deserted train. After an intolerable delay the train moved out of the station slowly. It crept onward among ruinous houses and over the twinkling river. At Westland Row Station a crowd of people pressed to the carriage doors; but the porters moved them back, saying that it was a special train for the bazaar. I remained alone in the bare carriage. In a few minutes the train drew up beside an improvised wooden platform. I passed out on to the road and saw by the lighted dial of a clock that it was ten minutes to ten. In front of me was a large building which displayed the magical name.

I could not find any sixpenny entrance and, fearing that the bazaar would be closed, I passed in quickly through a turnstile, handing a shilling to a weary-looking man. I found myself in a big hall girdled at half its height by a gallery. Nearly all the stalls were closed and the greater part of the hall was in darkness. I recognised a silence like that which pervades a church after a service. I walked into the centre of the bazaar timidly. A few people were gathered about the stalls which were still open. Before a curtain, over which the words *Café Chantant* were written in coloured lamps, two men were counting money on a salver. I listened to the fall of the coins.

Remembering with difficulty why I had come I went over to one of the stalls and examined porcelain vases and flowered tea-sets. At the door of the stall a young lady was talking and laughing with two young gentlemen. I remarked their English accents and listened vaguely to their conversation.

"O, I never said such a thing!"

"O, but you did!"

"O, but I didn't!"

"Didn't she say that?"

"Yes; I heard her."

"O, there's a . . . fib!"

Observing me the young lady came over and asked me did I wish to buy anything. The tone of her voice was not encouraging; she seemed to have spoken to me out of a sense of duty. I looked humbly at the great jars that stood like eastern guards at either side of the dark entrance to the stall and murmured:

"No, thank you."

The young lady changed the position of one of the vases and went back to the two young men. They began to talk of the same subject. Once or twice the young lady glanced at me over her shoulder.

I lingered before her stall, though I knew my stay was useless, to make my interest in her wares seem the more real. Then I turned away slowly and walked down the middle of the bazaar. I allowed the two pennies to fall against the sixpence in my pocket. I heard a voice call from one end of the gallery that the light was out. The upper part of the hall was now completely dark.

Gazing up into the darkness I saw myself as a creature driven and derided by vanity; and my eyes burned with anguish and anger.

James Joyce (1882-1941)   Born, raised, and educated in middle-class Dublin, the youthful Joyce rejected family, country, and religion, leaving Ireland in 1902 to spend the rest of his life (with only occasional brief exceptions) in Zurich, Paris, Trieste, and other European cities. In spite of this self-imposed exile, turn-of-the-century Dublin

and its people constitute the heart of Joyce's work, although the implications of his fiction are timeless and universal. When once asked if
he planned ever to return to Dublin, Joyce is said to have replied:
"Have I ever left it?"

The short stories of *Dubliners,* from which "Araby" and "A Little
Cloud" are taken, are Joyce's first significant literary achievement;
in toto, they are one of the permanent landmarks in the evolution of
the short story. The stories themselves were for the most part written
when Joyce was in his early twenties, but because of publishing difficulties (such as beset his entire literary career) the volume was not
brought out until 1914. In it, Joyce said, he had attempted to write a
"chapter" in the "moral history" of Ireland. Joyce's later works, together with *Dubliners,* constitute perhaps the major individual literary
achievement of the twentieth century; they include *A Portrait of the
Artist as a Young Man* (1916), *Ulysses* (1922), and *Finnegans Wake*
(1939).

It has been said that the Dublin of Joyce's stories is, in effect, a city
of the dead. Joyce himself spoke of the "special odour of corruption"
which, he hoped, "floated" over his stories, and once commented that
he would fill his books with the "odour of ashpits and old weeds and
offal." Like Chekhov, Joyce rejected what he considered the romantic
claptrap and elaborate improbability of many of his predecessors.
Like the unnamed narrator of "Araby," he sought his subject matter
in "places the most hostile to romance," in the streets and homes and
public places of "dear, dirty Dublin," and in the lives of insignificant
individuals like the "I" of "Araby" or Little Chandler of "A Little
Cloud."

The structural and technical simplicity of "Araby" and "A Little
Cloud" is a far cry from the complexities of Joyce's later fiction.
Typical of the later Joyce, however, is the preoccupation with character. By an action, or a statement, or a sudden moment of awareness,
or in terms of an incident, Joyce's people are revealed in moments of
crisis, as a landscape is suddenly illuminated by a flash of lightning.
Through participating in these revelations — epiphanies, Joyce called
them — we see beneath the surface of Joyce's men and women. We
are suddenly made aware of the essence of their harassed personalities. Once having been glimpsed in these moments of revelation,
characters like Little Chandler are likely to become part of the reader's
vicarious experience, to linger in his memory more enduringly than
most flesh-and-blood acquaintances.

Dubliners is available in the New American Library, the Modern
Library (with an Introduction by Padraic Colum), and the Viking
Portable Library (with an Introduction by Harry Levin).

Questions   1. It has been said that Joyce was so aware of the existence of powerful internal conflicts within essentially commonplace people that there was no need for him to look for literary material elsewhere. Do you believe that the conflict within the "I" of this story is a suitable theme or subject? What is the conflict? Is the conflict inevitable? Is it convincing?   2. In what ways, if any, is this a typical story of a young boy in love? In what ways, if any, do you find the story moving?   3. What part does setting play in this story? Consider some of the descriptive passages (for example, the third paragraph); is this, in your opinion, effective creation of mood, atmosphere, and background? Compare or contrast such a paragraph with the sequence at the bazaar.   4. What is the significance of the title of the story?   5. What is the purpose of such lines as "I imagined that I bore my chalice safely through a throng of foes"; "my body was like a harp and her words and gestures were like fingers running upon the wires"?

JAMES JOYCE

A Little Cloud

EIGHT YEARS before he had seen his friend off at the North Wall and wished him godspeed. Gallaher had got on. You could tell that at once by his travelled air, his well-cut tweed suit, and fearless accent. Few fellows had talents like his and fewer still could remain unspoiled by such success. Gallaher's heart was in the right place and he had deserved to win. It was something to have a friend like that.

Little Chandler's thoughts ever since lunchtime had been of his meeting with Gallaher, of Gallaher's invitation and of the great city London where Gallahaer lived. He was called Little Chandler because, though he was but slightly under the average stature, he gave one the idea of being a little man. His hands were white and small, his frame was fragile, his voice was quiet and his maanners were refined. He took the greatest care of his fair silken hair and moustache and used perfume discreetly on his handkerchief. The half-moons of his nails were perfect and when he smiled you caught a glimpse of a row of childish white teeth.

As he sat at his desk in the King's Inns he thought what changes those eight years had brought. The friend whom he had known under a shabby and necessitous guise had become a brilliant figure on the London Press. He turned often from his tiresome writing to gaze out of the office window. The glow of a

A LITTLE CLOUD From *The Portable James Joyce*. Copyright, 1946, 1947 by The Viking Press, Inc. Reprinted by permission of The Viking Press, Inc.

late autumn sunset covered the grass plots and walks. It cast a shower of kindly golden dust on the untidy nurses and decrepit old men who drowsed on the benches; it flickered upon all the moving figures — on the children who ran screaming along the gravel paths and on everyone who passed through the gardens. He watched the scene and thought of life; and (as always happened when he thought of life) he became sad. A gentle melancholy took possession of him. He felt how useless it was to struggle against fortune, this being the burden of wisdom which the ages had bequeathed to him.

He remembered the books of poetry upon his shelves at home. He had bought them in his bachelor days and many an evening, as he sat in the little room off the hall, he had been tempted to take one down from the bookshelf and read out something to his wife. But shyness had always held him back; and so the books had remained on their shelves. At times he repeated lines to himself and this consoled him.

When his hour had struck he stood up and took leave of his desk and of his fellow-clerks punctiliously. He emerged from under the feudal arch of the King's Inns, a neat modest figure, and walked swiftly down Henrietta Street. The golden sunset was waning and the air had grown sharp. A horde of grimy children populated the street. They stood or ran in the roadway or crawled up the steps before the gaping doors or squatted like mice upon the thresholds. Little Chandler gave them no thought. He picked his way deftly through all that minute vermin-like life and under the shadow of the gaunt spectral mansions in which the old nobility of Dublin had roystered. No memory of the past touched him, for his mind was full of a present joy.

He had never been in Corless's but he knew the value of the name. He knew that people went there after the theatre to eat oysters and drink liqueurs; and he had heard that the waiters there spoke French and German. Walking swiftly by at night he had seen cabs drawn up before the door and richly dressed ladies, escorted by cavaliers, alight and enter quickly. They wore noisy dresses and many wraps. Their faces were powdered and they caught up their dresses, when they touched earth, like alarmed Atalantas. He had always passed without turning his head to look. It was his habit to walk swiftly in the street even by day and whenever he found himself in the city late at night he hurried on his way apprehensively and excitedly. Sometimes, however, he courted the causes of his fear. He chose the darkest and narrowest streets and, as he walked boldly forward, the silence that was spread about his footsteps troubled him, the wandering, silent figures troubled him; and at times a sound of low fugitive laughter made him tremble like a leaf.

He turned to the right towards Capel Street. Ignatius Gallaher on the London Press! Who would have thought it possible eight years before? Still, now that he reviewed the past, Little Chandler could remember many signs of future greatness in his friend. People used to say that Ignatius Gallaher was wild. Of course, he did mix with a rakish set of fellows at that time, drank freely and borrowed money on all sides. In the end he had got mixed up in some shady affair, some money transaction: at least, that was one version of his flight. But nobody denied him talent. There was always a certain . . . something in Ignatius Gallaher that impressed you in spite of yourself. Even when he was out at elbows and at his wits' end for money he kept up a bold face. Little Chandler remembered (and the remembrance brought a slight flush of pride to his cheek) one of Ignatius Gallaher's sayings when he was in a tight corner:

"Half time now, boys," he used to say lightheartedly. "Where's my considering cap?"

That was Ignatius Gallaher all out; and, damn it, you couldn't but admire him for it.

Little Chandler quickened his pace. For the first time in his life he felt himself superior to the people he passed. For the first time his soul revolted against the dull inelegance of Capel Street. There was no doubt about it: if you wanted to succeed you had to go away. You could do nothing in Dublin. As he crossed Grattan Bridge he looked down the river towards the lower quays and pitied the poor stunted houses. They seemed to him a band of tramps, huddled together along the river-banks, their old coats covered with dust and soot, stupefied by the panorama of sunset and waiting for the first chill of night to bid them arise, shake themselves and begone. He wondered whether he could write a poem to express his idea. Perhaps Gallaher might be able to get it into some London paper for him. Could he write something original? He was not sure what idea he wished to express but

the thought that a poetic moment had touched him took life
within him like an infant hope. He stepped onward bravely.

Every step brought him nearer to London, farther from his
own sober inartistic life. A light began to tremble on the horizon
of his mind. He was not so old — thirty-two. His temperament
might be said to be just at the point of maturity. There were so
many different moods and impressions that he wished to express
in verse. He felt them within him. He tried to weigh his soul
to see if it was a poet's soul. Melancholy was the dominant note
of his temperament, he thought, but it was a melancholy tempered by recurrences of faith and resignation and simple joy. If
he could give expression to it in a book of poems perhaps men
would listen. He would never be popular: he saw that. He could
not sway the crowd but he might appeal to a little circle of
kindred minds. The English critics, perhaps, would recognise
him as one of the Celtic school by reason of the melancholy tone
of his poems; besides that, he would put in allusions. He began
to invent sentences and phrases from the notice which his book
would get. *"Mr. Chandler has the gift of easy and graceful
verse."* . . . *"A wistful sadness pervades these poems."* . . .
"The Celtic note." It was a pity his name was not more Irish-
looking. Perhaps it would be better to insert his mother's name
before the surname: Thomas Malone Chandler, or better still:
T. Malone Chandler. He would speak to Gallaher about it.

He pursued his revery so ardently that he passed his street and
had to turn back. As he came near Corless's his former agitation
began to overmaster him and he halted before the door in indecision. Finally he opened the door and entered.

The light and noise of the bar held him at the doorways for a
few moments. He looked about him, but his sight was confused
by the shining of many red and green wine-glasses. The bar
seemed to him to be full of people and he felt that the people
were observing him curiously. He glanced quickly to right and
left (frowning slightly to make his errand appear serious), but
when his sight cleared a little he saw that nobody had turned to
look at him: and there, sure enough, was Ignatius Gallaher
leaning with his back against the counter and his feet planted
far apart.

"Hallo, Tommy, old hero, here you are! What is it to be? What
will you have? I'm taking whisky: better stuff than we get

across the water. Soda? Lithia? No mineral? I'm the same.
Spoils the flavour. . . . Here, *garçon,* bring us two halves of malt
whisky, like a good fellow. . . . Well, and how have you been
pulling along since I saw you last? Dear God, how old we're
getting! Do you see any signs of aging in me — eh, what? A
little grey and thin on the top — what?"

Ignatius Gallaher took off his hat and displayed a large closely-
cropped head. His face was heavy, pale and clean-shaven. His
eyes, which were of bluish slate-colour, relieved his unhealthy
pallor and shone out plainly above the vivid orange tie he wore.
Between these rival features the lips appeared very long and
shapeless and colourless. He bent his head and felt with two
sympathetic fingers the thin hair at the crown. Little Chandler
shook his head as a denial. Ignatius Gallaher put on his hat
again.

"It pulls you down," he said, "press life. Always hurry and
scurry, looking for copy and sometimes not finding it; and then,
always to have something new in your stuff. Damn proofs and
printers, I say, for a few days. I'm deuced glad, I can tell you,
to get back to the old country. Does a fellow good, a bit of a
holiday. I feel a ton better since I landed again in dear dirty
Dublin. . . . Here you are, Tommy. Water? Say when."

Little Chandler allowed his whisky to be very much diluted.

"You don't know what's good for you, my boy," said Ignatius
Gallaher. "I drink mine neat."

"I drink very little as a rule," said Little Chandler modestly.
"An odd half-one or so when I meet any of the old crowd: that's
all."

"Ah, well," said Ignatius Gallaher, cheerfully, "here's to us and
to old times and old acquaintances."

They clinked glasses and drank the toast.

"I met some of the old gang today," said Ignatius Gallaher.
"O'Hara seems to be in a bad way. What's he he doing?"

"Nothing," said Little Chandler. "He's gone to the dogs."

"But Hogan has a good sit, hasn't he?"

"Yes; he's in the Land Commission."

"I met him one night in London and he seemed to be very
flush. . . . Poor O'Hara! Boose, I suppose?"

"Other things, too," said Little Chandler shortly.

Ignatius Gallaher laughed.

"Tommy," he said, "I see you haven't changed an atom. You're the very same serious person that used to lecture me on Sunday mornings when I had a sore head and a fur on my tongue. You'd want to knock about a bit in the world. Have you never been anywhere even for a trip?"

"I've been to the Isle of Man," said Little Chandler.

Ignatius Gallaher laughed.

"The Isle of Man!" he said. "Go to London or Paris: Paris, for choice. That'd do you good."

"Have you seen Paris?"

"I should think I have! I've knocked about there a little."

"And is it really so beautiful as they say?" asked Little Chandler.

He sipped a little of his drink while Ignatius Gallaher finished his boldly.

"Beautiful?" said Ignatius Gallaher, pausing on the word and on the flavour of his drink. "It's not so beautiful, you know. Of course, it is beautiful. . . . But it's the life of Paris; that's the thing. Ah, there's no city like Paris for gaiety, movement, excitement. . . ."

Little Chandler finished his whisky and, after some trouble, succeeded in catching the barman's eye. He ordered the same again.

"I've been to the Moulin Rouge," Ignatius Gallaher continued when the barman had removed their glasses, "and I've been to all the Bohemian cafés. Hot stuff! Not for a pious chap like you, Tommy."

Little Chandler said nothing until the barman returned with two glasses: then he touched his friend's glass lightly and reciprocated the former toast. He was beginning to feel somewhat disillusioned. Gallaher's accent and way of expressing himself did not please him. There was something vulgar in his friend which he had not observed before. But perhaps it was only the result of living in London amid the bustle and competition of the Press. The old personal charm was still there under this new gaudy manner. And, after all, Gallaher had lived, he had seen the world. Little Chandler looked at his friend enviously.

"Everything in Paris is gay," said Ignatius Gallaher. "They believe in enjoying life — and don't you think they're right? If you want to enjoy yourself properly you must go to Paris. And, mind

you, they've a great feeling for the Irish there. When they heard
I was from Ireland they were ready to eat me, man."

Little Chandler took four or five sips from his glass.

"Tell me," he said, "is it true that Paris is so . . . immoral as
they say?"

Ignatius Gallaher made a catholic gesture with his right arm.

"Every place is immoral," he said. "Of course you do find spicy
bits in Paris. Go to one of the students' balls, for instance. That's
lively, if you like, when the *cocottes* begin to let themselves loose.
You know what they are, I suppose?"

"I've heard of them," said Little Chandler.

Ignatius Gallaher drank off his whisky and shook his head.

"Ah," he said, "you may say what you like. There's no woman
like the Parisienne — for style, for go."

"Then it is an immoral city," said Little Chandler, with timid
insistence — "I mean, compared with London or Dublin?"

"London!" said Ignatius Gallaher. "It's six of one and half-a-
dozen of the other. You ask Hogan, my boy. I showed him a bit
about London when he was over there. He'd open your eye.
. . . I say, Tommy, don't make punch of that whisky; liquor up."

"No, really. . . ."

"O, come on, another one won't do you any harm. What is it?
The same again, I suppose?"

"Well . . . all right."

"*François*, the same again. . . . Will you smoke, Tommy?"

Ignatius Gallaher produced his cigar-case. The two friends lit
their cigars and puffed at them in silence until their drinks were
served.

"I'll tell you my opinion," said Ignatius Gallaher, emerging
after some time from the clouds of smoke in which he had taken
refuge, "it's a rum world. Talk of immorality! I've heard of cases
— what am I saying? — I've known them: cases of . . . immorality. . . ."

Ignatius Gallaher puffed thoughtfully at his cigar and then, in
a calm historian's tone, he proceeded to sketch for his friend some
pictures of the corruption which was rife abroad. He summarised
the vices of many capitals and seemed inclined to award the palm
to Berlin. Some things he could not vouch for (his friends had
told him), but of others he had had personal experience. He
spared neither rank nor caste. He revealed many of the secrets

of religious houses on the Continent and described some of the practices which were fashionable in high society and ended by telling, with details, a story about an English duchess — a story which he knew to be true. Little Chandler was astonished.

"Ah, well," said Ignatius Gallaher, "here we are in old jog-along Dublin where nothing is known of such things."

"How dull you must find it," said Little Chandler, "after all the other places you've seen!"

"Well," said Ignatius Gallaher, "it's a relaxation to come over here, you know. And, after all, it's the old country, as they say, isn't it? You can't help having a certain feeling for it. That's human nature. . . . But tell me something about yourself. Hogan told me you had . . . tasted the joys of connubial bliss. Two years ago, wasn't it?"

Little Chandler blushed and smiled.

"Yes," he said. "I was married last May twelve months."

"I hope it's not too late in the day to offer my best wishes," said Ignatius Gallaher. "I didn't know your address or I'd have done so at the time."

He extended his hand, which Little Chandler took.

"Well, Tommy," he said, "I wish you and yours every joy in life, old chap, and tons of money, and may you never die till I shoot you. And that's the wish of a sincere friend, an old friend. You know that?"

"I know that," said Little Chandler.

"Any youngsters?" said Ignatius Gallaher.

Little Chandler blushed again.

"We have one child," he said.

"Son or daughter?"

"A little boy."

Ignatius Gallaher slapped his friend sonorously on the back.

"Bravo," he said, "I wouldn't doubt you, Tommy."

Little Chandler smiled, looked confusedly at his glass and bit his lower lip with three childishly white front teeth.

"I hope you'll spend an evening with us," he said, "before you go back. My wife will be delighted to meet you. We can have a little music and—"

"Thanks awfully, old chap," said Ignatius Gallaher. "I'm sorry we didn't meet earlier. But I must leave tomorrow night."

"Tonight, perhaps . . . ?"

"I'm awfully sorry, old man. You see I'm over here with an-other fellow, clever young chap he is too, and we arranged to go to a little card-party. Only for that. . . ."

"O, in that case. . . ."

"But who knows?" said Ignatius Gallaher considerately. "Next year I may take a little skip over here now that I've broken the ice. It's only a pleasure deferred."

"Very well," said Little Chandler, "the next time you come we must have an evening together. That's agreed now, isn't it?"

"Yes, that's agreed," said Ignatius Gallaher. "Next year if I come, *parole d'honneur.*"

"And to clinch the bargain," said Little Chandler, "we'll just have one more now."

Ignatius Gallaher took out a large gold watch and looked at it.

"Is it to be the last?" he said. "Because you know, I have an a.p."

"O, yes, positively," said Little Chandler.

"Very well, then," said Ignatius Gallaher, "let us have another one as a *doec an doruis* — that's good vernacular for a small whisky, I believe."

Little Chandler ordered the drinks. The blush which had risen to his face a few moments before was establishing itself. A trifle made him blush at any time: and now he felt warm and excited. Three small whiskies had gone to his head and Galla-her's strong cigar had confused his mind, for he was a delicate and abstinent person. The adventure of meeting Gallaher after eight years, of finding himself with Gallaher in Corless's sur-rounded by lights and noise, of listening to Gallaher's stories and of sharing for a brief space Gallaher's vagrant and triumphant life, upset the equipoise of his sensitive nature. He felt acutely the contrast between his own life and his friend's, and it seemed to him unjust. Gallaher was his inferior in birth and education. He was sure that he could do something better than his friend had ever done, or could ever do, something higher than mere tawdry journalism if he only got the chance. What was it that stood in his way? His unfortunate timidity! He wished to vindi-cate himself in some way, to assert his manhood. He saw behind Gallaher's refusal of his invitation. Gallaher was only patronising him by his friendliness just as he was patronising Ireland by his visit.

The barman brought their drinks. Little Chandler pushed one glass towards his friend and took up the other boldly.

"Who knows?" he said, as they lifted their glasses. "When you come next year I may have the pleasure of wishing long life and happiness to Mr. and Mrs. Ignatius Gallaher."

Ignatius Gallaher in the act of drinking closed one eye expressively over the rim of his glass. When he had drunk he smacked his lips decisively, set down his glass and said:

"No blooming fear of that, my boy. I'm going to have my fling first and see a bit of life and the world before I put my head in the sack — if I ever do."

"Some day you will," said Little Chandler calmly.

Ignatius Gallaher turned his orange tie and slate-blue eyes full upon his friend.

"You think so?" he said.

"You'll put your head in the sack," repeated Little Chandler stoutly, "like everyone else if you can find the girl."

He had slightly emphasised his tone and he was aware that he had betrayed himself; but, though the colour had heightened in his cheek, he did not flinch from his friend's gaze. Ignatius Gallaher watched him for a few moments and then said:

"If ever it occurs, you may bet your bottom dollar there'll be no mooning and spooning about it. I mean to marry money. She'll have a good fat account at the bank or she won't do for me."

Little Chandler shook his head.

"Why, man alive," said Ignatius Gallaher, vehemently, "do you know what it is? I've only to say the word and tomorrow I can have the woman and the cash. You don't believe it? Well, I know it. There are hundreds — what am I saying? — thousands of rich Germans and Jews, rotten with money, that'd only be too glad. . . . You wait a while, my boy. See if I don't play my cards properly. When I go about a thing I mean business, I tell you. You just wait."

He tossed his glass to his mouth, finished his drink and laughed loudly. Then he looked thoughtfully before him and said in a calmer tone:

"But I'm in no hurry. They can wait. I don't fancy tying myself up to one woman, you know."

He imitated with his mouth the act of tasting and made a wry face.

"Must get a bit stale, I should think," he said.

.   .   .   .

Little Chandler sat in the room off the hall, holding a child in his arms. To save money they kept no servant but Annie's young sister Monica came for an hour or so in the morning and an hour or so in the evening to help. But Monica had gone home long ago. It was a quarter to nine. Little Chandler had come home late for tea, and, moreover, he had forgotten to bring Annie home the parcel of coffee from Bewley's. Of course she was in a bad humour and gave him short answers. She said she would do without any tea but when it came near the time at which the shop at the corner closed she decided to go out herself for a quarter of a pound of tea and two pounds of sugar. She put the sleeping child deftly in his arms and said:

"Here. Don't waken him."

A little lamp with a white china shade stood upon the table and its light fell over a photograph which was enclosed in a frame of crumpled horn. It was Annie's photograph. Little Chandler looked at it, pausing at the thin tight lips. She wore the pale blue summer blouse which he had brought her home as a present one Saturday. It had cost him ten and elevenpence; but what an agony of nervousness it had cost him! How he had suffered that day, waiting at the shop door until the shop was empty, standing at the counter and trying to appear at his ease while the girl piled ladies' blouses before him, paying at the desk and forgetting to take up the odd penny of his change, being called back by the cashier, and finally, striving to hide his blushes as he left the shop by examining the parcel to see if it was securely tied. When he brought the blouse home Annie kissed him and said it was very pretty and stylish; but when she heard the price she threw the blouse on the table and said it was a regular swindle to charge ten and elevenpence for it. At first she wanted to take it back but when she tried it on she was delighted with it, especially with the make of the sleeves, and kissed him and said he was very good to think of her.

Hm! . . .

He looked coldly into the eyes of the photograph and they

answered coldly. Certainly they were pretty and the face itself
was pretty. But he found something mean in it. Why was it so
unconscious and ladylike? The composure of the eyes irritated
him. They repelled him and defied him: there was no passion in
them, no rapture. He thought of what Gallaher had said about
rich Jewesses. Those dark Oriental eyes, he thought, how full
they are of passion, of voluptuous longing! . . . Why had he
married the eyes in the photograph?

He caught himself up at the question and glanced nervously
round the room. He found something mean in the pretty furniture which he had bought for his house on the hire system.
Annie had chosen it herself and it reminded him of her. It too
was prim and pretty. A dull resentment against his life awoke
within him. Could he not escape from his little house? Was it
too late for him to try to live bravely like Gallaher? Could he go
to London? There was the furniture still to be paid for. If he
could only write a book and get it published, that might open the
way for him.

A volume of Byron's poems lay before him on the table. He
opened it cautiously with his left hand lest he should waken the
child and began to read the first poem in the book:

> "Hushed are the winds and still the evening gloom,
>   Not e'en a Zephyr wanders through the grove,
> While I return to view my Margaret's tomb
>   And scatter flowers on the dust I love."

He paused. He felt the rhythm of the verse about him in the
room. How melancholy it was! Could he, too, write like that,
express the melancholy of his soul in verse? There were so many
things he wanted to describe: his sensation of a few hours before
on Grattan Bridge, for example. If he could get back again into
that mood. . . .

The child awoke and began to cry. He turned from the page
and tried to hush it: but it would not be hushed. He began to
rock it to and fro in his arms but its wailing cry grew keener. He
rocked it faster while his eyes began to read the second stanza:

> "Within this narrow cell reclines her clay,
>   That clay where once . . ."

It was useless. He couldn't read. He couldn't do anything. The wailing of the child pierced the drum of his ear. It was useless, useless! He was a prisoner for life. His arms trembled with anger and suddenly bending to the child's face he shouted:

"Stop!"

The child stopped for an instant, had a spasm of fright and began to scream. He jumped up from his chair and walked hastily up and down the room with the child in his arms. It began to sob piteously, losing its breath for four or five seconds, and then bursting out anew. The thin walls of the room echoed the sound. He tried to soothe it but it sobbed more convulsively. He looked at the contracted and quivering face of the child and began to be alarmed. He counted seven sobs without a break between them and caught the child to his breast in fright. If it died! . . .

The door was burst open and a young woman ran in, panting.

"What is it? What is it?" she cried.

The child, hearing its mother's voice, broke out into a paroxysm of sobbing.

"It's nothing, Annie . . . it's nothing. . . . He began to cry . . ."

She flung her parcels on the floor and snatched the child from him.

"What have you done to him?" she cried, glaring into his face.

Little Chandler sustained for one moment the gaze of her eyes and his heart closed together as he met the hatred in them. He began to stammer:

"It's nothing. . . . He . . . he began to cry. . . . I couldn't . . . I didn't do anything. . . . What?"

Giving no heed to him she began to walk up and down the room, clasping the child tightly in her arms and murmuring:

"My little man! My little mannie! Was 'ou frightened, love? . . . There now, love! There now! . . . Lambabaun! Mamma's little lamb of the world! . . . There now!"

Little Chandler felt his cheeks suffused with shame and he stood back out of the lamplight. He listened while the paroxysm of the child's sobbing grew less and less; and tears of remorse started to his eyes.

Questions   1. In what ways, if any, is Little Chandler the older counterpart of the young boy of "Araby"? Which is the more believable character? the more sympathetic?   2. What in common exists between the Paris of "A Little Cloud" and the bazaar of "Araby"? 3. Compare or contrast Chandler and Gallaher. Is Gallaher really the success Chandler thinks he is?   4. Will Little Chandler ever write the poems he dreams of? Does he possess anything in common with the poet (Byron) he so admires?   5. What is the purpose, or implication, of the final scene involving Little Chandler and his son? Do you sympathize more or less with Little Chandler during this scene? 6. It has been said that "entrapment" is the recurrent theme of *Dubliners*. Do you agree, as far as these two stories are concerned? Compare or contrast them with Anderson's "Adventure."   7. Are you *satisfied* by the endings of these stories? Why or why not? Are you *convinced* by them?

FRANZ KAFKA

A Country Doctor

I WAS in great perplexity; I had to start on an urgent journey; a seriously ill patient was waiting for me in a village ten miles off; a thick blizzard of snow filled all the wide spaces between him and me; I had a gig, a light gig with big wheels, exactly right for our country roads; muffled in furs, my bag of instruments in my hand, I was in the courtyard all ready for the journey; but there was no horse to be had, no horse. My own horse had died in the night, worn out by the fatigues of this icy winter; my servant girl was now running round the village trying to borrow a horse; but it was hopeless, I knew it, and I stood there forlornly, with the snow gathering more and more thickly upon me, more and more unable to move. In the gateway the girl appeared, alone, and waved the lantern; of course, who would lend a horse at this time for such a journey? I strode through the courtyard once more; I could see no way out; in my confused distress I kicked at the dilapidated door of the year-long uninhabited pigsty. It flew open and flapped to and fro on its hinges. A steam and smell as of horses came out from it. A dim stable lantern was swinging inside from a rope. A man, crouching on his hams in that low space, showed an open blue-eyed face. "Shall I yoke up?" he asked, crawling out on all fours. I did not know what to say and merely stooped down to see what else was in the sty. The servant

A COUNTRY DOCTOR   Reprinted from *The Penal Colony* by Franz Kafka, translated by Willa and Edwin Muir, by permission of Schocken Books, New York. Copyright 1948 by Schocken Books, New York.

girl standing beside me. "You never know what you're going to
find in your own house," she said, and we both laughed. "Hey
there, Brother, hey there, Sister!" called the groom, and two
horses, enormous creatures with powerful flanks, one after the
other, their legs tucked close to their bodies, each well-shaped
head lowered like a camel's, by sheer strength of buttocking
squeezed out through the door hole which they filled entirely.
But at once they were standing up, their legs long and their
bodies steaming thickly. "Give him a hand," I said, and the willing girl hurried to help the groom with the harnessing. Yet hardly
was she beside him when the groom clipped hold of her and
pushed his face against hers. She screamed and fled back to me;
on her cheek stood out in red the marks of two rows of teeth.
"You brute," I yelled in fury, "do you want a whipping?" but in
the same moment reflected that the man was a stranger; that I
did not know where he came from, and that of his own free will
he was helping me out when everyone else had failed me. As if
he knew my thoughts he took no offense at my threat but, still
busied with the horses, only turned round once towards me. "Get
in," he said then, and indeed: everything was ready. A magnificent pair of horses, I observed, such as I had never sat behind,
and I climbed in happily. "But I'll drive, you don't know the
way," I said. "Of course," said he, "I'm not coming with you
anyway, I'm staying with Rose." "No," shrieked Rose, fleeing
into the house with a justified presentiment that her fate was
inescapable; I heard the door chain rattle as she put it up; I heard
the key turn in the lock; I could see, moreover, how she put out
the lights in the entrance hall and in further flight all through the
rooms to keep herself from being discovered. "You're coming
with me," I said to the groom, "or I won't go, urgent as my
journey is. I'm not thinking of paying for it by handing the girl
over to you. "Gee up!" he said; clapped his hands; the gig
whirled off like a log in a freshet; I could just hear the door of
my house splitting and bursting as the groom charged at it and
then I was deafened and blinded by a storming rush that steadily
buffeted all my senses. But this only for a moment, since, as if
my patient's farmyard had opened out just before my courtyard
gate, I was already there; the horses had come quietly to a standstill; the blizzard had stopped; moonlight all around; my patient's
parents hurried out of the house, his sister behind them; I was

almost lifted out of the gig; from their confused ejaculations
I gathered not a word; in the sickroom the air was almost unbreathable; the neglected stove was smoking; I wanted to push
open a window; but first I had to look at my patient. Gaunt,
without any fever, not cold, not warm, with vacant eyes, without
a shirt, the youngster heaved himself up from under the feather
bedding, threw his arms around my neck, and whispered in my
ear: "Doctor, let me die." I glanced round the room; no one had
heard it; the parents were leaning forward in silence waiting for
my verdict; the sister had set a chair for my handbag; I opened
the bag and hunted among my instruments; the boy kept clutching at me from his bed to remind me of his entreaty; I picked up
a pair of tweezers, examined them in the candlelight and laid
them down again. "Yes," I thought blasphemously, "in cases like
this the gods are helpful, send the missing horse, add to it a
second because of the urgency, and to crown everything bestow
even a groom — " And only now did I remember Rose again;
what was I to do, how could I rescue her, how could I pull her
away from under that groom at ten miles' distance, with a team
of horses I couldn't control. These horses, now, they had somehow slipped the reins loose, pushed the window open from the
outside, I did not know how; each of them had stuck a head in at
a window and, quite unmoved by the startled cries of the family,
stood eyeing the patient. "Better go back at once," I thought, as
if the horses were summoning me to the return journey, yet I
permitted the patient's sister, who fancied that I was dazed by
the heat, to take my fur coat from me. A glass of rum was poured
out for me, the old man clapped me on the shoulder, a familiarity
justified by this offer of his treasure. I shook my head; in the
narrow confines of the old man's thoughts I felt ill; that was my
only reason for refusing the drink. The mother stood by the bed-
side and cajoled me towards it. I yielded, and, while one of the
horses whinnied loudly to the ceiling, laid my head to the boy's
breast, which shivered under my wet beard. I confirmed what I
already knew; the boy was quite sound, something a little wrong
with his circulation, saturated with coffee by his solicitous mother,
but sound and best turned out of bed with one shove. I am no
world reformer and so I let him lie. I was the district doctor and
did my duty to the uttermost, to the point where it became
almost too much. I was badly paid and yet generous and helpful

to the poor. I had still to see that Rose was all right, and then
the boy might have his way and I wanted to die too. What was I
doing there in that endless winter! My horse was dead, and not
a single person in the village would lend me another. I had to
get my team out of the pigsty; if they hadn't chanced to be horses
I should have had to travel with swine. That was how it was.
And I nodded to the family. They knew nothing about it, and,
had they known, would not have believed it. To write prescriptions is easy, but to come to an understanding with people is
hard. Well, this should be the end of my visit, I had once more
been called out needlessly, I was used to that, the whole district
made my life a torment with my night bell, but that I should have
to sacrifice Rose this time as well, the pretty girl who had lived
in my house for years almost without my noticing her — that sacrifice was too much to ask, and I had somehow to get it reasoned
out in my head with the help of what craft I could muster, in
order not to let fly at this family, which with the best will in the
world could not restore Rose to me. But as I shut my bag and put
an arm out for my fur coat, the family meanwhile standing together, the father sniffing at the glass of rum in his hand, the
mother, apparently disappointed in me — why, what do people
expect? — biting her lips with tears in her eyes, the sister fluttering a blood-soaked towel, I was somehow ready to admit con-
ditionally that the boy might be ill after all. I went towards him,
he welcomed me smiling as if I were bringing him the most
nourishing invalid broth — ah, now both horses were whinnying
together; the noise, I suppose, was ordained by heaven to assist
my examination of the patient — and this time I discovered that
the boy was indeed ill. In his right side, near the hip, was an
open wound as big as the palm of my hand. Rose-red, in many
variations of shade, dark in the hollows, lighter at the edges,
softly granulated, with irregular clots of blood, open as a surface
mine to the daylight. That was how it looked from a distance.
But on a closer inspection there was another complication. I
could not help a low whistle of surprise. Worms, as thick and
as long my little finger, themselves rose-red and blood-spotted
as well, were wriggling from their fastness in the interior of the
wound towards the light, with small white heads and many little
legs. Poor boy, you were past helping. I had discovered your
great wound; this blossom in your side was destroying you. The

family was pleased; they saw me busying myself; the sister told
the mother, the mother the father, the father told several guests
who were coming in, through the moonlight at the open door,
walking on tiptoe, keeping their balance with outstretched arms.
"Will you save me?" whispered the boy with a sob, quite blinded
by the life within his wound. That is what people are like in my
district. Always expecting the impossible from the doctor. They
have lost their ancient beliefs; the parson sits at home and un-
ravels his vestments, one after another; but the doctor is supposed
to be omnipotent with his merciful surgeon's hand. Well, as it
pleases them; I have not thrust my services on them; if they misuse me for sacred ends, I let that happen to me too; what better
do I want, old country doctor that I am, bereft of my servant
girl! And so they came, the family and the village elders, and
stripped my clothes off me; a school choir with the teacher at the
head of it stood before the house and sang these words to an
utterly simple tune:

> *Strip his clothes off, then he'll heal us,*
> *If he doesn't, kill him dead!*
> *Only a doctor, only a doctor.*

Then my clothes were off and I looked at the people quietly, my
fingers in my beard and my head cocked to one side. I was altogether composed and equal to the situation and remained so,
although it was no help to me, since they now took me by the
head and feet and carried me to the bed. They laid me down in
it next to the wall, on the side of the wound. Then they all left
the room; the door was shut; the singing stopped; clouds covered
the moon; the bedding was warm around me; the horses' heads
in the open windows wavered like shadows. "Do you know,"
said a voice in my ear, "I have very little confidence in you.
Why, you were only blown in here, you didn't come on your own
feet. Instead of helping me, you're cramping me on my death
bed. What I'd like best is to scratch your eyes out." "Right,"
I said, "it is a shame. And yet I am a doctor. What am I to do?
Believe me, it is not too easy for me either." "Am I supposed to
be content with this apology? Oh, I must be, I can't help it. I
always have to put up with things. A fine wound is all I brought
into the world; that was my sole endowment." "My young friend,"

said I, "your mistake is: you have not a wide enough view. I have been in all the sickrooms, far and wide, and I tell you: your wound is not so bad. Done in a tight corner with two strokes of the ax. Many a one proffers his side and can hardly hear the ax in the forest, far less that it is coming nearer to him." "Is that really so, or are you deluding me in my fever?" "It is really so, take the word of an official doctor." And he took it and lay still. But now it was time for me to think of escaping. The horses were still standing faithfully in their places. My clothes, my fur coat, my bag were quickly collected; I didn't want to waste time dressing; if the horses raced home as they had come, I should only be springing, as it were, out of this bed into my own. Obediently a horse backed away from the window; I threw my bundle into the gig; the fur coat missed its mark and was caught on a hook only by the sleeve. Good enough. I swung myself on to the horse. With the reins loosely trailing, one horse barely fastened to the other, the gig swaying behind, my fur coat last of all in the snow. "Geeup!" I said, but there was no galloping; slowly, like old men, we crawled through the snowy wastes; a long time echoed behind us the new but faulty song of the children:

> O be joyful, all you patients,
> The doctor's laid in bed beside you!

Never shall I reach home at this rate; my flourishing practice is done for; my successor is robbing me, but in vain, for he cannot take my place; in my house the disgusting groom is raging; Rose is his victim; I do not want to think about it any more. Naked, exposed to the frost of this most unhappy of ages, with an earthly vehicle, unearthly horses, old man that I am, I wander astray. My fur coat is hanging from the back of the gig, but I cannot reach it, and none of my limber pack of patients lifts a finger. Betrayed! Betrayed! A false alarm on the night bell once answered — it cannot be made good, not ever.

Franz Kafka (1883-1924)   Kafka was born in Prague of well-to-do Jewish parents. He studied law and interspersed a civil service career with a decade of intense literary activity. Only a few of his shorter works were published during his lifetime, and Kafka was virtually unknown for almost ten years after his early death from consumption. His major works include three novels (*The Trial, The Castle, Amerika*) and a volume of short stories and narrative sketches, *The Penal Colony*. Although Kafka's diaries and a volume of "parables" are now also available in American editions, a considerable portion of his work has not yet been translated into English.

Kafka's short fiction is a combination of basically antithetical elements — the familiar and the surrealistic, the commonplace and the grotesque, the factual and the fantastic. Although his narrative method is realistic, the ultimate effect of his stories is quite the opposite; Kafka leads the reader from the world of recognizable events into a strange land of his own creation. "A Country Doctor," with its matter-of-fact, almost prosaic beginning, is characteristic. In the enumeration of specific details ("a thick blizzard of snow," "a light gig with big wheels, exactly right for our country roads," "muffled in fur, my bag of instruments in my hand") the opening of the story sounds almost like a page from the journal of a rural doctor or from a novel by a circumstantial narrator such as Defoe. Almost immediately, however, a terrifying change occurs. With the appearance of the demoniacal groom and the pair of enormous horses, the doctor's wild journey begins and the world as we know it begins to fade away. In its place is a strange land of fantasy or nightmare inhabited by lonely, tormented, misunderstood individuals.

Traditional allegorists — such as Bunyan in *The Pilgrim's Progress* — assigned specific meanings to characters or events; such-and-such a character represents Gluttony, or Pride, or Avarice, and nothing else. Kafka's allegories, on the other hand, are conceived in terms of deliberate ambiguity. Thus no one can state categorically just what Kafka intends the groom or the boy's wound or the supernatural horses in "A Country Doctor" to represent; it is how the reader interprets them that determines his final analysis of the story. Kafka's symbols are subject to multiple interpretations, and as a result his stories exist on various levels of meaning. "A Hunger Artist," for example, has been called a commentary on the plight of religion in a world more interested in material than in spiritual values. Other critics have read it as a depiction of a neurotic personality, as an allegory of the fate of the artist in modern society, or as the conflict between the flesh and the spirit. Regardless of such varying interpretations, Kafka's fiction in general is concerned with the dilemma of mankind in a world almost totally lacking in spiritual, ethical, or moral values, a world devoid of reason, logic, or coherence.

Good editions of Kafka's short fiction are: *Selected Stories of Franz*

Kafka (Modern Library) and *The Penal Colony. Stories and Short Pieces* (Schocken).

Questions   1. What is the significance of the following comments of the doctor: "To write prescriptions is easy, but to come to an understanding with people is hard"; "They [people] have lost their ancient beliefs; the parson sits at home . . . but the doctor is supposed to be omnipotent. . . . I have not thrust my services on them; if they misuse me for sacred ends, I let that happen to me"; "Many a one proffers his side and can hardly hear the ax in the forest, far less that it is coming nearer to him"; "Betrayed! Betrayed! A false alarm on the night bell once answered — it cannot be made good, not ever." In what ways does the doctor appear to be a leader? a martyr? a messiah? How do you interpret the other characters — Rose, the groom, the sick boy ("A fine wound is all I brought into the world"), the boy's family, the neighbors?   2. How do you interpret such incidents as the sudden appearance of the horses, the doctor's journey from his home to that of the sick boy, the placing the doctor beside the sick boy, the fact that he is stripped when he starts to return home? 3. What is the purpose of the songs in the story:

> *Strip his clothes off, then he'll heal us,*
> *If he doesn't, kill him dead!*

> *O be joyful all you patients,*
> *The doctor's laid in bed beside you!*

4. Allen Tate and Caroline Gordon, in *The House of Fiction,* state that Hawthorne "was never able to bring his craft to the pitch of perfection which Kafka attained." Do you agree or disagree?   5. The same critics have commented on Flaubert's "great discovery that in fiction no object exists until it has acted upon or been acted upon by some other object." Does this comment have any meaning in connection with Kafka?

FRANZ KAFKA

A Hunger Artist

DURING these last decades the interest in professional fasting has markedly diminished. It used to pay very well to stage such great performances under one's own management, but today that is quite impossible. We live in a different world now. At one time the whole town took a lively interest in the hunger artist; from day to day of his fast the excitement mounted; everybody wanted to see him at least once a day; there were people who bought season tickets for the last few days and sat from morning till night in front of his small barred cage; even in the nighttime there were visiting hours, when the whole effect was heightened by torch flares; on fine days the cage was set out in the open air, and then it was the children's special treat to see the hunger artist; for their elders he was often just a joke that happened to be in fashion, but the children stood open-mouthed, holding each other's hands for greater security, marvelling at him as he sat there pallid in black tights, with his ribs sticking out so prominently, not even on a seat but down among straw on the ground, sometimes giving a courteous nod, answering questions with a constrained smile, or perhaps stretching an arm through the bars so that one might feel how thin it was, and then again withdrawing deep into himself, paying no attention to anyone or anything, not even to the all-important striking of the clock that was the only piece of furniture in his cage, but merely staring into vacancy with half-shut eyes, now and then taking a sip from a tiny glass of water to moisten his lips.

Besides casual onlookers there were also relays of permanent watchers selected by the public, usually butchers, strangely enough, and it was their task to watch the hunger artist day and night, three of them at a time, in case he should have some secret recourse to nourishment. This was nothing but a formality, instituted to reassure the masses, for the initiates knew well enough that during his fast the artist would never in any circumstances, not even under forcible compulsion, swallow the smallest morsel of food; the honor of his profession forbade it. Not every watcher, of course, was capable of understanding this, there were often groups of night watchers who were very lax in carrying out their duties and deliberately huddled together in a retired corner to play cards with great absorption, obviously intending to give the hunger artist the chance of a little refreshment, which they supposed he could draw from some private hoard. Nothing annoyed the artist more than such watchers; they made him miserable; they made his fast seem unendurable; sometimes he mastered his feebleness sufficiently to sing during their watch for as long as he could keep going, to show them how unjust their suspicions were. But that was of little use; they only wondered at his cleverness in being able to fill his mouth even while singing. Much more to his taste were the watchers who sat close up to the bars, who were not content with the dim night lighting of the hall but focused him in the full glare of the electric pocket torch given them by the impresario. The harsh light did not trouble him at all, in any case he could never sleep properly, and he could always drowse a little, whatever the light, at any hour, even when the hall was thronged with noisy onlookers. He was quite happy at the prospect of spending a sleepless night with such watchers; he was ready to exchange jokes with them, to tell them stories out of his nomadic life, anything at all to keep them awake and demonstrate to them again that he had no eatables in his cage and that he was fasting as not one of them could fast. But his happiest moment was when the morning came and an enormous breakfast was brought them, at his expense, on which they flung themselves with the keen appetite of healthy men after a weary night of wakefulness. Of course there were people who argued that this breakfast was an unfair attempt to bribe the watchers, but that was going rather too far, and when they were invited to take on a night's vigil without a breakfast, merely for the sake of the cause, they made themselves scarce, although they stuck stubbornly to their suspicions.

Such suspicions, anyhow, were a necessary accompaniment to the profession of fasting. No one could possibly watch the hunger artist continuously, day and night, and so no one could produce first-hand evidence that the fast had really been rigorous and continuous; only the artist himself could know that, he was therefore bound to be the sole completely satisfied spectator of his own fast. Yet for other reasons he was never satisfied; it was not perhaps mere fasting that had brought him to such skeleton thinness that many people had regretfully to keep away from his exhibitions, because the sight of him was too much for them, perhaps it was dissatisfaction with himself that had worn him down. For he alone knew, what no other initiate knew, how easy it was to fast. It was the easiest thing in the world. He made no secret of this, yet people did not believe him, at the best they set him down as modest, most of them, however, thought he was out for publicity or else was some kind of cheat who found it easy to fast because he had discovered a way of making it easy, and then had the impudence to admit the fact, more or less. He had to put up with all that, and in the course of time had got used to it, but his inner dissatisfaction always rankled, and never yet, after any term of fasting — this must be granted to his credit — had he left the cage of his own free will. The longest period of fasting was fixed by his impresario at forty days, beyond that term he was not allowed to go, not even in great cities, and there was good reason for it, too. Experience had proved that for about forty days the interest of the public could be stimulated by a steadily increasing pressure of advertisement, but after that the town began to lose interest, sympathetic support began notably to fall off; there were of course local variations as between one town and another or one country and another, but as a general rule forty days marked the limit. So on the fortieth day the flower-bedecked cage was opened, enthusiastic spectators filled the hall, a military band played, two doctors entered the cage to measure the results of the fast, which were announced through a megaphone, and finally two young ladies appeared, blissful at having been selected for the honor, to help the hunger artist down the few steps leading to a small table on which was spread a carefully chosen invalid repast. And at this very moment the artist always turned stubborn. True, he would entrust his bony arms to the outstretched helping hands of the ladies bending over him, but stand up he would not. Why stop fasting at this particular moment, after forty days of it? He had held out for a long time, an illimitably long time; why stop now, when he was in his best fasting form, or rather, not yet quite in his best fasting form? Why should he be cheated of the fame he would get for fasting longer, for being not only the record hunger artist of all time, which presumably he was already, but for beating his own record by a performance beyond human imagination, since he felt that there were no limits to his capacity for fasting? His public pretended to admire him so much, why should it have so little patience with him; if he could endure fasting longer, why shouldn't the public endure it? Besides, he was tired, he was comfortable sitting in the straw, and now he was supposed to lift himself to his full height and go down to a meal the very thought of which gave him a nausea that only the presence of the ladies kept him from betraying, and even that with an effort. And he looked up into the eyes of the ladies who were apparently so friendly and in reality so cruel, and shook his head, which felt too heavy on its strengthless neck. But then there happened yet again what always happened. The impresario came forward, without a word — for the band made speech impossible — lifted his arms in the air above the artist, as if inviting Heaven to look down upon its creature here in the straw, this suffering martyr, which indeed he was, although in quite another sense; grasped him round the emaciated waist, with exaggerated caution, so that the frail condition he was in might be appreciated; and committed him to the care of the blenching ladies, not without secretly giving him a shaking so that his legs and body tottered and swayed. The artist now submitted completely; his head lolled on his breast as if it had landed there by chance; his body was hollowed out; his legs in a spasm of self-preservation clung close to each other at the knees, yet scraped on the ground as if it were not really solid ground, as if they were only trying to find solid ground; and the whole weight of his body, a featherweight after all, relapsed onto one of the ladies, who, looking round for

help and panting a little — this post of honor was not at all what
she had expected it to be — first stretched her neck as far as she
could to keep her face at least free from contact with the artist,
then finding this impossible, and her more fortunate companion
not coming to her aid but merely holding extended on her own
trembling hand the little bunch of knucklebones that was the
artist's, to the great delight of the spectators, burst into tears and
had to be replaced by an attendant who had long been stationed
in readiness. Then came the food, a little of which the impresario
managed to get between the artist's lips, while he sat in a kind
of half-fainting trance, to the accompaniment of cheerful patter
designed to distract the public's attention from the artist's condition; after that, a toast was drunk to the public, supposedly
prompted by a whisper from the artist in the impresario's ear;
the band confirmed it with a mighty flourish, the spectators melted
away, and no one had any cause to be dissatisfied with the pro-
ceedings, no one except the hunger artist himself, he only, as
always.

So he lived for many years, with small regular intervals of re-
cuperation, in visible glory, honored by the world, yet in spite
of that troubled in spirit, and all the more troubled because no
one would take his trouble seriously. What comfort could he
possibly need? What more could he possibly wish for? And if
some good-natured person, feeling sorry for him, tried to console
him by pointing out that his melancholy was probably caused by
fasting, it could happen, especially when he had been fasting
for some time, that he reacted with an outburst of fury and to
the general alarm began to shake the bars of his cage like a wild
animal. Yet the impresario had a way of punishing these out-
breaks which he rather enjoyed putting into operation. He would
apologize publicly for the artist's behavior, which was only to
be excused, he admitted, because of the irritability caused by
fasting; a condition hardly to be understood by well-fed people;
then by natural transition he went on to mention the artist's
equally incomprehensible boast that he could fast for much longer
than he was doing; he praised the high ambition, the good will,
the great self-denial undoubtedly implicit in such a statement;
and then quite simply countered it by bringing out photographs,
which were also on sale to the public, showing the artist on the
fortieth day of a fast lying in bed almost dead from exhaustion.

This perversion of the truth, familiar to the artist though it was, always unnerved him afresh and proved too much for him. What was a consequence of the premature ending of his fast was here presented as the cause of it! To fight against this lack of understanding, against a whole world of non-understanding, was impossible. Time and again in good faith he stood by the bars listening to the impresario, but as soon as the photographs appeared he always let go and sank with a groan back on to his straw, and the reassured public could once more come close and gaze at him.

A few years later when the witnesses of such scenes called them to mind, they often failed to understand themselves at all. For meanwhile the aforementioned change in public interest had set in; it seemed to happen almost overnight; there may have been profound causes for it, but who was going to bother about that; at any rate the pampered hunger artist suddenly found himself deserted one fine day by the amusement seekers, who went streaming past him to other more favored attractions. For the last time the impresario hurried him over half Europe to discover whether the old interest might still survive here and there; all in vain; everywhere, as if by secret agreement, a positive revulsion from professional fasting was in evidence. Of course it could not really have sprung up so suddenly as all that, and many premonitory symptoms which had not been sufficiently remarked or suppressed during the rush and glitter of success now came retrospectively to mind, but it was now too late to take any countermeasures. Fasting would surely come into fashion again at some future date, yet that was no comfort for those living in the present. What, then, was the hunger artist to do? He had been applauded by thousands in his time and could hardly come down to showing himself in a street booth at village fairs, and as for adopting another profession, he was not only too old for that but too fanatically devoted to fasting. So he took leave of the impresario, his partner in an unparalleled career, and hired himself to a large circus; in order to spare his own feelings he avoided reading the conditions of his contract.

A large circus with its enormous traffic in replacing and recruiting men, animals and apparatus can always find a use for people at any time, even for a hunger artist, provided of course that he does not ask too much, and in this particular case anyhow it was not only the artist who was taken on but his famous and long-known name as well, indeed considering the peculiar nature of his performance, which was not impaired by advancing age, it could not be objected that here was an artist past his prime, no longer at the height of his professional skill, seeking a refuge in some quiet corner of a circus; on the contrary, the hunger artist averred that he could fast as well as ever, which was entirely credible, he even alleged that if he were allowed to fast as he liked, and this was at once promised him without more ado, he could astound the world by establishing a record never yet achieved, a statement which certainly provoked a smile among the other professionals, since it left out of account the change in public opinion, which the hunger artist in his zeal conveniently forgot.

He had not, however, actually lost his sense of the real situation and took it as a matter of course that he and his cage should be stationed, not in the middle of the ring as a main attraction, but outside, near the animal cages, on a site that was after all easily accessible. Large and gaily painted placards made a frame for the cage and announced what was to be seen inside it. When the public came thronging out in the intervals to see the animals, they could hardly avoid passing the hunger artist's cage and stopping there for a moment, perhaps they might even have stayed longer had not those pressing behind them in the narrow gangway, who did not understand why they should be held up on their way toward the excitements of the menagerie, made it impossible for anyone to stand gazing quietly for any length of time. And that was the reason why the hunger artist, who had of course been looking forward to these visiting hours as the main achievement of his life, began instead to shrink from them. At first he could hardly wait for the intervals; it was exhilarating to watch the crowds come streaming his way, until only too soon — not even the most obstinate self-deception, clung to almost consciously, could hold out against the fact — the conviction was borne in upon him that these people, most of them, to judge from their actions, again and again, without exception, were all on their way to the menagerie. And the first sight of them from the distance remained the best. For when they reached his cage he was at once deafened by the storm of shouting and abuse that arose from the two contending factions, which renewed them-

selves continuously, of those who wanted to stop and stare at him
— he soon began to dislike them more than the others — not out
of real interest but only out of obstinate self-assertiveness, and
those who wanted to go straight on to the animals. When the
first great rush was past, the stragglers came along, and these,
whom nothing could have prevented from stopping to look at
him as long as they had breath, raced past with long strides,
hardly even glancing at him, in their haste to get to the menagerie in time. And all too rarely did it happen that he had a stroke
of luck, when some father of a family fetched up before him
with his children, pointed a finger at the hunger artist and explained at length what the phenomenon meant, telling stories
of earlier years when he himself had watched similar but much
more thrilling performances, and the children, still rather un-
comprehending, since neither inside nor outside school had they
been sufficiently prepared for this lesson — what did they care
about fasting? — yet showed by the brightness of their intent
eyes that new and better times might be coming. Perhaps, said
the hunger artist to himself many a time, things would be a little
better if his cage were set not quite so near the menagerie. That
made it too easy for people to make their choice, to say nothing
of what he suffered from the stench of the menagerie, the animals' restlessness by night, the carrying past of raw lumps of flesh
for the beasts of prey, the roaring at feeding times, which depressed him continually. But he did not dare to lodge a complaint with the management; after all, he had the animals to
thank for the troops of people who passed his cage, among whom
there might always be one here and there to take an interest in
him, and who could tell where they might seclude him if he
called attention to his existence and thereby to the fact that,
strictly speaking, he was only an impediment on the way to the
menagerie.

A small impediment, to be sure, one that grew steadily less.
People grew familiar with the strange idea that they could be
expected, in times like these, to take an interest in a hunger
artist, and with this familiarity the verdict went out against him.
He might fast as much as he could, and he did so; but nothing
could save him now, people passed him by. Just try to explain to
anyone the art of fasting! Anyone who has no feeling for it cannot be made to understand it. The fine placards grew dirty and

illegible, they were torn down; the little notice board telling the number of fast days achieved, which at first was changed carefully every day, had long stayed at the same figure, for after the first few weeks even this small task seemed pointless to the staff; and so the artist simply fasted on and on, as he had once dreamed of doing, and it was no trouble to him, just as he had always foretold, but no one counted the days, no one, not even the artist himself, knew what records he was already breaking, and his heart grew heavy. And when once in a time some leisurely passerby stopped, made merry over the old figure on the board and spoke of swindling, that was in its way the stupidest lie ever invented by indifference and inborn malice, since it was not the hunger artist who was cheating; he was working honestly, but the world was cheating him of his reward.

Many more days went by, however, and that too came to an end. An overseer's eye fell on the cage one day and he asked the attendants why this perfectly good cage should be left standing there unused with dirty straw inside it; nobody knew, until one man, helped out by the notice board, remembered about the hunger artist. They poked into the straw with sticks and found him in it. "Are you still fasting?" asked the overseer. "When on earth do you mean to stop?" "Forgive me, everybody," whispered the hunger artist; only the overseer, who had his ear to the bars, understood him. "Of course," said the overseer, and tapped his forehead with a finger to let the attendants know what state the man was in, "we forgive you." "I always wanted you to admire my fasting," said the hunger artist. "We do admire it," said the overseer, affably. "But you shouldn't admire it," said the hunger artist. "Well, then we don't admire it," said the overseer, "but why shouldn't we admire it?" "Because I have to fast, I can't help it," said the hunger artist. "What a fellow you are," said the overseer, "and why can't you help it?" "Because," said the hunger artist, lifting his head a little and speaking, with his lips pursed, as if for a kiss, right into the overseer's ear, so that no syllable might be lost, "because I couldn't find the food I liked. If I had found it, believe me, I should have made no fuss and stuffed myself like you or anyone else." These were his last words, but in his dimming eyes remained the firm though no longer proud persuasion that he was still continuing to fast.

"Well, clear this out now!" said the overseer, and they buried the hunger artist, straw and all. Into the cage they put a young panther. Even the most insensitive felt it refreshing to see this wild creature leaping around the cage that had so long been dreary. The panther was all right. The food he liked was brought him without hesitation by the attendants; he seemed not even to miss his freedom; his noble body, furnished almost to the bursting point with all that it needed, seemed to carry freedom around with it too; somewhere in his jaws it seemed to lurk; and the joy of life streamed with such ardent passion from his throat that for the onlookers it was not easy to stand the shock of it. But they braced themselves, crowded round the cage, and did not want ever to move away.

Questions   1. In what ways does the hunger artist resemble the country doctor? In what ways are the characters different?   2. What is the significance of the fact that the impresario fixes the fasting period at forty days? What is suggested by the celebrations which follow the fast ("So on the fortieth day the flower-bedecked cage was opened, enthusiastic spectators filled the hall, a military band played" and so forth)?   3. Discuss the contrast between the young panther and the artist. Why are the people relieved and "refreshed" to see this "wild creature leaping around the cage that had so long been dreary"?   4. Discuss the artist's comment, made shortly before his death, that he fasted "because I couldn't find the food I liked. If I had found it, believe me, I should have made no fuss and stuffed myself like you or anyone else." Do you believe it?   5. In what ways, if any, do these two stories by Kafka remind you of "Young Goodman Brown" or "Rappaccini's Daughter"?

D. H. LAWRENCE

Tickets, Please

THERE is in the Midlands a single-line tramway system which boldly leaves the county town and plunges off into the black, industrial countryside, up hill and down dale, through the long, ugly villages of workmen's houses, over canals and railways, past churches perched high and nobly over the smoke and shadows, through stark, grimy, cold little market-places, tilting away in a rush past cinemas and shops down to the hollow where the collieries are, then up again, past a little rural church, under the ash trees, on in a rush to the terminus, the last little ugly place of industry, the cold little town that shivers on the edge of the wild, gloomy country beyond. There the green and creamy coloured tram-car seems to pause and purr with curious satisfaction. But in a few minutes — the clock on the turret of the Co-operative Wholesale Society's Shops gives the time — away it starts once more on the adventure. Again there are the reckless swoops downhill, bouncing the loops: again the chilly wait in the hill-top market-place: again the breathless slithering round the precipitous drop under the church: again the patient halts at the loops, waiting for the outcoming car: so on and on, for two long hours, till at last the city looms beyond the fat gas-works, the narrow factories draw near, we are in the sordid streets of the great town, once more we sidle to a standstill at our terminus, abashed

TICKETS, PLEASE From *England, My England* by D. H. Lawrence, included in *The Portable D. H. Lawrence*. Copyright 1922 by Thomas Seltzer, Inc., 1950 by Frieda Lawrence. Reprinted by permission of The Viking Press, Inc.

by the great crimson and cream-coloured city cars, but still perky,
jaunty, somewhat dare-devil, green as a jaunty sprig of parsley
out of a black colliery garden.

To ride on these cars is always an adventure. Since we are in
war-time, the drivers are men unfit for active service: cripples
and hunchbacks. So they have the spirit of the devil in them.
The ride becomes a steeple-chase. Hurray! we have leapt in a
clear jump over the canal bridges — now for the four-lane corner.
With a shriek and a trail of sparks we are clear again. To be
sure, a tram often leaps the rails — but what matter! It sits in a
ditch till other trams come to haul it out. It is quite common for
a car, packed with one solid mass of living people, to come to a
dead halt in the midst of unbroken blackness, the heart of nowhere on a dark night, and for the driver and the girl conductor
to call, "All get off — car's on fire!" Instead, however, of rushing
out in a panic, the passengers stolidly reply: "Get on — get on!
We're not coming out. We're stopping where we are. Push on,
George." So till flames actually appear.

The reason for this reluctance to dismount is that the nights
are howlingly cold, black, and windswept, and a car is a haven
of refuge. From village to village the miners travel, for a change
of cinema, of girl, of pub. The trams are desperately packed.
Who is going to risk himself in the black gulf outside, to wait
perhaps an hour for another tram, then to see the forlorn notice
"Depot Only," because there is something wrong! or to greet a
unit of three bright cars all so tight with people that they sail
past with a howl of derision. Trams that pass in the night.

This, the most dangerous tram-service in England, as the authorities themselves declare, with pride, is entirely conducted by
girls, and driven by rash young men, a little crippled, or by delicate young men, who creep forward in terror. The girls are
fearless young hussies. In their ugly blue uniform, skirts up to
their knees, shapeless old peaked caps on their heads, they have
all the sang-froid of an old non-commissioned officer. With a
tram packed with howling colliers, roaring hymns downstairs and
a sort of antiphony of obscenities upstairs, the lasses are perfectly
at their ease. They pounce on the youths who try to evade their
ticket-machine. They push off the men at the end of their distance. They are not going to be done in the eye — not they.
They fear nobody — and everybody fears them.

"Hello, Annie!"

"Hello, Ted!"

"Oh, mind my corn, Miss Stone. It's my belief you've got a heart of stone, for you've trod on it again."

"You should keep it in your pocket," replies Miss Stone, and she goes sturdily upstairs in her high boots.

"Tickets, please."

She is peremptory, suspicious, and ready to hit first. She can hold her own against ten thousand. The step of that tram-car is her Thermopylæ.

Therefore, there is a certain wild romance aboard these cars — and in the sturdy bosom of Annie herself. The time for soft romance is in the morning, between ten o'clock and one, when things are rather slack: that is, except market-day and Saturday. Thus Annie has time to look about her. Then she often hops off her car and into a shop where she has spied something, while the driver chats in the main road. There is very good feeling between the girls and the drivers. Are they not companions in peril, shipments aboard this careering vessel of a tram-car, for ever rocking on the waves of a stormy land.

Then, also, during the easy hours, the inspectors are most in evidence. For some reason, everybody employed in this tram-service is young: there are no grey heads. It would not do. Therefore the inspectors are of the right age, and one, the chief, is also good-looking. See him stand on a wet, gloomy morning, in his long oilskin, his peaked cap well down over his eyes, waiting to board a car. His face is ruddy, his small brown moustache is weathered, he has a faint impudent smile. Fairly tall and agile, even in his waterproof, he springs aboard a car and greets Annie.

"Hello, Annie! Keeping the wet out?"

"Trying to."

There are only two people in the car. Inspecting is soon over. Then for a long and impudent chat on the footboard, a good, easy, twelve-mile chat.

The inspector's name is John Thomas Raynor — always called John Thomas, except sometimes, in malice, Coddy. His face sets in fury when he is addressed, from a distance, with this abbreviation. There is considerable scandal about John Thomas in half a dozen villages. He flirts with the girl conductors in the morning and walks out with them in the dark night, when they leave their

tram-car at the depot. Of course, the girls quit the service frequently. Then he flirts and walks out with the newcomer: always
providing she is sufficiently attractive, and that she will consent
to walk. It is remarkable, however, that most of the girls are
quite comely, they are all young, and this roving life aboard the
car gives them a sailor's dash and recklessness. What matter how
they behave when the ship is in port. Tomorrow they will be
aboard again.

Annie, however, was something of a Tartar, and her sharp
tongue had kept John Thomas at arm's length for many months.
Perhaps, therefore, she liked him all the more: for he always came
up smiling, with impudence. She watched him vanquish one
girl, then another. She could tell by the movement of his mouth
and eyes, when he flirted with her in the morning, that he had
been walking out with this lass, or the other, the night before.
A fine cock-of-the-walk he was. She could sum him up pretty
well.

In this subtle antagonism they knew each other like old friends,
they were as shrewd with one another almost as man and wife.
But Annie had always kept him sufficiently at arm's length. Besides, she had a boy of her own.

The Statutes fair, however, came in November, at Bestwood.
It happened that Annie had the Monday night off. It was a
drizzling ugly night, yet she dressed herself up and went to the
fair ground. She was alone, but she expected soon to find a pal
of some sort.

The roundabouts were veering round and grinding out their
music, the side shows were making as much commotion as possible. In the cocoanut shies there were no cocoanuts, but artificial war-time substitutes, which the lads declared were fastened
into the irons. There was a sad decline in brilliance and luxury.
None the less, the ground was muddy as ever, there was the
same crush, the press of faces lighted up by the flares and the
electric lights, the same smell of naphtha and a few fried potatoes, and of electricity.

Who should be the first to greet Miss Annie, on the show
ground, but John Thomas. He had a black overcoat buttoned up
to his chin, and a tweed cap pulled down over his brows, his face
between was ruddy and smiling and handy as ever. She knew so
well the way his mouth moved.

She was very glad to have a "boy." To be at the Statutes without a fellow was no fun. Instantly, like the gallant he was, he took her on the Dragons, grim-toothed, roundabout switchbacks. It was not nearly so exciting as a tram-car actually. But, then, to be seated in a shaking green dragon, uplifted above the sea of bubble faces, careering in a rickety fashion in the lower heavens, whilst John Thomas leaned over her, his cigarette in his mouth, was after all the right style. She was a plump, quick, alive little creature. So she was quite excited and happy.

John Thomas made her stay on for the next round. And therefore she could hardly for shame repulse him when he put his arm round her and drew her a little nearer to him, in a very warm and cuddly manner. Besides, he was fairly discreet, he kept his movement as hidden as possible. She looked down and saw that his red, clean hand was out of sight of the crowd. And they knew each other so well. So they warmed up to the fair.

After the dragons they went on the horses. John Thomas paid each time, so she could but be complaisant. He, of course, sat astride on the outer horse — named "Black Bess" — and she sat sideways, towards him, on the inner horse — named "Wildfire." But of course John Thomas was not going to sit discreetly on "Black Bess," holding the brass bar. Round they spun and heaved, in the light. And round he swung on his wooden steed, flinging one leg across her mount, and perilously tipping up and down, across the space, half lying back, laughing at her. He was perfectly happy; she was afraid her hat was on one side, but she was excited.

He threw quoits on a table and won for her two large, pale-blue hat-pins. And then, hearing the noise of the cinemas, announcing another performance, they climbed the boards and went in.

Of course, during these performances pitch darkness falls from time to time, when the machine goes wrong. Then there is a wild whooping, and a loud smacking of simulated kisses. In these moments John Thomas drew Annie towards him. After all, he had a wonderfully warm, cosy way of holding a girl with his arm, he seemed to make such a nice fit. And after all, it was pleasant to be so held: so very comforting and cosy and nice. He leaned over her and she felt his breath on her hair; she knew he wanted to kiss her on the lips. And after all, he was so warm and she fitted in to him so softly. After all, she wanted him to touch her lips.

But the light sprang up; she also started electrically, and put her hat straight. He left his arm lying nonchalantly behind her. Well, it was fun, it was exciting to be at the Statutes with John Thomas.

When the cinema was over they went for a walk across the dark, damp fields. He had all the arts of love-making. He was especially good at holding a girl, when he sat with her on a stile in the black, drizzling darkness. He seemed to be holding her in space, against his own warmth and gratification. And his kisses were soft and slow and searching.

So Annie walked out with John Thomas, though she kept her own boy dangling in the distance. Some of the tram-girls chose to be huffy. But there, you must take things as you find them, in this life.

There was no mistake about it, Annie liked John Thomas a good deal. She felt so rich and warm in herself whenever he was near. And John Thomas really liked Annie more than usual. The soft, melting way in which she could flow into a fellow, as if she melted into his very bones, was something rare and good. He fully appreciated this.

But with a developing acquaintance there began a developing intimacy. Annie wanted to consider him a person, a man; she wanted to take an intelligent interest in him, and to have an intelligent response. She did not want a mere nocturnal presence, which was what he was so far. And she prided herself that he could not leave her.

Here she made a mistake. John Thomas intended to remain a nocturnal presence; he had no idea of becoming an all-round individual to her. When she started to take an intelligent interest in him and his life and his character, he sheered off. He hated intelligent interest. And he knew that the only way to stop it was to avoid it. The possessive female was aroused in Annie. So he left her.

It is no use saying she was not surprised. She was at first startled, thrown out of her count. For she had been so *very* sure of holding him. For a while she was staggered, and everything became uncertain to her. Then she wept with fury, indignation, desolation, and misery. Then she had a spasm of despair. And then, when he came, still impudently, on to her car, still familiar, but letting her see by the movement of his head that he had gone away to somebody else for the time being and was enjoying pastures new, then she determined to have her own back.

She had a very shrewd idea what girls John Thomas had taken out. She went to Nora Purdy. Nora was a tall, rather pale, but well-built girl, with beautiful yellow hair. She was rather secretive.

"Hey!" said Annie, accosting her; then softly, "Who's John Thomas on with now?"

"I don't know," said Nora.

"Why tha does," said Annie, ironically lapsing into dialect. "Tha knows as well as I do."

"Well, I do, then," said Nora. "It isn't me, so don't bother."

"It's Cissy Meakin, isn't it?"

"It is, for all I know."

"Hasn't he got a face on him!" said Annie. "I don't half like his cheek. I could knock him off the footboard when he comes round at me."

"He'll get dropped-on one of these days," said Nora.

"Ay, he will when somebody makes up their mind to drop it on him. I should like to see him taken down a peg or two, shouldn't you?"

"I shouldn't mind," said Nora.

"You've got quite as much cause to as I have," said Annie. "But we'll drop on him one of these days, my girl. What? Don't you want to?"

"I don't mind," said Nora.

But as a matter of fact, Nora was much more vindictive than Annie.

One by one Annie went the round of the old flames. It so happened that Cissy Meakin left the tramway service in quite a short time. Her mother made her leave. Then John Thomas was on the qui-vive. He cast his eyes over his old flock. And his eyes lighted on Annie. He thought she would be safe now. Besides, he liked her.

She arranged to walk home with him on Sunday night. It so happened that her car would be in the depot at half-past nine: the last car would come in at ten-fifteen. So John Thomas was to wait for her there.

At the depot the girls had a little waiting-room of their own. It was quite rough, but cosy, with a fire and an oven and a mirror, and table and wooden chairs. The half dozen girls who knew John Thomas only too well had arranged to take service this Sunday afternoon. So, as the cars began to come in, early, the girls dropped into the waiting-room. And instead of hurrying off home, they sat around the fire and had a cup of tea. Outside was the darkness and lawlessness of war-time.

John Thomas came on the car after Annie, at about a quarter to ten. He poked his head easily into the girls' waiting-room.

"Prayer-meeting?" he asked.

"Ay," said Laura Sharp. "Ladies only."

"That's me!" said John Thomas. It was one of his favourite exclamations.

"Shut the door, boy," said Muriel Baggaley.

"On which side of me?" said John Thomas.

"Which tha likes," said Polly Birkin.

He had come in and closed the door behind him. The girls moved in their circle, to make a place for him near the fire. He took off his great-coat and pushed back his hat.

"Who handles the teapot?" he said.

Nora Purdy silently poured him out a cup of tea.

"Want a bit o' my bread and drippin'?" said Muriel Baggaley to him.

"Ay, give us a bit."

And he began to eat his piece of bread.

"There's no place like home, girls," he said.

They all looked at him as he uttered this piece of impudence. He seemed to be sunning himself in the presence of so many damsels.

"Especially if you're not afraid to go home in the dark," said Laura Sharp.

"Me! By myself I am."

They sat till they heard the last tram come in. In a few minutes Emma Houselay entered.

"Come on, my old duck!" cried Polly Birkin.

"It *is* perishing," said Emma, holding her fingers to the fire.

"But — I'm afraid to, go home in, the dark," sang Laura Sharp, the tune having got into her mind.

"Who're you going with tonight, John Thomas?" asked Muriel Baggaley, coolly.

"Tonight?" said John Thomas. "Oh, I'm going home by myself tonight — all on my lonely-O."

"That's me!" said Nora Purdy, using his own ejaculation.

The girls laughed shrilly.

"Me as well, Nora," said John Thomas.

"Don't know what you mean," said Laura.

"Yes, I'm toddling," said he, rising and reaching for his overcoat.

"Nay," said Polly. "We're all here waiting for you."

"We've got to be up in good time in the morning," he said in the benevolent official manner.

They all laughed.

"Nay," said Muriel. "Don't leave us all lonely, John Thomas. Take one!"

"I'll take the lot, if you like," he responded gallantly.

"That you won't, either," said Muriel. "Two's company; seven's too much of a good thing."

"Nay — take one," said Laura. "Fair and square, all above board and say which."

"Ay," cried Annie, speaking for the first time. "Pick, John Thomas; let's hear thee."

"Nay," he said. "I'm going home quiet tonight. Feeling good, for once."

"Whereabouts?" said Annie. "Take a good un, then. But tha's got to take one of us!"

"Nay, how can I take one," he said, laughing uneasily. "I don't want to make enemies."

"You'd only make *one*," said Annie.

"The chosen *one*," added Laura.

"Oh, my! Who said girls!" exclaimed John Thomas, again turning, as if to escape. "Well — good-night."

"Nay, you've got to make your pick," said Muriel. "Turn your face to the wall and say which one touches you. Go on — we shall only just touch your back — one of us. Go on — turn your face to the wall, and don't look, and say which one touches you."

He was uneasy, mistrusting them. Yet he had not the courage to break away. They pushed him to a wall and stood him there with his face to it. Behind his back they all grimaced, tittering. He looked so comical. He looked around uneasily.

"Go on!" he cried.

"You're looking — you're looking!" they shouted.

He turned his head away. And suddenly, with a movement like a swift cat, Annie went forward and fetched him a box on the side of the head that set his cap flying, and himself staggering. He started round.

But at Annie's signal they all flew at him, slapping him, pinching him, pulling his hair, though more in fun than in spite or anger. He, however, saw red. His blue eyes flamed with strange fear as well as fury, and he butted through the girls to the door. It was locked. He wrenched at it. Roused, alert, the girls stood round and looked at him. He faced them, at bay. At that moment they were rather horrifying to him, as they stood in their short uniforms. He was distinctly afraid.

"Come on, John Thomas! Come on! Choose!" said Annie.

"What are you after? Open the door," he said.

"We sha'n't — not till you've chosen!" said Muriel.

"Chosen what?" he said.

"Chosen the one you're going to marry," she replied.

He hesitated a moment.

"Open the blasted door," he said, "and get back to your senses." He spoke with official authority.

"You've got to choose!" cried the girls.

"Come on!" cried Annie, looking him in the eye. "Come on! Come on!"

He went forward, rather vaguely. She had taken off her belt, and swinging it, she fetched him a sharp blow over the head with the buckle end. He sprang and seized her. But immediately the other girls rushed upon him, pulling and tearing and beating him. Their blood was now thoroughly up. He was their sport now. They were going to have their own back, out of him. Strange, wild creatures, they hung on him and rushed at him to bear him down. His tunic was torn right up the back, Nora had hold at the back of his collar, and was actually strangling him. Luckily the button burst. He struggled in a wild frenzy of fury and terror, almost mad terror. His tunic was simply torn off his back, his shirt-sleeves were torn away, his arms were naked. The girls rushed at him, clenched their hands on him and pulled at him: or they rushed at him and pushed him, butted him with all their might: or they struck him wild blows. He ducked and cringed and struck sideways. They became more intense.

At last he was down. They rushed on him, kneeling on him. He had neither breath nor strength to move. His face was bleeding with a long scratch, his brow was bruised.

Annie knelt on him, the other girls knelt and hung on to him. Their faces were flushed, their hair wild, their eyes were all glittering strangely. He lay at last quite still, with face averted, as an animal lies when it is defeated and at the mercy of the captor. Sometimes his eye glanced back at the wild faces of the girls. His breast rose heavily, his wrists were torn.

"Now, then, my fellow!" gasped Annie at length. "Now then — now —— "

At the sound of her terrifying cold triumph, he suddenly started to struggle as an animal might, but the girls threw themselves upon him with unnatural strength and power, forcing him down.

"Yes — now, then!" gasped Annie at length.

And there was a dead silence, in which the thud of heart-beating was to be heard. It was a suspense of pure silence in every soul.

"Now you know where you are," said Annie.

The sight of his white, bare arm maddened the girls. He lay in a kind of trance of fear and antagonism. They felt themselves filled with supernatural strength.

Suddenly Polly started to laugh — to giggle wildly — helplessly — and Emma and Muriel joined in. But Annie and Nora and Laura remained the same, tense, watchful, with gleaming eyes. He winced away from these eyes.

"Yes," said Annie, in a curious low tone, secret and deadly. "Yes! You've got it now! You know what you've done, don't you? You know what you've done."

He made no sound nor sign, but lay with bright, averted eyes, and averted, bleeding face.

"You ought to be *killed*, that's what you ought," said Annie tensely. "You ought to be *killed*." And there was a terrifying lust in her voice.

Polly was ceasing to laugh, and giving long-drawn oh-h-hs and sighs as she came to herself.

"He's got to choose," she said vaguely.

"Oh, yes, he has," said Laura, with vindictive decision.

"Do you hear — do you hear?" said Annie. And with a sharp movement that made him wince, she turned his face to her.

"Do you hear?" she repeated, shaking him.

But he was quite dumb. She fetched him a sharp slap on the face. He started, and his eyes widened. Then his face darkened with defiance, after all.

"Do you hear?" she repeated.

He only looked at her with hostile eyes.

"Speak!" she said, putting her face devilishly near his.

"What?" he said, almost overcome.

"You've got to *choose!*" she cried, as if it were some terrible menace, and as if it hurt her that she could not exact more.

"What?" he said in fear.

"Choose your girl, Coddy. You've got to choose her now. And you'll get your neck broken if you play any more of your tricks, my boy. You're settled now."

There was a pause. Again he averted his face. He was cunning in his overthrow. He did not give in to them really — no, not if they tore him to bits.

"All right, then," he said, "I choose Annie." His voice was strange and full of malice. Annie let go of him as if he had been a hot coal.

"He's chosen Annie!" said the girls in chorus.

"Me!" cried Annie. She was still kneeling, but away from him. He was still lying prostrate, with averted face. The girls grouped uneasily around.

"Me!" repeated Annie, with a terrible bitter accent.

Then she got up, drawing away from him with strange disgust and bitterness.

"I wouldn't touch him," she said.

But her face quivered with a kind of agony, she seemed as if she would fall. The other girls turned aside. He remained lying on the floor, with his torn clothes and bleeding, averted face.

"Oh, if he's chosen —— " said Polly.

"I don't want him — he can choose again," said Annie, with the same rather bitter hopelessness.

"Get up," said Polly, lifting his shoulder. "Get up."

He rose slowly, a strange, ragged, dazed creature. The girls eyed him from a distance, curiously, furtively, dangerously.

"Who wants him?" cried Laura roughly.

"Nobody," they answered with contempt. Yet each one of them waited for him to look at her, hoped he would look at her. All except Annie, and something was broken in her.

He, however, kept his face closed and averted from them all. There was a silence of the end. He picked up the torn pieces of his tunic, without knowing what to do with them. The girls stood about uneasily, flushed, panting, tidying their hair and their dress unconsciously, and watching him. He looked at none of them. He espied his cap in a corner and went and picked it up. He put it on his head, and one of the girls burst into a shrill, hysteric laugh at the sight he presented. He, however, took no heed but went straight to where his overcoat hung on a peg. The girls moved away from contact with him as if he had been an electric wire. He put on his coat and buttoned it down. Then he rolled his tunic-rags into a bundle, and stood before the locked door, dumbly.

"Open the door, somebody," said Laura.

"Annie's got the key," said one.

Annie silently offered the key to the girls. Nora unlocked the door.

"Tit for tat, old man," she said. "Show yourself a man, and don't bear a grudge."

But without a word or sign he had opened the door and gone, his face closed, his head dropped.

"That'll learn him," said Laura.

"Coddy!" said Nora.

"Shut up, for God's sake!" cried Annie fiercely, as if in torture.

"Well, I'm about ready to go, Polly. Look sharp!" said Muriel.

The girls were all anxious to be off. They were tidying themselves hurriedly, with mute, stupefied faces.

D(avid) H(erbert) Lawrence (1885-1930)   Lawrence was born in a small English mining town of Nottinghamshire. His early years were darkened by poverty, hard work, and the growing friction between his heavy-drinking coal-mining father and his sensitive, ambitious mother. Ill health and a burning ambition to write caused him to abandon the profession of schoolteacher, and eventually led him across the world — from England to Australia to Mexico and the American Southwest, and finally to the south of France where he died of tuberculosis at the age of forty-five. His ashes were flown back to America and repose in the Lawrence shrine near Taos, New Mexico, where Lawrence and his wife Frieda had lived for several years.

A prolific writer, Lawrence produced approximately fifty volumes of novels, short stories, translations, plays, poems, critical material, journals, and essays. Literary creation to him was a necessity, a compulsion, and a catharsis: "One sheds one's sicknesses," he said, "in books." His career was one of continuous controversy, evoked almost as much by Lawrence's dogmatic personality and revolutionary beliefs as by his outspoken, iconoclastic, often brutal books. His best novels (*Sons and Lovers, The Rainbow, Lady Chatterley's Lover*) and collections of short stories (*The Prussian Officer and Other Stories, The Lovely Lady, A Modern Lover*) are important both in themselves and as the culmination of the fiction writer's fight for freedom of expression; with Joyce and Lawrence, the battle was finally won. In spite of the unevenness of much of his work, Lawrence is one of the towering literary figures of the twentieth century.

The Tales of D. H. Lawrence (London: Heinemann) contains forty-six of his short stories. No similar American edition exists, although several of his best stories are included in *The Portable D. H. Lawrence* (ed. Diana Trilling, Viking).

Questions   1. Compare the long descriptive opening paragraph of "Tickets, Please" with descriptive openings of such stories as "The Fall of the House of Usher" and "Araby." What are the purpose and function of this opening?   2. From whose point of view is the story narrated? Do we ever get within the consciousness of any of the characters, or are they observed "from the outside"?   3. What is the significance of the reference to Annie: "The step of that tram-car is her Thermopylae"?   4. Violence or the threat of violence frequently figures in Lawrence's fiction. Does Lawrence prepare the reader for the sudden outbreak of violence in the waiting room of the depot? How do you explain the mob action of the girls? Can this action be justified? Is John Thomas, in other words, the victim of an unreasonable attack, or does he "have it coming to him"?   5. How do you explain Annie's reaction when John Thomas "chooses" her? Why is "something broken in her"; why are her last words in the story spoken "as if in torture"?   6. What is the significance of the wartime background of the story?

KATHERINE MANSFIELD

Marriage
à la Mode

ON HIS WAY to the station William remembered with a fresh pang of disappointment that he was taking nothing down to the kiddies. Poor little chaps! It was hard lines on them. Their first words always were as they ran to greet him, "What have you got for me, daddy?" and he had nothing. He would have to buy them some sweets at the station. But that was what he had done for the past four Saturdays; their faces had fallen last time when they saw the same old boxes produced again.

"And Paddy had said, "I had red ribbing on mine *bee*-fore!"

And Johnny had said, "It's always pink on mine. I hate pink."

But what was William to do? The affair wasn't so easily settled. In the old days, of course, he would have taken a taxi off to a decent toyshop and chosen them something in five minutes. But nowadays they had Russian toys, French toys, Serbian toys — toys from God knows where. It was over a year since Isabel had scrapped the old donkeys and engines and so on because they were so "dreadfully sentimental" and "so appallingly bad for the babies' sense of form."

"It's so important," the new Isabel had explained, "that they

MARRIAGE À LA MODE   Reprinted from *The Short Stories of Katherine Mansfield,* by permission of Alfred A. Knopf, Inc. Copyright 1922, 1937 by Alfred A. Knopf, Inc.

should like the right things from the very beginning. It saves so
much time later on. Really, if the poor pets have to spend their
infant years staring at these horrors, one can imagine them growing up and asking to be taken to the Royal Academy."

And she spoke as though a visit to the Royal Academy was
certain immediate death to any one. . . .

"Well, I don't know," said Williams slowly. "When I was their
age I used to go to bed hugging an old towel with a knot in it."

The new Isabel looked at him, her eyes narrowed, her lips
apart.

"*Dear* William! I'm sure you did!" She laughed in the new
way.

Sweets it would have to be, however, thought William gloomily, fishing in his pockets for change for the taxi-man. And he
saw the kiddies handing the boxes round — they were awfully
generous little chaps — while Isabel's precious friends didn't
hesitate to help themselves. . . .

What about fruit? William hovered before a stall just inside
the station. What about a melon each? Would they have to share
that, too? Or a pineapple for Pad, and a melon for Johnny?
Isabel's friends could hardly go sneaking up to the nursery at the
children's meal-times. All the same, as he bought the melon
William had a horrible vision of one of Isabel's young poets lap-
ping up a slice, for some reason, behind the nursery door.

With his two very awkward parcels he strode off to his train.
The platform was crowded, the train was in. Doors banged open
and shut. There came such a loud hissing from the engine that
people looked dazed as they scurried to and fro. William made
straight for a first-class smoker, stowed away his suit-case and
parcels, and taking a huge wad of papers out of his inner pocket,
he flung down in the corner and began to read.

"Our client moreover is positive. . . . We are inclined to re-
consider . . . in the event of — " Ah, that was better. William
pressed back his flattened hair and stretched his legs across the
carriage floor. The familiar dull gnawing in his breast quietened
down. "With regard to our decision — " He took out a blue pencil and scored a paragraph slowly.

Two men came in, stepped across him, and made for the farther corner. A young fellow swung his golf clubs into the rack
and sat down opposite. The train gave a gentle lurch, they were

off. William glanced up and saw the hot, bright station slipping away. A red-faced girl raced along by the carriages, there was something strained and almost desperate in the way she waved and called. "Hysterical!" thought William dully. Then a greasy, black-faced workman at the end of the platform grinned at the passing train. And William thought, "A filthy life!" and went back to his papers.

When he looked up again there were fields, and beasts standing for shelter under the dark trees. A wide river, with naked children splashing in the shallows, glided into sight and was gone again. The sky shone pale, and one bird drifted high like a dark fleck in a jewel.

"We have examined our client's correspondence files. . . ." The last sentence he had read echoed in his mind. "We have examined . . ." William hung on to that sentence, but it was no good; it snapped in the middle, and the fields, the sky, the sailing bird, the water, all said, "Isabel." The same thing happened every Saturday afternoon. When he was on his way to meet Isabel there began those countless imaginary meetings. She was at the station, standing just a little apart from everybody else; she was sitting in the open taxi outside; she was at the garden gate; walking across the parched grass; at the door, or just inside the hall.

And her clear, light voice said, "It's William," or "Hillo, William!" or "So William has come!" He touched her cool hand, her cool cheek.

The exquisite freshness of Isabel! When he had been a little boy, it was his delight to run into the garden after a shower of rain and shake the rosebush over him. Isabel was that rosebush, petal-soft, sparkling and cool. And he was still that little boy. But there was no running into the garden now, no laughing and shaking. The dull, persistent gnawing in his breast started again. He drew up his legs, tossed the papers aside, and shut his eyes.

"What is it, Isabel? What is it?" he said tenderly. They were in their bedroom in the new house. Isabel sat on a painted stool before the dressing-table that was strewn with little black and green boxes.

"What is what, William?" And she bent forward, and her fine light hair fell over her cheeks.

"Ah, you know!" He stood in the middle of the strange room

and he felt a stranger. At that Isabel wheeled round quickly and faced him.

"Oh, William!" she cried imploringly, and she held up the hair-brush. "Please! Please don't be so dreadfully stuffy and — tragic. You're always saying or looking or hinting that I've changed. Just because I've got to know really congenial people, and go about more, and am frightfully keen on — on everything, you behave as though I'd — " Isabel tossed back her hair and laughed — "killed our love or something. It's so awfully absurd" — she bit her lip — "and it's so maddening, William. Even this new house and the servants you grudge me."

"Isabel!"

"Yes, yes, it's true in a way," said Isabel quickly. "You think they are another bad sign. Oh, I know you do. I feel it," she said softly, "every time you come up the stairs. But we couldn't have gone on living in that other poky little hole, William. Be practical, at least! Why, there wasn't enough room for the babies even."

No, it was true. Every morning when he came back from chambers it was to find the babies with Isabel in the back drawing-room. They were having rides on the leopard skin thrown over the sofa back, or they were playing shops with Isabel's desk for a counter, or Pad was sitting on the hearthrug rowing away for dear life with a little brass fire shovel, while Johnny shot at pirates with the tongs. Every evening they each had a pick-a-back up the narrow stairs to their fat old Nanny.

Yes, he supposed it was a poky little house. A little white house with blue curtains and a windowbox of petunias. William met their friends at the door with "Seen our petunias? Pretty terrific for London, don't you think?"

But the imbecile thing, the absolutely extraordinary thing was that he hadn't the slightest idea that Isabel wasn't as happy as he. God, what blindness! He hadn't the remotest notion in those days that she really hated that inconvenient little house, that she thought the fat Nanny was ruining the babies, that she was desperately lonely, pining for new people and new music and pictures and so on. If they hadn't gone to that studio party at Moira Morrison's — if Moira Morrison hadn't said as they were leaving, "I'm going to rescue your wife, selfish man. She's

like an exquisite little Titania" — if Isabel hadn't gone with Moira
to Paris — if — if . . .

The train stopped at another station. Bettingford. Good
heavens! They'd be there in ten minutes. William stuffed the
papers back into his pockets; the young man opposite had long
since disappeared. Now the other two got out. The late afternoon sun shone on women in cotton frocks and little sunburnt,
barefoot children. It blazed on a silky yellow flower with coarse
leaves which sprawled over a bank of rock. The air ruffling
through the window smelled of the sea. Had Isabel the same
crowd with her this week-end, wondered William?

And he remembered the holidays they used to have, the four of
them, with a little farm girl, Rose, to look after the babies.
Isabel wore a jersey and her hair in a plait; she looked about
fourteen. Lord! how his nose used to peel! And the amount they
ate, and the amount they slept in that immense feather bed with
their feet locked together. . . . William couldn't help a grim
smile as he thought of Isabel's horror if she knew the full extent
of his sentimentality.

.   .   .   .

"Hillo, William!" She was at the station after all, standing just
as he had imagined, apart from the others, and — William's heart
leapt — she was alone.

"Hallo, Isabel!" William stared. He thought she looked so
beautiful that he had to say something. "You look very cool."

"Do I?" said Isabel. "I don't feel very cool. Come along, your
horrid old train is late. The taxi's outside." She put her hand
lightly on his arm as they passed the ticket collector. "We've
all come to meet you," she said. "But we've left Bobby Kane at
the sweet shop, to be called for."

"Oh!" said William. It was all he could say for the moment.

There in the glare waited the taxi, with Bill Hunt and Dennis
Green sprawling on one side, their hats tilted over their faces,
while on the other, Moira Morrison, in a bonnet like a huge
strawberry, jumped up and down.

"No ice! No ice! No ice!" she shouted gaily.

And Dennis chimed in from under his hat. "*Only* to be had
from the fishmonger's."

And Bill Hunt, emerging, added, "With *whole* fish in it."

"Oh, what a bore!" wailed Isabel. And she explained to William how they had been chasing round the town for ice while she waited for him. "Simply everything is running down the steep cliffs into the sea, beginning with the butter."

"We shall have to anoint ourselves with the butter," said Dennis. "May thy head, William, lack not ointment."

"Look here," said William, "how are we going to sit? I'd better get up by the driver."

"No, Bobby Kane's by the driver," said Isabel. "You're to sit between Moira and me." The taxi started. "What have you got in those mysterious parcels?"

"De-cap-it-ated heads!" said Bill Hunt, shuddering beneath his hat.

"Oh, fruit!" Isabel sounded very pleased. "Wise William! A melon and a pineapple. How too nice!"

"No, wait a bit," said William, smiling. But he really was anxious. "I brought them down for the kiddies."

"Oh, my dear!" Isabel laughed, and slipped her hand through his arm. "They'd be rolling in agonies if they were to eat them. No" — she patted his hand — "you must bring them something next time. I refuse to part with my pineapple."

"Cruel Isabel! Do let me smell it!" said Moira. She flung her arms across William appealingly. "Oh!" The strawberry bonnet fell forward: she sounded quite faint.

"A Lady in Love with a Pineapple," said Dennis, as the taxi drew up before a little shop with a striped blind. Out came Bobby Kane, his arms full of little packets.

"I do hope they'll be good. I've chosen them because of the colours. There are some round things which really look too divine. And just look at this nougat," he cried ecstatically, "just look at it! It's a perfect little ballet."

But at that moment the shopman appeared. "Oh, I forgot. They're none of them paid for," said Bobby, looking frightened. Isabel gave the shopman a note, and Bobby was radiant again. "Hallo, William! I'm sitting by the driver." And bareheaded, all in white, with his sleeves rolled up to the shoulders, he leapt into his place. "Avanti!" he cried. . . .

After tea the others went off to bathe, while William stayed and made his peace with the kiddies. But Johnny and Paddy were asleep, the rose-red glow had paled, bats were flying, and

still the bathers had not returned. As William wandered downstairs, the maid crossed the hall carrying a lamp. He followed her
into the sitting-room. It was a long room, coloured yellow. On
the wall opposite William some one had painted a young man,
over life-size, with very wobbly legs, offering a wide-eyed daisy
to a young woman who had one very short arm and one very
long, thin one. Over the chairs and sofa there hung strips of
black material, covered with big splashes like broken eggs, and
everywhere one looked there seemed to be an ash-tray full of
cigarette ends. William sat down in one of the arm-chairs. Nowadays, when one felt with one hand down the sides, it wasn't
to come upon a sheep with three legs or a cow that had lost one
horn, or a very fat dove out of the Noah's Ark. One fished up yet
another little paper-covered book of smudged-looking poems. . . .
He thought of the wad of papers in his pocket, but he was too
hungry and tired to read. The door was open; sounds came
from the kitchen. The servants were talking as if they were alone
in the house. Suddenly there came a loud screech of laughter
and an equally loud "Sh!" They had remembered him. William
got up and went through the French windows into the garden,
and as he stood there in the shadow he heard the bathers coming
up the sandy road; their voices rang through the quiet.

"I think it's up to Moira to use her little arts and wiles."

A tragic moan from Moira.

"We ought to have a gramophone for the week-ends that
played 'The Maid of the Mountains.'"

"Oh no! Oh no!" cried Isabel's voice. "That's not fair to
William. Be nice to him, my children! He's only staying until to-
morrow evening."

"Leave him to me," cried Bobby Kane. "I'm awfully good at
looking after people."

The gate swung open and shut. William moved on the terrace;
they had seen him. "Hallo, William!" And Bobby Kane, flapping
his towel, began to leap and pirouette on the parched lawn.
"Pity you didn't come, William. The water was divine. And we
all went to a little pub afterwards and had sloe gin."

The others had reached the house. "I say, Isabel," called
Bobby, "would you like me to wear my Nijinsky dress to-night?"

"No," said Isabel, "nobody's going to dress. We're all starving.

William's starving, too. Come along, *mes amis*, let's begin with sardines."

"I've found the sardines," said Moira, and she ran into the hall, holding a box high in the air.

"A Lady with a Box of Sardines," said Dennis gravely.

"Well, William, and how's London?" asked Bill Hunt, drawing the cork out of a bottle of whisky.

"Oh, London's not much changed," answered William.

"Good old London," said Bobby, very hearty, spearing a sardine.

But a moment later William was forgotten. Moira Morrison began wondering what colour one's legs really were under water.

"Mine are the palest, palest mushroom colour."

Bill and Dennis ate enormously. And Isabel filled glasses, and changed plates, and found matches, smiling blissfully. At one moment she said, "I do wish, Bill, you'd paint it."

"Paint what?" said Bill loudly, stuffing his mouth with bread.

"Us," said Isabel, "round the table. It would be so fascinating in twenty years' time."

Bill screwed up his eyes and chewed. "Light's wrong," he said rudely, "far too much yellow"; and went on eating. And that seemed to charm Isabel, too.

But after supper they were all so tired they could do nothing but yawn until it was late enough to go to bed. . . .

It was not until William was waiting for his taxi the next afternoon that he found himself alone with Isabel. When he brought his suit-case down into the hall, Isabel left the others and went over to him. She stooped down and picked up the suit-case. "What a weight!" she said, and she gave a little awkward laugh. "Let me carry it! To the gate!"

"No, why should you?" said William. "Of course, not. Give it to me."

"Oh, please do let me," said Isabel. "I want to, really." They walked together silently. William felt there was nothing to say now.

"There," said Isabel triumphantly, setting the suit-case down, and she looked anxiously along the sandy road. "I hardly seem to have seen you this time," she said breathlessly. "It's so short, isn't it? I feel you've only just come. Next time —" The taxi came into sight. "I hope they look after you properly in London.

I'm so sorry the babies have been out all day, but Miss Neil had arranged it. They'll hate missing you. Poor William, going back to London." The taxi turned. "Good-bye!" She gave him a little hurried kiss; she was gone.

Fields, trees, hedges streamed by. They shook through the empty, blind-looking little town, ground up the steep pull to the station.

The train was in. William made straight for a first-class smoker, flung back into the corner, but this time he let the papers alone. He folded his arms against the dull, persistent gnawing, and began in his mind to write a letter to Isabel.

. . . .

The post was late as usual. They sat outside the house in long chairs under coloured parasols. Only Bobby Kane lay on the turf at Isabel's feet. It was dull, stifling; the day drooped like a flag.

"Do you think there will be Mondays in Heaven?" asked Bobby childishly.

And Dennis murmured, "Heaven will be one long Monday."

But Isabel couldn't help wondering what had happened to the salmon they had for supper last night. She had meant to have fish mayonnaise for lunch and now . . .

Moira was asleep. Sleeping was her latest discovery. "It's *so* wonderful. One simply shuts one's eyes, that's all. It's *so* delicious."

When the old ruddy postman came beating along the sandy road on his tricycle one felt the handle-bars ought to have been oars.

Bill Hunt put down his book. "Letters," he said complacently, and they all waited. But, heartless postman — O malignant world! There was only one, a fat one for Isabel. Not even a paper.

"And mine's only from William," said Isabel mournfully.

"From William — already?"

"He's sending you back your marriage lines as a gentle reminder."

"Does everybody have marriage lines? I thought they were only for servants."

"Pages and pages! Look at her! A Lady reading a Letter," said Dennis.

My darling, precious Isabel. Pages and pages there were. As Isabel read on her feeling of astonishment changed to a stifled feeling. What on earth had induced William . . . ? How extraordinary it was. . . . What could have made him . . . ? She felt confused, more and more excited, even frightened. It was just like William. Was it? It was absurd, of course, it must be absurd, ridiculous. "Ha, ha, ha! Oh dear!" What was she to do? Isabel flung back in her chair and laughed till she couldn't stop laughing.

"Do, do tell us," said the others. "You must tell us."

"I'm longing to," gurgled Isabel. She sat up, gathered the letter, and waved it at them. "Gather round," she said. "Listen, it's too marvellous. A love-letter!"

"A love-letter! But how divine!" *Darling, precious Isabel.* But she had hardly begun before their laughter interrupted her.

"Go on, Isabel, it's perfect."

"It's the most marvellous find."

"Oh, do go on, Isabel!"

God forbid, my darling, that I should be a drag on your happiness.

"Oh! oh! oh!"

"Sh! sh! sh!"

And Isabel went on. When she reached the end they were hysterical. Bobby rolled on the turf and almost sobbed.

"You must let me have it just as it is, entire, for my new book," said Dennis firmly. "I shall give it a whole chapter."

"Oh, Isabel," moaned Moira, "that wonderful bit about holding you in his arms!"

"I always thought those letters in divorce cases were made up. But they pale before this."

"Let me hold it. Let me read it, mine own self," said Bobby Kane.

But, to their surprise, Isabel crushed the letter in her hand. She was laughing no longer. She glanced quickly at them all; she looked exhausted. "No, not just now. Not just now," she stammered.

And before they could recover she had run into the house, through the hall, up the stairs into her bedroom. Down she sat on the side of the bed. "How vile, odious, abominable, vulgar," muttered Isabel. She pressed her eyes with her knuckles and rocked to and fro. And again she saw them, but not four, more like forty, laughing, sneering, jeering, stretching out their hands while she read them William's letter. Oh, what a loathsome thing to have done. How could she have done it! *God forbid, my darling, that I should be a drag on your happiness.* William! Isabel pressed her face into the pillow. But she felt that even the grave bedroom knew her for what she was, shallow, tinkling, vain. . . .

Presently from the garden below there came voices.

"Isabel, we're all going for a bathe. Do come!"

"Come, thou wife of William!"

"Call her once before you go, call once yet!"

Isabel sat up. Now was the moment, now she must decide. Would she go with them, or stay here and write to William? Which, which should it be? "I must make up my mind." Oh, but how could there be any question? Of course she would stay here and write.

"Titania!" piped Moira.

"Isa-bel?"

No, it was too difficult. "I'll — I'll go with them, and write to William later. Some other time. Later. Not now. But I shall *certainly* write," thought Isabel hurriedly.

And, laughing in the new way, she ran down the stairs.

Katherine (Beauchamp) Mansfield (1888-1923)   Katherine Mansfield was born in Wellington, New Zealand, the third daughter of a family which had lived in Australia and New Zealand for three generations. At the age of thirteen she was sent to England to be educated, and there, after an unhappy return to New Zealand, she settled permanently in 1909. A "writer" since childhood (one of her stories appeared in print when she was nine), she saw her first important stories published in *The New Age;* these pieces, based on her experiences in Germany while recuperating from an illness, were published as a book in 1911, *In a German Pension.* In 1913 she married John Middleton Murry, English critic, editor, and friend of D. H. Lawrence; many of her stories originally appeared in journals he edited. Like Lawrence, Miss Mansfield was plagued by ill health and traveled extensively in search of a beneficent climate. She died suddenly in Fontainebleau at the age of thirty-five. During her brief lifetime she published approximately seventy stories, collected in such volumes as *Bliss* (1920) and *The Garden Party and Other Stories* (1922).

Like Henry James, Katherine Mansfield is an artist striving constantly to attain the unattainable; the truth and nothing but the truth was her goal. Her ironic, sometimes malicious, always perceptive commentaries on life around her are characterized by their admirable form and their delicacy of technique. Although she is often spoken of as a disciple of Chekhov — whose work she greatly admired — her fiction is essentially her own, essentially *Mansfieldian*. As her husband has commented, her similarity to Chekhov is more one of temperament than of technique, and her affinities are more with the English poets than with any specific fiction writer or group of fiction writers. The world of her fiction is a limited one; within its boundaries, however, she worked with precision, subtlety, and intelligence.

The Short Stories of Katherine Mansfield (Knopf) contains the author's major work, as well as several stories which were unfinished at the time of her death; a good selection is in *Stories by Katherine Mansfield* (ed. Elizabeth Bowen, Vintage).

Questions   1. What do we learn about Isabel *before* she actually appears in the story? Are her subsequent actions in keeping with this foreshadowing of her personality? Are you convinced by her brief moments of remorse later in the story?   2. Several shifts occur during the story: shifts from present to past time and events, from William's point of view to that of other characters, from the recording of external events to the depiction of a character's thoughts, reveries, or reminiscences. Are these shifts necessary? Are they effective? Make lists of these and other similar shifts.   3. Contrast plays a particularly important part in this story: contrasts between William and Isabel, between William and Isabel's friends, between the old and the "new" way of life lived by Isabel. Are there any other contrasts in the story?   4. What is the reason for mentioning the "red-faced girl" and the "greasy, black-faced workman" whom William sees from the train at the beginning of the story?   5. Notice one of Miss Mansfield's many devices for characterization: Dennis' routine with "A Lady in Love with a Pineapple" and "A Lady with a Box of Sardines." What does this tell us about Dennis? What other methods of characterization are employed?   6. Are Isabel's friends *real* artists? Are they admirable people? Do they seem like real individuals or more like caricatures of real individuals?

PÄR LAGERKVIST

The Children's Campaign

EVEN THE CHILDREN at that time received military training, were assembled in army units and exercised just as though on active service, had their own headquarters and annual maneuvers when everything was conducted as in a real state of war. The grown-ups had nothing directly to do with this training; the children actually exercised themselves and all command was entrusted to them. The only use made of adult experience was to arrange officers' training courses for specially suitable boys, who were chosen with the greatest care and who were then put in charge of the military education of their comrades in the ranks.

These schools were of high standing and there was hardly a boy throughout the land who did not dream of going to them. But the entrance tests were particularly hard; not only a perfect physique was required but also a highly developed intelligence and character. The age of admission was six to seven years and the small cadets then received an excellent training, both purely military and in all other respects, chiefly the further molding of character. It was also greatly to one's credit in after life to have passed through one of these schools. It was really on the splendid

THE CHILDREN'S CAMPAIGN From *The Eternal Smile and Other Stories*, by Pär Lagerkvist. Copyright 1954 by Random House, Inc. Reprinted by permission.

foundation laid here that the quality, organization and efficiency of the child army rested.

Thereafter, as already mentioned, the grownups in no way interfered but everything was entrusted to the children themselves. No adult might meddle in the command, in organizational details or matters of promotion. Everything was managed and supervised by the children; all decisions, even the most vital, being reached by their own little general staff. No one over fourteen was allowed. The boys then passed automatically into the first age group of the regular troops with no mean military training already behind them.

The large child army, which was the object of the whole nation's love and admiration, amounted to three army corps of four divisions: infantry, light field artillery, medical and service corps. All physically fit boys were enrolled in it and a large number of girls belonged to it as nurses, all volunteers.

Now it so happened that a smaller, quite insignificant nation behaved in a high-handed and unseemly way toward its powerful neighbor, and the insult was all the greater since this nation was by no means an equal. Indignation was great and general and, since people's feelings were running high, it was necessary to rebuke the malapert and at the same time take the chance to subjugate the country in question. In this situation the child army came forward and through its high command asked to be charged with the crushing and subduing of the foe. The news of this caused a sensation and a wave of fervor throughout the country. The proposal was given serious consideration in supreme quarters and as a result the commission was given, with some hesitation, to the children. It was in fact a task well suited to this army, and the people's obvious wishes in the matter had also to be met, if possible.

The Foreign Office therefore sent the defiant country an unacceptable ultimatum and, pending the reply, the child army was mobilized within twenty-four hours. The reply was found to be unsatisfactory and war was declared immediately.

Unparalleled enthusiasm marked the departure for the front. The intrepid little youngsters had green sprigs in the barrels of their rifles and were pelted with flowers. As is so often the case, the campaign was begun in the spring, and this time the general opinion was that there was something symbolic in it. In the capi-

tal the little commander in chief and chief of general staff, in the
presence of huge crowds, made a passionate speech to the troops
in which he expressed the gravity of the hour and his conviction
of their unswerving valor and willingness to offer their lives for
their country.

The speech, made in a strong voice, aroused the greatest ecstasy. The boy — who had a brilliant career behind him and
had reached his exalted position at the age of only twelve and a
half — was acclaimed with wild rejoicing and from this moment
was the avowed hero of the entire nation. There was not a dry
eye and those of the many mothers especially shone with pride
and happiness. For them it was the greatest day in their lives.
The troops marched past below fluttering banners, each regiment
with its music corps at the head. It was an unforgettable spectacle.

There were also many touching incidents, evincing a proud
patriotism, as when a little four-year-old, who had been lifted up
on his mother's arm so that he could see, howled with despair
and shouted, "I want to go, too. I want to go, too!" while his
mother tried to hush him, explaining that he was too small.
"Small am I, eh?" he exclaimed, punching her face so that her
nose bled. The evening papers were full of such episodes showing the mood of the people and of the troops who were so sure
of victory. The big march past was broadcast and the c in c's
speech, which had been recorded, was broadcast every evening
during the days that followed, at 7:15 P.M.

Military operations had already begun, however, and reports
of victory began to come in at once from the front. The children
had quickly taken the offensive and on one sector of the front
had inflicted a heavy defeat on the enemy, seven hundred dead
and wounded and over twelve hundred prisoners, while their own
losses amounted to only a hundred or so fallen. The victory was
celebrated at home with indescribable rejoicing and with thanks-
giving services in the churches. The newspapers were filled with
accounts of individual instances of valor and pictures several
columns wide of the high command, of which the leading personalities, later so well-known, began to appear now for the first
time. In their joy, mothers and aunts sent so much chocolate and
other sweets to the army that headquarters had to issue a strict
order that all such parcels were, for the time being at any rate,

forbidden, since they had made whole regiments unfit for battle and these in their turn had nearly been surrounded by the enemy.

For the child army was already far inside enemy territory and still managed to keep the initiative. The advance sector did retreat slightly in order to establish contact with its wings but only improved its positions by so doing. A stalemate ensued in the theater of war for some time after this.

During July, however, troops were concentrated for a big attack along the whole line and huge reserves — the child army's, in comparison with those of its opponent, were almost inexhaustible — were mustered to the front. The new offensive, which lasted for several weeks, resulted, too, in an almost decisive victory for the whole army, even though casualties were high. The children defeated the enemy all along the line but did not manage to pursue him and thereby exploit their success to the full, because he was greatly favored by the fact that his legs were so much longer, an advantage of which he made good use. By dint of forced marches, however, the children finally succeeded in cutting the enemy's right flank to pieces. They were now in the very heart of the country and their outposts were only a few days' march from the capital.

It was a pitched battle on a big scale and the newspapers had enormous headlines every day which depicted the dramatic course of events. At set hours the radio broadcast the gunfire and a résumé of the position. The war correspondents described in rapturous words and vivid colors the state of affairs at the front — the children's incredible feats, their indomitable courage and self-sacrifice, the whole morale of the army. It was no exaggeration. The youngsters showed the greatest bravery; they really behaved like heroes. One only had to see their discipline and contempt of death during an attack, as though they had been grown-up men at least.

It was an unforgettable sight to see them storm ahead under murderous machine gun fire and the small medical orderlies dart nimbly forward and pick them up as they fell. Or the wounded and dying who were moved behind the front, those who had had a leg shot away or their bellies ripped open by a bayonet so that their entrails hung out — but without one sound of complaint crossing their small lips. The hand-to-hand fighting had been very fierce and a great number of children fell in this, while they were superior in the actual firing. Losses were estimated at 4,000 on the enemy side and 7,000 among the children, according to the secret reports. The victory had been hard won but all the more complete.

This battle became very famous and was also of far greater importance than any previously. It was now clear beyond all doubt that the children were incomparably superior in tactics, discipline and individual courage. At the same time, however, it was admitted by experts that the enemy's headlong retreat was very skillfully carried out, that his strength was evidently in defense and that he should not be underrated too much. Toward the end, also, he had unexpectedly made a stubborn resistance which had prevented any further penetration.

This observation was not without truth. In actual fact the enemy was anything but a warlike nation, and indeed his forces found it very difficult to hold their own. Nevertheless, they improved with practice during the fighting and became more efficient as time went on. This meant that they caused the children a good deal of trouble in each succeeding battle. They also had certain advantages on their side. As their opponents were so small, for instance, it was possible after a little practice to spit several of them on the bayonet at once, and often a kick was enough to fell them to the ground.

But against this, the children were so much more numerous and also braver. They were everywhere. They swarmed over one and in between one's legs and the unwarlike people were nearly demented by all these small monsters who fought like fiends. Little fiends was also what they were generally called — not without reason — and this name was even adopted in the children's homeland, but there it was a mark of honor and a pet name. The enemy troops had all their work cut out merely defending themselves. At last, however, they were able to check the others' advance and even venture on one or two counterattacks. Everything then came to a standstill for a while and there was a breathing space.

The children were now in possession of a large part of the country. But this was not always so easy. The population did not particularly like them and proved not to be very fond of children. It was alleged that snipers fired on the boys from houses and that they were ambushed when they moved in small detachments. Children had even been found impaled on stakes or with their eyes gouged out, so it was said. And in many cases these stories were no doubt true. The population had quite lost their heads, were obviously goaded into a frenzy, and as they were of little use as a warlike nation and their cruelty could therefore find no natural outlet, they tried to avenge themselves by atrocities. They felt overrun by all the foreign children as by troublesome vermin and, being at their wits' end, they simply killed whenever they had the chance. In order to put an end to these outrages the children burned one village after the other and shot hundreds of people daily, but this did not improve matters. The despicable deeds of these craven guerrillas caused them endless trouble.

At home, the accounts of all this naturally aroused the most bitter resentment. People's blood boiled to think that their small soldiers were treated in this way by those who had nothing to do with the war, by barbarous civilians who had no notion of established and judicial forms. Even greater indignation was caused, however, by an incident that occurred inside the occupied area some time after the big summer battle just mentioned.

A lieutenant who was out walking in the countryside came to a stream where a large, fat woman knelt washing clothes. He asked her the way to a village close by. The woman, who probably suspected him of evil intent, retorted, "What are you doing here? You ought to be at home with your mother." Whereupon the lieutenant drew his saber to kill her, but the woman grabbed hold of him and, putting him over her knee, thwacked him black and blue with her washboard so that he was unable to sit down for several days afterward. He was so taken aback that he did nothing, armed though he was to the teeth. Luckily no one saw the incident, but there were orders that all outrages on the part of the population were to be reported to headquarters. The lieutenant therefore duly reported what had happened to him. True, it gave him little satisfaction, but as he had to obey orders he had no choice. And so it all came out.

The incident aroused a storm of rage, particularly among those at home. The infamous deed was a humiliation for the country, an insult which nothing could wipe out. It implied a deliberate violation by this militarily ignorant people of the simplest rules of warfare. Everywhere, in the press, in propaganda speeches, in ordinary conversation, the deepest contempt and disgust for the deed was expressed. The lieutenant who had so flagrantly shamed the army had his officer's epaulettes ripped off in front of the assembled troops and was declared unworthy to serve any longer in the field. He was instantly sent home to his parents, who belonged to one of the most noted families but who now had to retire into obscurity in a remote part of the country.

The woman, on the other hand, became a heroic figure among her people and the object of their rapturous admiration. During the whole of the war she and her deed were a rallying national symbol which people looked up to and which spurred them on to further effort. She subsequently became a favorite motif in the profuse literature about their desperate struggle for freedom; a vastly popular figure, brought to life again and again as time passed, now in a rugged, everyday way which appealed to the man in the street, now in heroic female form on a grandiose scale, to become gradually more and more legendary, wreathed in saga and myth. In some versions she was shot by the enemy; in others she lived to a ripe old age, loved and revered by her people.

This incident, more than anything else, helped to increase the bad feelings between the two countries and to make them wage the war with ever greater ruthlessness. In the late summer, before the autumn rains began, both armies, ignorant of each other's plans, simultaneously launched a violent offensive, which devastated both sides. On large sectors of the front the troops completely annihilated each other so that there was not a single survivor left. Any peaceful inhabitants thereabouts who were still alive and ventured out of their cellars thought that the war was over, because all were slain.

But soon new detachments came up and began fighting again. Great confusion arose in other quarters from the fact that in the heat of attack men ran past each other and had to turn around in order to go on fighting; and that some parts of the line rushed ahead while others came behind, so that the troops were both in front of and behind where they should have been and time and again attacked each other in the rear. The battle raged in this way with extreme violence and shots were fired from all directions at once.

When at last the fighting ceased and stock was taken of the

situation, it appeared that no one had won. On both sides there
was an equal number of fallen, 12,924, and after all attacks and
retreats the position of the armies was exactly the same as at the
start of the battle. It was agreed that both should claim the victory. Thereafter the rain set in and the armies went to earth in
trenches and put up barbed wire entanglements.

The children were the first to finish their trenches, since they
had had more to do with that kind of thing, and settled down in
them as best they could. They soon felt at home. Filthy and
lousy, they lived there in the darkness as though they had never
done anything else. With the adaptability of children they
quickly got into the way of it. The enemy found this more
difficult; he felt miserable and homesick for the life above ground
to which he was accustomed. Not so the children. When one
saw them in their small gray uniforms, which were caked thick
with mud, and their small gas masks, one could easily think they
had been born to this existence. They crept in and out of the
holes down into the earth and scampered about the passages like
mice. When their burrows were attacked they were instantly up
on the parapet and snapped back in blind fury. As the months
passed, this hopeless, harrowing life put endurance to an increasingly severe test. But they never lost courage or the will to fight.

For the enemy the strain was often too much; the glaring pointlessness of it all made many completely apathetic. But the little
ones did not react like this. Children are really more fitted for
war and take more pleasure in it, while grownups tire of it after
a while and think it is boring. The boys continued to find the
whole thing exciting and they wanted to go on living as they were
now. They also had a more natural herd instinct; their unity and
camaraderie helped them a great deal, made it easier to hold out.

But, of course, even they suffered great hardship. Especially
when winter set in with its incessant rain, a cold sleet which made
everything sodden and filled the trenches with mud. It was
enough to unman anyone. But it would never have entered their
heads to complain. However bad things were, nothing could have
made them admit it. At home everyone was very proud of them.
All the cinemas showed parades behind the front and the little
c in c and his generals pinning medals for bravery on their soldiers' breasts. People thought of them a great deal out there, of
their little fiends, realizing that they must be having a hard time.

At Christmas, in particular, thoughts went out to them, to the lighted Christmas trees and all the sparkling childish eyes out in the trenches; in every home people sat wondering how they were faring. But the children did not think of home. They were soldiers out and out, absorbed by their duty and their new life. They attacked in several places on the morning of Christmas Eve, inflicting fairly big losses on the enemy in killed and wounded, and did not stop until it was time to open their parcels. They had the real fighting spirit which might have been a lesson even to adults.

There was nothing sentimental about them. The war had hardened and developed them, made them men. It did happen that one poor little chap burst into tears when the Christmas tree was lighted, but he was made the laughing-stock of them all. "Are you homesick for your mummy, you bastard?" they said, and kept on jeering at him all evening. He was the object of their scorn all through Christmas; he behaved suspiciously and tried to keep to himself. Once he walked a hundred yards away from the post and, because he might well have been thinking of flight, he was seized and court-martialed. He could give no reason for having absented himself and since he had obviously intended to desert he was shot.

If those at home had been fully aware of the morale out there, they need not have worried. As it was, they wondered if the children could really hold their ground and half-regretted having entrusted them with the campaign, now that it was dragging on so long because of this nerve-racking stationary warfare. After the New Year help was even offered in secret, but it was rejected with proud indignation.

The morale of the enemy, on the other hand, was not so high. They did intend to fight to the last man, but the certainty of a complete victory was not so general as it should have been. They could not help thinking, either, how hopeless their fight really was; that in the long run they could not hold their own against these people who were armed to the very milk teeth, and this often dampened their courage.

Hardly had nature begun to come to life and seethe with the newly awakened forces of spring before the children started with incredible intensity to prepare for the decisive battle. Heavy mechanized artillery was brought up and placed in strong positions; huge troop movements went on night and day; all available fighting forces were concentrated in the very front lines. After murderous gunfire which lasted for six days, an attack was launched with great force and extreme skill. Individual bravery was, if possible, more dazzling than ever. The whole army was also a year older, and that means much at that age. But their opponents, too, were determined to do their utmost. They had assembled all their reserves, and their spirits, now that the rain had stopped and the weather was fine, were full of hope.

It was a terrible battle. The hospital trains immediately started going back from both sides packed with wounded and dying. Machine guns, tanks and gas played fearful havoc. For several days the outcome was impossible to foresee, since both armies appeared equally strong and the tide of battle constantly changed. The position gradually cleared, however. The enemy had expected the main attack in the center, but the child army turned out to be weakest there. Use was made of this, especially because they themselves were best prepared at this very point, and this part of the children's front was soon made to waver and was forced farther and farther back by repeated attack. Advantage was also taken of an ideal evening breeze from just the right quarter to gas the children in thousands. Encouraged by their victory, the troops pursued the offensive with all their might and with equal success.

The child army's retreat, however, turned out to be a stratagem, brilliantly conceived and carried out. Its center gave way more and more and the enemy, giving all his attention to this, forgot that at the same time he himself was wavering on both wings. In this way he ran his head into a noose. When the children considered that they had retreated far enough they halted, while the troops on the outermost wings, already far ahead, advanced swiftly until they met behind the enemy's back. The latter's entire army was thereby surrounded and in the grip of an iron hand. All the children's army had to do now was to draw the noose tighter. At last the gallant defenders had to surrender and let themselves be taken prisoner, which in fact they already were. It was the most disastrous defeat in history; not a single one escaped other than by death.

This victory became much more famous than any of the others and was eagerly studied at all military academies on account of its brilliantly executed, doubly effective encircling movement.

The great general Sludelsnorp borrowed its tactics outright seventy years later at his victory over the Slivokvarks in the year 2048.

The war could not go on any longer now, because there was nothing left to fight, and the children marched to the capital with the imprisoned army between them to dictate the peace terms. These were handed over by the little commander in chief in the hall of mirrors in the stately old palace at a historic scene which was to be immortalized time and again in art and even now was reproduced everywhere in the weekly press. The film cameras whirred, the flashlights hissed and the radio broadcast the great moment to the world. The commander in chief, with austere and haughty mien and one foot slightly in front of the other, delivered the historic document with his right hand. The first and most important condition was the complete cession of the country, besides which the expenses of its capture were to be borne by the enemy, who thus had to pay the cost of the war on both sides, the last clause on account of the fact that he had been the challenging party and, according to his own admission, the cause of the war. The document was signed in dead silence, the only sound was the scratching of the fountain pen, which, according to the commentator's whisper, was solid gold and undoubtedly a future museum piece.

With this, everything was settled and the children's army returned to its own country, where it was received with indescribable rapture. Everywhere along the roads the troops were greeted with wild rejoicing; their homecoming was one long victory parade. The march into the capital and the dismissal there of the troops, which took place before vast crowds, were especially impressive. People waved and shouted in the streets as they passed, were beside themselves with enthusiasm, bands played, eyes were filled with tears of joy. Some of the loudest cheering was for the small invalids at the rear of the procession, blind and with limbs amputated, who had sacrificed themselves for their country. Many of them had already got small artificial arms and legs so that they looked just the same as before. The victory salute thundered, bayonets flashed in the sun. It was an unforgettable spectacle.

A strange, new leaf was written in the great book of history which would be read with admiration in time to come. The nation had seen many illustrious deeds performed, but never anything as proud as this. What these children had done in their devotion and fervent patriotism could never be forgotten.

Nor was it. Each spring, on the day of victory, school children marched out with flags in their hands to the cemeteries with all the small graves where the heroes rested under their small white crosses. The mounds were strewn with flowers and passionate speeches were made, reminding everyone of the glorious past, their imperishable honor and youthful, heroic spirit of self-sacrifice. The flags floated in the sun and the voices rang out clear as they sang their rousing songs, radiant childish eyes looking ahead to new deeds of glory.

Pär Lagerkvist (1891-)   Born in a provincial town in Sweden, Pär Lagerkvist was educated at the Swedish University of Upsala. Except for long visits to Denmark, France, and Italy, Lagerkvist has spent most of his life in his native country. In 1940 he was elected one of the "Immortals" of the Swedish Academy, and was later awarded an honorary doctorate from the University of Gothenberg. The author of some thirty-five books and plays, he had been recognized in Europe as a poet, dramatist, essayist, and fiction writer for years before he was awarded, in 1952, the Nobel Prize for literature. At that time, however, only two of his works of fiction (the novels *Barrabas* and *The Dwarf*) were in print in America, although a volume of his short fiction appeared two years later: *The Eternal Smile and Other Stories* (Random House).

Lagerkvist's short fiction is remarkable for its variety and its high quality. It ranges from brief fables, parables, or allegories to longer stories or novellas like "The Eternal Smile," which is a surging, almost symphonic fictional commentary on mankind's attempts to discover God. It includes realistic or autobiographical stories and angry Swiftian satires like "The Children's Campaign." In spite of his preoccupation with violent, dark, or sinister materials, Lagerkvist's fiction is affirmative rather than negative, for it suggests man's need for spiritual values in a disturbing moral universe.

In "The Children's Campaign" Lagerkvist works up his effects realistically, in a method reminiscent of Defoe or Swift ("On both sides there was an equal number of fallen, 12,924, and after all attacks and retreats the position of the armies was exactly the same as at the start of the battle"). The contrast between this matter-of-fact, prosy style and the emotion-charged subject matter is the source of much of the power of the story. Only occasionally does Lagerkvist comment on the action ("the glaring pointlessness of it all"); the contrast between the "barbarous civilians who had no notion of established and judicial forms" and the children engaged in their meaningless slaughter carries its own message. The final irony is reserved until the very last sentence which describes the children, singing, with "radiant childish eyes looking ahead to new deeds of glory."

Questions   1. Why does the author continually emphasize the fact that the enemy is not a "warlike nation" and refer several times to the "despicable deeds of these craven guerrillas"?   2. What is the irony implicit in the statement that "children are really more fitted for war" than adults?   3. What is accomplished by such details as the enemy woman's spanking the child lieutenant, the Christmas Eve incident and the subsequent court-martial, the green sprigs in the barrels of the children's rifles?   4. Is any attempt made to individualize the characters in this story? Why or why not?   5. Compare or contrast this story with other satires you may have read, such as Jonathan Swift's "A Modest Proposal" or *Gulliver's Travels*.

WILLIAM FAULKNER

That
Evening Sun

I

MONDAY is no different from any other weekday in Jefferson now. The streets are paved now, and the telephone and electric companies are cutting down more and more of the shade trees — the water oaks, the maples and locusts and elms — to make room for iron poles bearing clusters of bloated and ghostly and bloodless grapes; and we have a city laundry which makes the rounds on Monday morning, gathering the bundles of clothes into bright-colored, specially-made motorcars: the soiled wearing of a whole week now flees apparitionlike behind alert and irritable electric horns, with a long diminishing noise of rubber and asphalt like tearing silk, and even the Negro women who still take in white people's washing after the old custom, fetch and deliver it in automobiles.

But fifteen years ago, on Monday morning the quiet, dusty, shady streets would be full of Negro women with, balanced on their steady, turbaned heads, bundles of clothes tied up in sheets, almost as large as cotton bales, carried so without touch of hand between the kitchen door of the white house and the blackened washpot beside a cabin door in Negro Hollow.

Nancy would set her bundle on the top of her head, then upon the bundle in turn she would set the black straw sailor hat which she wore winter and summer. She was tall, with a high, sad face sunken a little where her teeth were missing. Sometimes we would go a part of the way down the lane and across the pasture with her, to watch the balanced bundle and the hat that never bobbed nor wavered, even when she walked down into the ditch and up the other side and stooped through the fence. She would go down on her hands and knees and crawl through the gap, her head rigid, uptilted, the bundle steady as a rock or a balloon, and rise to her feet again and go on.

Sometimes the husbands of the washing women would fetch and deliver the clothes, but Jesus never did that for Nancy, even before Father told him to stay away from our house, even when Dilsey was sick and Nancy would come to cook for us.

And then about half the time we'd have to go down the lane to Nancy's cabin and tell her to come on and cook breakfast. We would stop at the ditch, because Father told us not to have anything to do with Jesus — he was a short black man, with a razor scar down his face — and we would throw rocks at Nancy's house until she came to the door, leaning her head around it without any clothes on.

"What yawl mean, chunking my house?" Nancy said. "What you little devils mean?"

"Father says for you to come on and get breakfast," Caddy said. "Father says it's over a half an hour now, and you've got to come this minute."

"I ain't studying no breakfast," Nancy said. "I going to get my sleep out."

"I bet you're drunk," Jason said. "Father says you're drunk. Are you drunk, Nancy?"

"Who says I is?" Nancy said. "I got to get my sleep out. I ain't studying no breakfast."

So after a while we quit chunking the cabin and went back home. When she finally came, it was too late for me to go to school. So we thought it was whiskey until that day they arrested her again and they were taking her to jail and they passed Mr. Stovall. He was the cashier in the bank and a deacon in the Baptist church, and Nancy began to say:

"When you going to pay me, white man? When you going to

pay me, white man? It's been three times now since you paid
me a cent — " Mr. Stovall knocked her down, but she kept on
saying, "When you going to pay me, white man? It's been three
times now since — " until Mr. Stovall kicked her in the mouth
with his heel and the marshal caught Mr. Stovall back, and
Nancy lying in the street, laughing. She turned her head and
spat out some blood and teeth and said, "It's been three times
now since he paid me a cent."

That was how she lost her teeth, and all that day they told
about Nancy and Mr. Stovall, and all that night the ones that
passed the jail could hear Nancy singing and yelling. They could
see her hands holding to the window bars, and a lot of them
stopped along the fence, listening to her and to the jailer trying to
make her stop. She didn't shut up until almost daylight, when
the jailer began to hear a bumping and scraping upstairs and he
went up there and found Nancy hanging from the window bar.
He said that it was cocaine and not whiskey, because no nigger
would try to commit suicide unless he was full of cocaine, because a nigger full of cocaine wasn't a nigger any longer.

The jailer cut her down and revived her; then he beat her,
whipped her. She had hung herself with her dress. She had fixed
it all right, but when they arrested her she didn't have on anything except a dress and so she didn't have anything to tie her
hands with and she couldn't make her hands let go of the window
ledge. So the jailer heard the noise and ran up there and found
Nancy hanging from the window, stark naked, her belly already
swelling out a little, like a little balloon.

When Dilsey was sick in her cabin and Nancy was cooking for
us, we could see her apron swelling out; that was before Father
told Jesus to stay away from the house. Jesus was in the kitchen,
sitting behind the stove, with his razor scar on his black face like
a piece of dirty string. He said it was a watermelon that Nancy
had under her dress.

"It never come off of your vine, though," Nancy said.

"Off of what vine?" Caddy said.

"I can cut down the vine it did come off of," Jesus said.

"What makes you want to talk like that before these chillen?"
Nancy said. "Whyn't you go on to work? You done et. You want
Mr. Jason to catch you hanging around his kitchen, talking that
way before these chillen?"

"Talking what way?" Caddy said. "What vine?"

"I can't hang around white man's kitchen," Jesus said. "But white man can hang around mine. White man can come in my house, but I can't stop him. When white man want to come in my house, I ain't got no house. I can't stop him, but he can't kick me outen it. He can't do that."

Dilsey was still sick in her cabin. Father told Jesus to stay off our place. Dilsey was still sick. It was a long time. We were in the library after supper.

"Isn't Nancy through in the kitchen yet?" Mother said. "It seems to me that she has had plenty of time to have finished the dishes."

"Let Quentin go and see," Father said. "Go and see if Nancy is through, Quentin. Tell her she can go on home."

I went to the kitchen. Nancy was through. The dishes were put away and the fire was out. Nancy was sitting in a chair, close to the cold stove. She looked at me.

"Mother wants to know if you are through," I said.

"Yes," Nancy said. She looked at me. "I done finished." She looked at me.

"What is it?" I said. "What is it?"

"I ain't nothing but a nigger," Nancy said. "It ain't none of my fault."

She looked at me, sitting in the chair before the cold stove, the sailor hat on her head. I went back to the library. It was the cold stove and all, when you think of a kitchen being warm and busy and cheerful. And with a cold stove and the dishes all put away, and nobody wanting to eat at that hour.

"Is she through?" Mother said.

"Yessum," I said.

"What is she doing?" Mother said.

"She's not doing anything. She's through."

"I'll go and see," Father said.

"Maybe she's waiting for Jesus to come and take her home," Caddy said.

"Jesus is gone," I said. Nancy told us how one morning she woke up and Jesus was gone.

"He quit me," Nancy said. "Done gone to Memphis, I reckon. Dodging them city *po*-lice for a while, I reckon."

"And a good riddance," Father said. "I hope he stays there."

"Nancy's scaired of the dark," Jason said.

"So are you," Caddy said.

"I'm not," Jason said.

"Scairy cat," Caddy said.

"I'm not," Jason said.

"You, Candace!" Mother said. Father came back.

"I am going to walk down the lane with Nancy," he said. "She says that Jesus is back."

"Has she seen him?" Mother said.

"No. Some Negro sent her word that he was back in town. I won't be long."

"You'll leave me alone, to take Nancy home?" Mother said. "Is her safety more precious to you than mine?"

"I won't be long," Father said.

"You'll leave these children unprotected, with that Negro about?"

"I'm going too," Caddy said. "Let me go, Father."

"What would he do with them, if he were unfortunate enough to have them?" Father said.

"I want to go, too," Jason said.

"Jason!" Mother said. She was speaking to Father. You could tell that by the way she said the name. Like she believed that all day Father had been trying to think of doing the thing she wouldn't like the most, and that she knew all the time that after a while he would think of it. I stayed quiet, because Father and I both knew that Mother would want him to make me stay with her if she just thought of it in time. So Father didn't look at me. I was the oldest. I was nine and Caddy was seven and Jason was five.

"Nonsense," Father said. "We won't be long."

Nancy had her hat on. We came to the lane. "Jesus always been good to me," Nancy said. "Whenever he had two dollars, one of them was mine." We walked in the lane. "If I can just get through the lane," Nancy said, "I be all right then."

The lane was always dark. "This is where Jason got scaired on Hallowe'en," Caddy said.

"I didn't," Jason said.

"Can't Aunt Rachel do anything with him?" Father said. Aunt Rachel was old. She lived in a cabin beyond Nancy's, by herself. She had white hair and she smoked a pipe in the door, all day

long; she didn't work any more. They said she was Jesus' mother.
Sometimes she said she was and sometimes she said she wasn't
any kin to Jesus.

"Yes you did," Caddy said. "You were scairder than Frony.
You were scairder than T.P. even. Scairder than niggers."

"Can't nobody do nothing with him," Nancy said. "He say I
done woke up the devil in him and ain't but one thing going to
lay it down again."

"Well, he's gone now," Father said. "There's nothing for you
to be afraid of now. And if you'd just let white men alone."

"Let what white men alone?" Caddy said. "How let them
alone?"

"He ain't gone nowhere," Nancy said. "I can feel him. I can
feel him now, in this lane. He hearing us talk, every word, hid
somewhere, waiting. I ain't seen him, and I ain't going to see him
again but once more, with that razor in his mouth. That razor
on that string down his back, inside his shirt. And then I ain't
going to be even surprised."

"I wasn't scaired," Jason said.

"If you'd behave yourself, you'd have kept out of this," Father
said. "But it's all right now. He's probably in Saint Louis now.
Probably got another wife by now and forgot all about you."

"If he has, I better not find out about it," Nancy said. "I'd
stand there right over them, and every time he wropped her, I'd
cut that arm off. I'd cut his head off and I'd slit her belly and
I'd shove — "

"Hush," Father said.

"Slit whose belly, Nancy?" Caddy said.

"I wasn't scaired," Jason said. "I'd walk right down this lane
by myself."

"Yah," Caddy said. "You wouldn't dare to put your foot down
in it if we were not here too."

II

Dilsey was still sick, so we took Nancy home every night until
Mother said, "How much longer is this going on? I to be left
alone in this big house while you take home a frightened Negro?"

We fixed a pallet in the kitchen for Nancy. One night we
waked up, hearing the sound. It was not singing and it was not
crying, coming up the dark stairs. There was a light in Mother's

room and we heard Father going down the hall, down the back stairs, and Caddy and I went into the hall. The floor was cold. Our toes curled away from it while we listened to the sound. It was like singing and it wasn't like singing, like the sound that Negroes make.

Then it stopped and we heard Father going down the back stairs, and went to the head of the stairs. Then the sound began again, in the stairway, not loud, and we could see Nancy's eyes halfway up the stairs, against the wall. They looked like cat's eyes do, like a big cat against the wall, watching us. When we came down the steps to where she was, she quit making the sound again, and we stood there until Father came back up from the kitchen, with his pistol in his hand. He went back down with Nancy and they came back with Nancy's pallet.

We spread the pallet in our room. After the light in Mother's room went off, we could see Nancy's eyes again. "Nancy," Caddy whispered, "are you asleep, Nancy?"

Nancy whispered something. It was oh or no, I don't know which. Like nobody had made it, like it came from nowhere and went nowhere, until it was like Nancy was not there at all; that I had looked so hard at her eyes on the stairs that they had got printed on my eyeballs, like the sun does when you have closed your eyes and there is no sun. "Jesus," Nancy whispered. "Jesus."

"Was it Jesus?" Caddy said. "Did he try to come into the kitchen?"

"Jesus," Nancy said. Like this: Jeeeeeeeeeeeeeeeesus, until the sound went out, like a match or a candle does.

"It's the other Jesus she means," I said.

"Can you see us, Nancy?" Caddy whispered. "Can you see our eyes too?"

"I ain't nothing but a nigger," Nancy said. "God knows. God knows."

"What did you see down there in the kitchen?" Caddy whispered. "What tried to get in?"

"God knows," Nancy said. We could see her eyes. "God knows."

Dilsey got well. She cooked dinner. "You'd better stay in bed a day or two longer," Father said.

"What for?" Dilsey said. "If I had been a day later, this place would be to rack and ruin. Get on out of here now, and let me get my kitchen straight again."

Dilsey cooked supper too. And that night, just before dark, Nancy came into the kitchen.

"How do you know he's back?" Dilsey said. "You ain't seen him."

"Jesus is a nigger," Jason said.

"I can feel him," Nancy said. "I can feel him laying yonder in the ditch."

"Tonight?" Dilsey said. "Is he there tonight?"

"Dilsey's a nigger too," Jason said.

"You try to eat something," Dilsey said.

"I don't want nothing," Nancy said.

"I ain't a nigger," Jason said.

"Drink some coffee," Dilsey said. She poured a cup of coffee for Nancy. "Do you know he's out there tonight? How come you know it's tonight?"

"I know," Nancy said. "He's there, waiting. I know. I done lived with him too long. I know what he is fixing to do fore he know it himself."

"Drink some coffee," Dilsey said. Nancy held the cup to her mouth and blew into the cup. Her mouth pursed out like a spreading adder's, like a rubber mouth, like she had blown all the color out of her lips with blowing the coffee.

"I ain't a nigger," Jason said. "Are you a nigger, Nancy?"

"I hellborn, child," Nancy said. "I won't be nothing soon. I going back where I come from soon."

III

She began to drink the coffee. While she was drinking, holding the cup in both hands, she began to make the sound again. She made the sound into the cup and the coffee sploshed out onto her hands and her dress. Her eyes looked at us and she sat there, her elbows on her knees, holding the cup in both hands, looking at us across the wet cup, making the sound.

"Look at Nancy," Jason said. "Nancy can't cook for us now. Dilsey's got well now."

"You hush up," Dilsey said. Nancy held the cup in both hands, looking at us, making the sound, like there were two of them: one looking at us and the other making the sound. "Whyn't you let

Mr. Jason telefoam the marshal?" Dilsey said. Nancy stopped then, holding the cup in her long brown hands. She tried to drink some coffee again, but it sploshed out of the cup, onto her hands and her dress, and she put the cup down. Jason watched her.

"I can't swallow it," Nancy said. "I swallows but it won't go down me."

"You go down to the cabin," Dilsey said. "Frony will fix you a pallet and I'll be there soon."

"Won't no nigger stop him," Nancy said.

"I ain't a nigger," Jason said. "Am I, Dilsey?"

"I reckon not," Dilsey said. She looked at Nancy. "I don't reckon so. What you going to do, then?"

Nancy looked at us. Her eyes went fast, like she was afraid there wasn't time to look, without hardly moving at all. She looked at us, at all three of us at one time. "You member that night I stayed in yawls' room?" she said. She told about how we waked up early the next morning, and played. We had to play quiet, on her pallet, until Father woke up and it was time to get breakfast. "Go and ask your maw to let me stay here tonight," Nancy said. "I won't need no pallet. We can play some more."

Caddy asked Mother. Jason went too. "I can't have Negroes sleeping in the bedrooms," Mother said. Jason cried. He cried until Mother said he couldn't have any dessert for three days if he didn't stop. Then Jason said he would stop if Dilsey would make a chocolate cake. Father was there.

"Why don't you do something about it?" Mother said. "What do we have officers for?"

"Why is Nancy afraid of Jesus?" Caddy said. "Are you afraid of Father, Mother?"

"What could the officers do?" Father said. "If Nancy hasn't seen him, how could the officers find him?"

"Then why is she afraid?" Mother said.

"She says he is there. She says she knows he is there tonight."

"Yet we pay taxes," Mother said. "I must wait here alone in this big house while you take a Negro woman home."

"You know that I am not lying outside with a razor," Father said.

"I'll stop if Dilsey will make a chocolate cake," Jason said. Mother told us to go out and Father said he didn't know if Jason would get a chocolate cake or not, but he knew what Jason was going to get in about a minute. We went back to the kitchen and told Nancy.

"Father said for you to go home and lock the door, and you'll be all right," Caddy said. "All right from what, Nancy? Is Jesus mad at you?" Nancy was holding the coffee cup in her hands again, her elbows on her knees and her hands holding the cup between her knees. She was looking into the cup. "What have you done that made Jesus mad?" Caddy said. Nancy let the cup go. It didn't break on the floor, but the coffee spilled out, and Nancy sat there with her hands still making the shape of the cup. She began to make the sound again, not loud. Not singing and not unsinging. We watched her.

"Here," Dilsey said. "You quit that, now. You get aholt of yourself. You wait here. I going to get Versh to walk home with you." Dilsey went out.

We looked at Nancy. Her shoulders kept shaking, but she quit making the sound. We watched her.

"What's Jesus going to do to you?" Caddy said. "He went away."

Nancy looked at us. "We had fun that night I stayed in yawls' room, didn't we?"

"I didn't," Jason said. "I didn't have any fun."

"You were asleep in Mother's room," Caddy said. "You were not there."

"Let's go down to my house and have some more fun," Nancy said.

"Mother won't let us," I said. "It's too late now."

"Don't bother her," Nancy said. "We can tell her in the morning. She won't mind."

"She wouldn't let us," I said.

"Don't ask her now," Nancy said. "Don't bother her now."

"She didn't say we couldn't go," Caddy said.

"We didn't ask," I said.

"If you go, I'll tell," Jason said.

"We'll have fun," Nancy said. "They won't mind, just to my house. I been working for yawl a long time. They won't mind."

"I'm not afraid to go," Caddy said. "Jason is the one that's afraid. He'll tell."

"I'm not," Jason said.

"Yes, you are," Caddy said. "You'll tell."

"I won't tell," Jason said. "I'm not afraid."

"Jason ain't afraid to go with me," Nancy said. "Is you, Jason?"

"Jason is going to tell," Caddy said. The lane was dark. We passed the pasture gate. "I bet if something was to jump out from behind that gate, Jason would holler."

"I wouldn't," Jason said. We walked down the lane. Nancy was talking loud.

"What are you talking so loud for, Nancy?" Caddy said.

"Who, me?" Nancy said. "Listen at Quentin and Caddy and Jason saying I'm talking loud."

"You talk like there was five of us here," Caddy said. "You talk like Father was here too."

"Who; me talking loud, Mr. Jason?" Nancy said.

"Nancy called Jason 'Mister,'" Caddy said.

"Listen how Caddy and Quentin and Jason talk," Nancy said.

"We're not talking loud," Caddy said. "You're the one that's talking like Father — "

"Hush," Nancy said; "hush, Mr. Jason."

"Nancy called Jason 'Mister' aguh — "

"Hush," Nancy said. She was talking loud when we crossed the ditch and stooped through the fence where she used to stoop through with the clothes on her head. Then we came to her house. We were going fast then. She opened the door. The smell of the house was like the lamp and the smell of Nancy was like the wick, like they were waiting for one another to begin to smell. She lit the lamp and closed the door and put the bar up. Then she quit talking loud, looking at us.

"What're we going to do?" Caddy said.

"What do yawl want to do?" Nancy said.

"You said we would have some fun," Caddy said.

There was something about Nancy's house; something you could smell besides Nancy and the house. Jason smelled it, even. "I don't want to stay here," he said. "I want to go home."

"Go home, then," Caddy said.

"I don't want to go by myself," Jason said.

"We're going to have some fun," Nancy said.

"How?" Caddy said.

Nancy stood by the door. She was looking at us, only it was like she had emptied her eyes, like she had quit using them. "What do you want to do?" she said.

"Tell us a story," Caddy said. "Can you tell a story?"

"Yes," Nancy said.

"Tell it," Caddy said. We looked at Nancy. "You don't know any stories."

"Yes," Nancy said. "Yes I do."

She came and sat in a chair before the hearth. There was a little fire there. Nancy built it up, when it was already hot inside. She built a good blaze. She told a story. She talked like her eyes looked, like her eyes watching us and her voice talking to us did not belong to her. Like she was living somewhere else, waiting somewhere else. She was outside the cabin. Her voice was inside and the shape of her, the Nancy that could stoop under a barbed wire fence with a bundle of clothes balanced on her head as though without weight, like a balloon, was there. But that was all. "And so this here queen come walking up to the ditch, where that bad man was hiding. She was walking up to the ditch, and she say, 'If I can just get past this here ditch,' was what she say . . ."

"What ditch?" Caddy said. "A ditch like that one out there? Why did a queen want to go into a ditch?"

"To get to her house," Nancy said. She looked at us. "She had to cross the ditch to get into her house quick and bar the door."

"Why did she want to go home and bar the door?" Caddy said.

IV

Nancy looked at us. She quit talking. She looked at us. Jason's legs stuck straight out of his pants where he sat on Nancy's lap. "I don't think that's a good story," he said. "I want to go home."

"Maybe we had better," Caddy said. She got up from the floor. "I bet they are looking for us right now." She went toward the door.

"No," Nancy said. "Don't open it." She got up quick and passed Caddy. She didn't touch the door, the wooden bar.

"Why not?" Caddy said.

"Come back to the lamp," Nancy said. "We'll have fun. You don't have to go."

"We ought to go," Caddy said. "Unless we have a lot of fun." She and Nancy came back to the fire, the lamp.

"I want to go home," Jason said. "I'm going to tell."

"I know another story," Nancy said. She stood close to the lamp. She looked at Caddy, like when your eyes look up at a stick balanced on your nose. She had to look down to see Caddy, but her eyes looked like that, like when you are balancing a stick.

"I won't listen to it," Jason said. "I'll bang on the floor."

"It's a good one," Nancy said. "It's better than the other one."

"What's it about?" Caddy said. Nancy was standing by the lamp. Her hand was on the lamp, against the light, long and brown.

"Your hand is on that hot globe," Caddy said. "Don't it feel hot to your hand?"

Nancy looked at her hand on the lamp chimney. She took her hand away, slow. She stood there, looking at Caddy, wringing her long hand as though it were tied to her wrist with a string.

"Let's do something else," Caddy said.

"I want to go home," Jason said.

"I got some popcorn," Nancy said. She looked at Caddy and then at Jason and then at me and then at Caddy again. "I got some popcorn."

"I don't like popcorn," Jason said. "I'd rather have candy."

Nancy looked at Jason. "You can hold the popper." She was still wringing her hand; it was long and limp and brown.

"All right," Jason said. "I'll stay a while if I can do that. Caddy can't hold it. I'll want to go home again if Caddy holds the popper."

Nancy built up the fire. "Look at Nancy putting her hands in the fire," Caddy said. "What's the matter with you, Nancy?"

"I got popcorn," Nancy said. "I got some." She took the popper from under the bed. It was broken. Jason began to cry.

"Now we can't have any popcorn," he said.

"We ought to go home, anyway," Caddy said. "Come on, Quentin."

"Wait," Nancy said; "wait. I can fix it. Don't you want to help me fix it?"

"I don't think I want any," Caddy said. "It's too late now."

"You help me, Jason," Nancy said. "Don't you want to help me?"

"No," Jason said. "I want to go home."

"Hush," Nancy said; "hush. Watch. Watch me. I can fix it so

Jason can hold it and pop the corn." She got a piece of wire and fixed the popper.

"It won't hold good," Caddy said.

"Yes it will," Nancy said. "Yawl watch. Yawl help me shell some corn."

The popcorn was under the bed too. We shelled it into the popper and Nancy helped Jason hold the popper over the fire.

"It's not popping," Jason said. "I want to go home."

"You wait," Nancy said. "It'll begin to pop. We'll have fun then."

She was sitting close to the fire. The lamp was turned up so high it was beginning to smoke. "Why don't you turn it down some?" I said.

"It's all right," Nancy said. "I'll clean it. Yawl wait. The popcorn will start in a minute."

"I don't believe it's going to start," Caddy said. "We ought to start home, anyway. They'll be worried."

"No," Nancy said. "It's going to pop. Dilsey will tell um yawl with me. I been working for yawl long time. They won't mind if yawl at my house. You wait, now. It'll start popping any minute now."

Then Jason got some smoke in his eyes and he began to cry. He dropped the popper into the fire. Nancy got a wet rag and wiped Jason's face, but he didn't stop crying.

"Hush," she said. "Hush." But he didn't hush. Caddy took the popper out of the fire.

"It's burned up," she said. "You'll have to get some more popcorn, Nancy."

"Did you put all of it in?" Nancy said.

"Yes," Caddy said. Nancy looked at Caddy. Then she took the popper and opened it and poured the cinders into her apron and began to sort the grains, her hands long and brown, and we watching her.

"Haven't you got any more?" Caddy said.

"Yes," Nancy said; "yes. Look. This here ain't burnt. All we need to do is — "

"I want to go home," Jason said. "I'm going to tell."

"Hush," Caddy said. We all listened. Nancy's head was already turned toward the barred door, her eyes filled with red lamplight. "Somebody is coming," Caddy said.

Then Nancy began to make that sound again, not loud, sitting there above the fire, her long hands dangling between her knees; all of a sudden water began to come out on her face in big drops, running down her face, carrying in each one a little turning ball of firelight like a spark until it dropped off her chin. "She's not crying," I said.

"I ain't crying," Nancy said. Her eyes were closed. "I ain't crying. Who is it?"

"I don't know," Caddy said. She went to the door and looked out. "We've got to go now," she said. "Here comes Father."

"I'm going to tell," Jason said. "Yawl made me come."

The water still ran down Nancy's face. She turned in her chair. "Listen. Tell him. Tell him we going to have fun. Tell him I take good care of yawl until in the morning. Tell him to let me come home with yawl and sleep on the floor. Tell him I won't need no pallet. We'll have fun. You member last time how we had so much fun?"

"I didn't have fun," Jason said. "You hurt me. You put smoke in my eyes. I'm going to tell."

v

Father came in. He looked at us. Nancy did not get up.

"Tell him," she said.

"Caddy made us come down here," Jason said. "I didn't want to."

Father came to the fire. Nancy looked up at him. "Can't you go to Aunt Rachel's and stay?" he said. Nancy looked up at Father, her hands between her knees. "He's not here," Father said. "I would have seen him. There's not a soul in sight."

"He in the ditch," Nancy said. "He waiting in the ditch yonder."

"Nonsense," Father said. He looked at Nancy. "Do you know he's there?"

"I got the sign," Nancy said.

"What sign?"

"I got it. It was on the table when I come in. It was a hogbone, with blood meat still on it, laying by the lamp. He's out there. When yawl walk out that door, I gone."

"Gone where, Nancy?" Caddy said.

"I'm not a tattletale," Jason said.

"Nonsense," Father said.

"He out there," Nancy said. "He looking through that window this minute, waiting for yawl to go. Then I gone."

"Nonsense," Father said. "Lock up your house and we'll take you on to Aunt Rachel's."

" 'Twon't do no good," Nancy said. She didn't look at Father now, but he looked down at her, at her long, limp, moving hands. "Putting it off won't do no good."

"Then what do you want to do?" Father said.

"I don't know," Nancy said. "I can't do nothing. Just put it off. And that don't do no good. I reckon it belong to me. I reckon what I going to get ain't no more than mine."

"Get what?" Caddy said. "What's yours?"

"Nothing," Father said. "You all must get to bed."

"Caddy made me come," Jason said.

"Go on to Aunt Rachel's," Father said.

"It won't do no good," Nancy said. She sat before the fire, her elbows on her knees, her long hands between her knees. "When even your own kitchen wouldn't do no good. When even if I was sleeping on the floor in the room with your chillen, and the next morning there I am, and blood — "

"Hush," Father said. "Lock the door and put out the lamp and go to bed."

"I scaired of the dark," Nancy said. "I scaired for it to happen in the dark."

"You mean you're going to sit right here with the lamp lighted?" Father said. Then Nancy began to make the sound again, sitting before the fire, her long hands between her knees. "Ah, damnation," Father said. "Come along, chillen. It's past bedtime."

"When yawl go home, I gone," Nancy said. She talked quieter now, and her face looked quiet, like her hands. "Anyway, I got my coffin money saved up with Mr. Lovelady." Mr. Lovelady was a short, dirty man who collected the Negro insurance, coming around to the cabins or the kitchens every Saturday morning, to collect fifteen cents. He and his wife lived at the hotel. One morning his wife committed suicide. They had a child, a little girl. He and the child went away. After a week or two he came back alone. We would see him going along the lanes and the back streets on Saturday mornings.

"Nonsense," Father said. "You'll be the first thing I'll see in the kitchen tomorrow morning."

"You'll see what you'll see, I reckon," Nancy said. "But it will take the Lord to say what that will be."

VI

We left her sitting before the fire.

"Come and put the bar up," Father said. But she didn't move. She didn't look at us again, sitting quietly there between the lamp and the fire. From some distance down the lane we could look back and see her through the open door.

"What, Father?" Caddy said. "What's going to happen?"

"Nothing," Father said. Jason was on Father's back, so Jason was the tallest of all of us. We went down into the ditch. I looked at it, quiet. I couldn't see much where the moonlight and the shadows tangled.

"If Jesus *is* hid here, he can see us, can't he?" Caddy said.

"He's not there," Father said. "He went away a long time ago."

"You made me come," Jason said, high; against the sky it looked like Father had two heads, a little one and a big one. "I didn't want to."

We went up out of the ditch. We could still see Nancy's house and the open door, but we couldn't see Nancy now, sitting before the fire with the door open, because she was tired. "I just done got tired," she said. "I just a nigger. It ain't no fault of mine."

But we could hear her, because she began just after we came up out of the ditch, the sound that was not singing and not un-singing. "Who will do our washing now, Father?" I said.

"I'm not a nigger," Jason said, high and close above Father's head.

"You're worse," Caddy said, "you are a tattletale. If something was to jump out, you'd be scairder than a nigger."

"I wouldn't," Jason said.

"You'd cry," Caddy said.

"Caddy," Father said.

"I wouldn't!" Jason said.

"Scairy cat," Caddy said.

"Candace!" Father said.

William Faulkner (1897-   )   William Faulkner was born in New Albany, Mississippi, of a family which had played a significant role in the history of Mississippi and the South. He left high school before graduating, was an air cadet in Canada during World War I, worked at odd jobs to earn a living, studied intermittently at the University of Mississippi and drifted around the country, and finally began to write. As he has said, "I wrote a book and discovered that my doom, fate, was to keep on writing books." His first book was a volume of poems, *The Marble Faun*, published in 1924; his first novel, *Soldiers' Pay*, was written in New Orleans with the encouragement of Sherwood Anderson and published in 1926. Since that time Faulkner, with only occasional and relatively recent exceptions, has lived in central Mississippi; this region, which corresponds to the "Yoknapatawpha" of his fiction, has furnished the background and in effect forms the very center of his many novels and short stories which span more than a century of Mississippi life. After years of neglect, indifference, and misunderstanding, the magnitude of his literary achievement was finally recognized; since his receipt of the Nobel Prize for literature in 1950 he has been increasingly regarded as the major American fiction writer of the past four decades.

What one critic has called the "charted chaos" of Faulkner's fiction grows out of a complex and often complicated narrative method, an extended and elaborate use of stream-of-consciousness, a constant experimentation with chronology and point of view, a fondness for indirection and obliquity of approach, and a highly individualistic, at times almost idiosyncratic language, sentence structure, and syntax. "That Evening Sun" and "A Bear Hunt" suggest both the variety of his short fiction and the nature of his narrative method. Each story depends for much of its effect on the interplay or counterpointing between past time and present events. The narrative unfolding of each story is indirect and ingenious; the full meaning of a story is not revealed until the very end when all the details of the story contribute to the total effect of the completed work. "A Bear Hunt" is characteristic; not until Ash's final comments to Ratliff does the narrative wheel, as it were, come full circle; then and only then does the reader understand the significance of the apparently irrelevant comment about the incident, twenty years earlier, involving the "Provine gang" with their drawn pistols and freshly lit cigars and the burning of the celluloid collars of the Negro men. Each story is narrated from more than one point of view or contains a kind of "multiple point of view." In "That Evening Sun," for example, Nancy is the focal character and Quentin the character from whose point of view the events are seen and recorded; however, particularly in the early sections of the story, the attitudes of various characters are presented — that of Jesus, of Dilsey, of various members of the family, and so forth. In each story, mood and atmosphere are evoked with meticulous artistry; Faulkner is as masterful in his creation of the essence of a place, a time, and a way of life as he is in the creation of not one but many completely realized individuals.

The most satisfactory single volume of Faulkner's short stories is *Collected Stories of William Faulkner* (Random House); good samplings are included in *A Faulkner Reader* (Modern Library) and *The Portable Faulkner* (ed. Malcolm Cowley, Viking).

Questions   1. Is there one protagonist, or major character, in this story? Or could it more properly be called a story of interacting groups — what has been termed "the multiplicity story"? Examine, for example, the relationship between Negroes and whites in the story; then consider the relationships within the individual groups. What different attitudes towards Nancy, for example, are displayed by the children, by the mother, and by the father? Examine the Negroes themselves, Nancy, Jesus, and Dilsey. Faulkner's Negroes exist both as individuals and in terms of racial situations; what different racial attitudes are embodied in Nancy, Dilsey, and Jesus? Compare or contrast the white attitudes towards the Negro as suggested by Mr. Stovall, the jailer, or the children's father.   2. What does Faulkner gain by having the events in the story narrated by Quentin, a nine-year-old boy? Notice, for example, the last scene in Nancy's cabin when events which to Nancy are a life-and-death matter seem to the children a kind of game. What, too, is gained by the children's lack of awareness of the sexual incidents involved?   3. Is Nancy a simple or complex character? Is she, as she says, "hellborn"? What is the significance of her lament "I won't be nothing soon. I going back where I come from soon"?   4. The town of Jefferson, the setting of this story, like the characters themselves, appears and reappears in many of Faulkner's stories and novels. Write an essay describing the town from what you learn about it in this story.   5. What is the purpose of the first few paragraphs of the story in which Jefferson "now" and Jefferson "fifteen years ago" are described?   6. It has been said that although Faulkner is first of all a Mississippian and second a Southerner, he is no "local colorist" or regionalist in any limited use of the term. His fiction is universal, concerned with what can be called archetypal experiences, in spite of the fact that it is so deeply rooted in time and place that it is impossible to think of as taking place anywhere but in "Yoknapatawpha." Can you see a basis for comparison, in this respect, with Hawthorne's New England stories or Joyce's stories of Dublin?

WILLIAM FAULKNER

A Bear Hunt

RATLIFF is telling this. He is a sewing-machine agent; time was when he traveled about our county in a light, strong buckboard drawn by a sturdy, wiry, mismatched team of horses; now he uses a model T Ford, which also carries his demonstrator machine in a tin box on the rear, shaped like a dog kennel and painted to resemble a house.

Ratliff may be seen anywhere without surprise — the only man present at the bazaars and sewing bees of farmers' wives; moving among both men and women at all-day singings at country churches, and singing, too, in a pleasant barytone. He was even at this bear hunt of which he speaks, at the annual hunting camp of Major de Spain in the river bottom twenty miles from town, even though there was no one there to whom he might possibly have sold a machine, since Mrs. de Spain doubtless already owned one, unless she had given it to one of her married daughters, and the other man — the man called Lucius Provine — with whom he became involved, to the violent detriment of his face and other members, could not have bought one for his wife even if he would, without Ratliff sold it to him on indefinite credit.

Provine is also a native of the county. But he is forty now and most of his teeth are gone, and it is years now since he and his dead brother and another dead and forgotten contemporary named Jack Bonds were known as the Provine gang and terrorized

A BEAR HUNT From *Collected Stories of William Faulkner.* Copyright 1934 by William Faulkner. Reprinted by permission of Random House, Inc.

our quiet town after the unimaginative fashion of wild youth by letting off pistols on the square late Saturday nights or galloping their horses down scurrying and screaming lanes of churchgoing ladies on Sunday morning. Younger citizens of the town do not know him at all save as a tall, apparently strong and healthy man who loafs in a brooding, saturnine fashion wherever he will be allowed, never exactly accepted by any group, and who makes no effort whatever to support his wife and three children.

There are other men among us now whose families are in want; men who, perhaps, would not work anyway, but who now, since the last few years, cannot find work. These all attain and hold to a certain respectability by acting as agents for the manufacturers of minor articles like soap and men's toilet accessories and kitchen objects, being seen constantly about the square and the streets carrying small black sample cases. One day, to our surprise, Provine also appeared with such a case, though within less than a week the town officers discovered that it contained whisky in pint bottles. Major de Spain extricated him somehow, as it was Major de Spain who supported his family by eking out the money which Mrs. Provine earned by sewing and such — perhaps as a Roman gesture of salute and farewell to the bright figure which Provine had been before time whipped him.

For there are older men who remember the Butch — he has even lost somewhere in his shabby past the lusty dare-deviltry of the nickname — Provine of twenty years ago; that youth without humor, yet with some driving, inarticulate zest for breathing which has long since burned out of him, who performed in a fine frenzy, which was, perhaps, mostly alcohol, certain outrageous and spontaneous deeds, one of which was the Negro-picnic business. The picnic was at a Negro church a few miles from town. In the midst of it, the two Provines and Jack Bonds, returning from a dance in the country, rode up with drawn pistols and freshly lit cigars; and taking the Negro men one by one, held the burning cigar ends to the popular celluloid collars of the day, leaving each victim's neck ringed with an abrupt and faint and painless ring of carbon. This is he of whom Ratliff is talking.

But there is one more thing more which must be told here in order to set the stage for Ratliff. Five miles farther down the river from Major de Spain's camp, and in an even wilder part of the river's jungle of cane and gum and pin oak, there is an

Indian mound. Aboriginal, it rises profoundly and darkly enigmatic, the only elevation of any kind in the wild, flat jungle of river bottom. Even to some of us — children though we were, yet we were descended of literate, town-bred people — it possessed inferences of secret and violent blood, of savage and sudden destruction, as though the yells and hatchets which we associated with Indians through the hidden and secret dime novels which we passed among ourselves were but trivial and momentary manifestations of what dark power still dwelled or lurked there, sinister, a little sardonic, like a dark and nameless beast lightly and lazily slumbering with bloody jaws — this, perhaps, due to the fact that a remnant of a once powerful clan of the Chickasaw tribe still lived beside it under Government protection. They now had American names and they lived as the sparse white people who surrounded them in turn lived.

Yet we never saw them, since they never came to town, having their own settlement and store. When we grew older we realized that they were no wilder or more illiterate than the white people, and that probably their greatest deviation from the norm — and this, in our country, no especial deviation — was the fact that they were a little better than suspect to manufacture moonshine whisky back in the swamps. Yet to us, as children, they were a little fabulous, their swamp-hidden lives inextricable from the life of the dark mound, which some of us had never seen, yet of which we had all heard, as though they had been set by the dark powers to be guardians of it.

As I said, some of us had never seen the mound, yet all of us had heard of it, talked of it as boys will. It was as much a part of our lives and background as the land itself, as the lost Civil War and Sherman's march, or that there were Negroes among us living in economic competition who bore our family names; only more immediate, more potential and alive. When I was fifteen, a companion and I, on a dare, went into the mound one day just at sunset. We saw some of those Indians for the first time; we got directions from them and reached the top of the mound just as the sun set. We had camping equipment with us, but we made no fire. We didn't even make down our beds. We just sat side by side on that mound until it became light enough to find our way back to the road. We didn't talk. When we looked at each other in the gray dawn, our faces were gray, too, quiet, very grave. When we reached town again, we didn't talk either. We just parted and went home and went to bed. That's what we thought, felt, about the mound. We were children, it is true, yet we were descendants of people who read books and who were — or should have been — beyond superstition and impervious to mindless fear.

Now Ratliff tells about Lucius Provine and his hiccup.

When I got back to town, the first fellow I met says, "What happened to your face, Ratliff? Was De Spain using you in place of his bear hounds?"

"No, boys," I says. "Hit was a cattymount."

"What was you trying to do to hit, Ratliff?" a fellow says.

"Boys," I says, "be dog if I know."

And that was the truth. Hit was a good while after they had done hauled Luke Provine offen me that I found that out. Because I never knowed who Old Man Ash was, no more than Luke did. I just knowed that he was Major's nigger, a-helping around camp. All I knowed, when the whole thing started, was what I thought I was aiming to do — to maybe help Luke sho enough, or maybe at the outside to just have a little fun with him without hurting him, or even maybe to do Major a little favor by getting Luke outen camp for a while. And then hyer hit is about midnight and that durn fellow comes swurging outen the woods wild as a skeered deer, and runs in where they are setting at the poker game, and I says, "Well, you ought to be satisfied. You done run clean out from under them." And he stopped dead still and give me a kind of glare of wild astonishment; he didn't even know that they had quit; and then he swurged all over me like a barn falling down.

Hit sho stopped that poker game. Hit taken three or four of them to drag him offen me, with Major turned in his chair with a set of threes in his hand, a-hammering on the table and hollering cusses. Only a right smart of the helping they done was stepping on my face and hands and feet. Hit was like a fahr — the fellows with the water hose done the most part of the damage.

"What the tarnation hell does this mean?" Major hollers, with three or four fellows holding Luke, and him crying like a baby.

"He set them on me!" Luke says. "He was the one sent me up there, and I'm a-going to kill him!"

"Set who on you?" Major says.

"Them Indians," Luke says, crying. Then he tried to get at me again, flinging them fellows holding his arms around like they was rag dolls, until Major pure cussed him quiet. He's a man yet. Don't let hit fool you none because he claims he ain't strong enough to work. Maybe hit's because he ain't never wore his strength down toting around one of them little black satchels full of pink galluses and shaving soap. Then Major asked me what hit was all about, and I told him how I had just been trying to help Luke get shed of them hiccups.

Be dog if I didn't feel right sorry for him. I happened to be passing out that way, and so I just thought I would drop in on them and see what luck they was having, and I druv up about sundown, and the first fellow I see was Luke. I wasn't surprised, since this here would be the biggest present gathering of men in the county, let alone the free eating and whisky, so I says, "Well, this is a surprise." And he says:

"Hic-uh! Hic-ow! Hic-oh! Hic — oh, God!" He had done already had them since nine o'clock the night before; he had been teching the jug ever' time Major offered him one and ever' time he could get to hit when Old Man Ash wasn't looking; and two days before Major had killed a bear, and I reckon Luke had already et more possum-rich bear pork — let alone the venison they had, with maybe a few coons and squirls throwed in for seasoning — than he could have hauled off in a waggin. So here he was, going three times to the minute, like one of these here clock bombs; only hit was bear meat and whisky instead of dynamite, and so he couldn't explode and put himself outen his misery.

They told me how he had done already kept ever'body awake most of the night before, and how Major got up mad anyway, and went off with his gun and Ash to handle them two bear hounds, and Luke following — outen pure misery, I reckon, since he hadn't slept no more than nobody else — walking along behind Major, saying, "Hic-ah! Hic-ow! Hic-oh! Hic — oh, Lord!" until Major turns on him and says:

"Get to hell over yonder with them shotgun fellows on the deer stands. How do you expect me to walk up on a bear or even hear the dogs when they strike? I might as well be riding a motorcycle."

So Luke went on back to where the deer standers was along the log-line levee. I reckon he never so much went away as he kind of died away in the distance like that ere motorcycle Major mentioned. He never tried to be quiet. I reckon he knowed hit wouldn't be no use. He never tried to keep to the open, neither. I reckon he thought that any fool would know from his sound that he wasn't no deer. No. I reckon he was so mizzable by then that he hoped somebody would shoot him. But nobody never, and he come to the first stand, where Uncle Ike McCaslin was, and set down on a log behind Uncle Ike with his elbows on his knees and his face in his hands, going, "Hic-uh! Hic-uh! Hic-uh! Hic-uh!" until Uncle Ike turns and says:

"Confound you, boy; get away from here. Do you reckon any varmint in the world is going to walk up to a hay baler? Go drink some water."

"I done already done that," Luke says, without moving. "I been drinking water since nine o'clock last night. I done already drunk so much water that if I was to fall down I would gush like a artesian well."

"Well, go away anyhow," Uncle Ike says. "Get away from here."

So Luke gets up and kind of staggers away again, kind of dying away again like he was run by one of these hyer one-cylinder gasoline engines, only a durn sight more often and regular. He went on down the levee to where the next stand was, and they druv him way from there, and he went on toward the next one. I reckon he was still hoping that somebody would take pity on him and shoot him, because now he kind of seemed to give up. Now, when he come to the "oh, God" part of hit, they said you could hyear him clean back to camp. They said he would echo back from the canebrake across the river like one of these hyer loud-speakers down in a well. They said that even the dogs on the trail quit baying, and so they all come up and made him come back to camp. That's where he was when I come in. And Old Man Ash was there, too, where him and Major had done come in so Major could take a nap, and neither me nor Luke noticing him except as just another nigger around.

That was hit. Neither one of us knowed or even thought about him. I be dog if hit don't look like sometimes that when a fellow sets out to play a joke, hit ain't another fellow he's playing that joke on; hit's a kind of big power laying still somewhere in the dark that he sets out to prank with without knowing hit, and hit all depends on whether that ere power is in the notion to take a joke or not, whether or not hit blows up right in his face like this one did in mine. Because I says, "You done had them since nine o'clock yesterday? That's nigh twenty-four hours. Seems like to me you'd 'a' done something to try to stop them." And him looking at me like he couldn't make up his mind whether to jump up and bite my head off or just to try and bite hisn off, saying "Hic-uh! Hic-uh!" slow and regular. Then he says,

"I don't want to get shed of them. I like them. But if you had them, I would get shed of them for you. You want to know how?"

"How?" I says.

"I'd just tear your head off. Then you wouldn't have nothing to hiccup with. They wouldn't worry you then. I'd be glad to do hit for you."

"Sho now," I says, looking at him setting there on the kitchen steps — hit was after supper, but he hadn't et none, being as his throat had done turned into a one-way street on him, you might say — going "Hic-uh! Hic-oh! Hic-oh! Hic-uh!" because I reckon Major had done told him what would happen to him if he taken to hollering again. I never meant no harm. Besides, they had done already told me how he had kept everybody awake all night the night before and had done skeered all the game outen that part of the bottom, and besides, the walk might help him to pass his own time. So I says, "I believe I know how you might get shed of them. But, of course, if you don't want to get shed of them——"

And he says, "I just wish somebody would tell me how. I'd pay ten dollars just to set here for one minute without saying 'hic'——" Well, that set him off sho enough. Hit was like up to that time his insides had been satisfied with going "'hic-uh" steady, but quiet, but now, when he reminded himself, hit was like he had done opened a cut-out, because right away he begun hollering, "Hic—— oh, God!" like when them fellows on the deer stands had made him come back to camp, and I heard Major's feet coming bup-bup-bup across the floor. Even his feet sounded mad, and I says quick,

"Sh-h-h-h! You don't want to get Major mad again, now."

So he quieted some, setting there on the kitchen steps, with Old Man Ash and the other niggers moving around inside the kitchen, and he says, "I will try anything you can sujest. I done tried ever'thing I knowed and ever'thing anybody else told me to. I done held my breath and drunk water until I feel just like one of these hyer big automobile tahrs they use to advertise with, and I hung by my knees offen that limb yonder for fifteen minutes and drunk a pint bottle full of water upside down, and somebody said to swallow a buckshot and I done that. And still I got them. What do you know that I can do?"

"Well," I say, "I don't know what you would do. But if hit was me that had them, I'd go up to the mound and get old John Basket to cure me."

Then he set right still, and then he turned slow and looked at me; I be dog if for a minute he didn't even hiccup. "John Basket?" he says.

"Sho," I says. "Them Indians knows all sorts of dodges that white doctors ain't hyeard about yet. He'd be glad to do that much for a white man, too, them, pore aboriginees would, because the white folks have been so good to them — not only letting them keep that ere hump of dirt that don't nobody want noways, but letting them use names like ourn and selling them flour and sugar and farm tools at not no more than a fair profit above what they would cost a white man. I hyear tell how pretty soon they are even going to start letting them come to town once a week. Old Basket would be glad to cure them hiccups for you."

"John Basket," he says; "them Indians," he says, hiccuping slow and quiet and steady. Then he says right sudden, "I be dog if I will!" Then I be dog if hit didn't sound like he was crying. He jumped up and stood there cussing, sounding like he was crying. "Hit ain't a man hyer has got any mercy on me, white or black. Hyer I done suffered and suffered more than twenty-four hours without food or sleep, and not a sonabitch of them has any mercy or pity on me!"

"Well, I was trying to," I says. "Hit ain't me that's got them. I just thought, seeing as how you had done seemed to got to the

place where couldn't no white man help you. But hit ain't no
law making you go up there and get shed of them." So I made
like I was going away. I went back around the corner of the
kitchen and watched him set down on the steps again, going
"Hic-uh! Hic-uh!" slow and quiet again; and then I seen, through
the kitchen window, Old Man Ash standing just inside the
kitchen door, right still, with his head bent like he was listening.
But still I never suspected nothing. No even did I suspect nothing when, after a while, I watched Luke get up again, sudden
but quiet, and stand for a minute looking at the window where
the poker game and the folks was, and then look off into the dark
towards the road that went down the bottom. Then he went
into the house, quiet, and come out a minute later with a lighted
lantrun and a shotgun. I don't know whose gun hit was and I
don't reckon he did, nor cared neither. He just come out kind
of quiet and determined, and went on down the road. I could
see the lantrun, but I could hyear him a long time after the
lantrun had done disappeared. I had come back around the
kitchen then and I was listening to him dying away down the
bottom, when old Ash says behind me:

"He gwine up dar?"

"Up where?" I says.

"Up to de mound," he says.

"Why, I be dog if I know," I says. "The last time I talked to
him he never sounded like he was fixing to go nowhere. Maybe
he just decided to take a walk. Hit might do him some good;
make him sleep tonight and help him get up a appetite for breakfast maybe. What do you think?"

But Ash never said nothing. He just went on back into the
kitchen. And still I never suspected nothing. How could I? I
hadn't never even seen Jefferson in them days. I hadn't never
even seen a pair of shoes, let alone two stores in a row or a arc
light.

So I went on in where the poker game was, and I says, "Well,
gentlemen, I reckon we might get some sleep tonight." And I
told them what had happened, because more than like he would
stay up there until daylight rather than walk them five miles
back in the dark, because maybe them Indians wouldn't mind a
little thing like a fellow with hiccups, like white folks would.
And I be dog if Major didn't rear up about hit.

"Dammit, Ratliff," he says, "you ought not to done that."

"Why, I jest sujested hit to him, Major, for a joke," I says. "I just told him about how old Basket was a kind of doctor. I never expected him to take hit serious. Maybe he ain't even going up there. Maybe he's just went out after a coon."

But most of them felt about hit like I did. "Let him go," Mr. Fraser says. "I hope he walks around all night. Damn if I slept a wink for him all night long. . . . Deal the cards, Uncle Ike."

"Can't stop him now, noways," Uncle Ike says, dealing the cards. "And maybe John Basket can do something for his hiccups. Durn young fool, eating and drinking himself to where he can't talk nor swallow neither. He set behind me on a log this morning, sounding just like a hay baler. I thought once I'd have to shoot him to get rid of him. . . . Queen bets a quarter, gentlemen."

So I set there watching them, thinking now and then about that durn fellow with his shotgun and his lantrun stumbling and blundering along through the woods, walking five miles in the dark to get shed of his hiccups, with the varmints all watching him and wondering just what kind of a hunt this was and just what kind of a two-leg varmint hit was that made a noise like that, and about them Indians up at the mound when he would come walking in, and I would have to laugh until Major says, "What in hell are you mumbling and giggling at?"

"Nothing," I says. "I was just thinking about a fellow I know."

"And damn if you hadn't ought to be out there with him," Major says. Then he decided hit was about drink time and he begun to holler for Ash. Finally I went to the door and hollered for Ash towards the kitchen, but hit was another one of the niggers that answered. When he come in with the demijohn and fixings, Major looks up and says, "Where's Ash?"

"He done gone," the nigger says.

"Gone?" Major says. "Gone where?"

"He say he gwine up to'ds de mound," the nigger says. And still I never knowed, never suspected. I just thought to myself, "That old nigger has turned powerful tender-hearted all of a sudden, being skeered for Luke Provine to walk around by himself in the dark. Or maybe Ash likes to listen to them hiccups," I thought to myself.

"Up to the mound?" Major says. "By dad, if he comes back

here full of John Basket's bust-skull whisky I'll skin him alive."

"He ain't say what he gwine fer," the nigger says. "All he tell me when he left, he gwine up to'ds de mound and he be back by daylight."

"He better be," Major says. "He better be sober too."

So we set there and they went on playing and me watching them like a durn fool, not suspecting nothing, just thinking how hit was a shame that that durned old nigger would have to come in and spoil Luke's trip, and hit come along towards eleven o'clock and they begun to talk about going to bed, being as they was all going out on stand tomorrow, when we hyeard the sound. Hit sounded like a drove of wild horses coming up that road, and we hadn't no more than turned towards the door, a-asking one another what in tarnation hit could be, with Major just saying, "What in the name of —— " when hit come across the porch like a harrycane and down the hall, and the door busted open and there Luke was. He never had no gun and lantrun then, and his clothes was nigh tore clean offen him, and his face looked wild as ere a man in the Jackson a-sylum. But the main thing I noticed was that he wasn't hiccuping now. And this time, too, he was nigh crying.

"They was fixing to kill me!" he says. "They was going to burn me to death! They had done tried me and tied me onto the pile of wood, and one of them was coming with the fahr when I managed to bust loose and run!"

"Who was?" Major says. "What in the tarnation hell are you talking about?"

"Them Indians!" Luke says. "They was fixing to —— "

"What?" Major hollers. "Damn to blue blazes, what?"

And that was where I had to put my foot in hit. He hadn't never seen me until then. "At least they cured your hiccups," I says.

Hit was then that he stopped right still. He hadn't never even seen me, but he seen me now. He stopped right still and looked at me with that ere wild face that looked like hit had just escaped from Jackson and had ought to be took back there quick.

"What?" he says.

"Anyway, you done run out from under them hiccups," I says.

Well, sir, he stood there for a full minute. His eyes had done gone blank, and he stood there with his head cocked a little, listen-

ing to his own insides. I reckon hit was the first time he had
took time to find out that they was gone. He stood there right
still for a full minute while that ere kind of shocked astonishment come onto his face. Then he jumped on me. I was still
setting in my chair, and I be dog if for a minute I didn't think
the roof had done fell in.

Well, they got him offen me at last and got him quieted down,
and then they washed me off and give me a drink, and I felt
better. But even with that drink I never felt so good but what I
felt hit was my duty to my honor to call him outen the back
yard, as the fellow says. No, sir. I know when I done made a
mistake and guessed wrong; Major de Spain wasn't the only man
that caught a bear on that hunt; no, sir. I be dog, if it had been
daylight, I'd a hitched up my Ford and taken out of there. But
hit was midnight, and besides, that nigger, Ash, was on my mind
then. I had just begun to suspect that hit was more to this business than met the nekkid eye. And hit wasn't no good time then
to go back to the kitchen then and ask him about hit, because
Luke was using the kitchen. Major had given him a drink, too,
and he was back there, making up for them two days he hadn't
et, talking a right smart about what he aimed to do to such and
such a sonabitch that would try to play his durn jokes on him,
not mentioning no names, but mostly laying himself in a new set
of hiccups, though I ain't going back to see.

So I waited until daylight, until I hyeard the niggers stirring
around in the kitchen; then I went back there. And there was
old Ash, looking like he always did, oiling Major's boots and
setting them behind the stove and then taking up Major's rifle
and beginning to load the magazine. He just looked once at my
face when I come in, and went on shoving ca'tridges into the gun.

"So you went up to the mound last night," I says. He looked
up at me again, quick, and then down again. But he never said
nothing, looking like a durned old frizzle-headed ape. "You must
know some of them folks up there," I says.

"I knows some of um," he says, shovin ca'tridges into the gun.

"You know old John Basket?" I says.

"I knows some of um," he says, not looking at me.

"Did you see him last night?" I says. He never said nothing
at all. So then I changed my tone, like a fellow has to do to get
anything outen a nigger. "Look here," I says. "Look at me." He

looked at me. "Just what did you do up there last night?"

"Who, me?" he says.

"Come on," I says. "Hit's all over now. Mr. Provine has done got over his hiccups and we done both forgot about anything that might have happened when he got back last night. You never went up there just for fun last night. Or maybe hit was something you told them up there, told old man Basket. Was that hit?" He had done quit looking at me, but he never stopped shoving ca'tridges into that gun. He looked quick to both sides. "Come on," I says. "Do you want to tell me what happened up there, or do you want me to mention to Mr. Provine that you was mixed up in hit some way?" He never stopped loading the rifle and he never looked at me, but I be dog if I couldn't almost see his mind working. "Come on," I says. "Just what was you doing up there last night?"

Then he told me. I reckon he knowed hit wasn't no use to try to hide hit then; that if I never told Luke, I could still tell Major. "I jest dodged him and got dar first en told um he was a new revenue agent coming up dar tonight, but dat he warn't much en dat all dey had to do was to give um a good skeer en likely he would go away. En dey did en he did."

"Well!" I says. "Well! I always thought I was pretty good at joking folks," I says, "but I take a back seat for you. What happened?" I says. "Did you see hit?"

"Never much happened," he says. "Dey jest went down de road a piece en atter a while hyer he come a-hickin' en a-blumpin' up de road wid de lant'un en de gun. They took de lant'un en de gun away frum him en took him up pon topper de mound en talked de Injun language at him fer a while. Den dey piled up some wood en fixed him on hit so he could git loose in a minute, en den one of dem come up de hill wid de fire, en he done de rest."

"Well!" I says. "Well, I'll be eternally durned!" And then all on a sudden hit struck me. I had done turned and was going out when hit struck me, and I stopped and I says, "There's one more thing I want to know. Why did you do hit?"

Now he set there on the wood box, rubbing the gun with his hand, not looking at me again. "I wuz jest helping you kyo him of dem hiccups."

"Come on," I says. "That wasn't your reason. What was hit?

Remember, I got a right smart I can tell Mr. Provine and Major both now. I don't know what Major will do, but I know what Mr. Provine will do if I was to tell him."

And he set there, rubbing that ere rifle with his hand. He was kind of looking down, like he was thinking. Not like he was trying to decide whether to tell me or not, but like he was remembering something from a long time back. And that's exactly what he was doing, because he says:

"I ain't skeered for him to know. One time dey was a picnic. Hit was a long time back, nigh twenty years ago. He was a young man den, en in de middle of de picnic, him en he brother en nudder white man — I fergit he name — dey rid up wid dey pistols out en cotch us niggers one at a time en burned our collars off. Hit was him dat burnt mine."

"And you waited all this time and went to all this trouble, just to get even with him?" I says.

"Hit warn't dat," he says, rubbing the rifle with his hand. "Hit wuz de collar. Back in dem days a top nigger hand made two dollars a week. I paid fo' bits fer dat collar. Hit wuz blue, wid a red picture of de race betwixt de Natchez en de Robert E. Lee running around hit. He burnt hit up. I makes ten dollars a week now. En I jest wish I knowed where I could buy another collar like dat un fer half of hit. I wish I did."

Questions   1. Compare or contrast the opening of this story with that of "That Evening Sun." Why does Faulkner begin the story with a kind of prologue? What are the characteristics of the unnamed narrator of this prologue? What is his attitude towards Ratliff and "the Provine gang"? In what ways is this narrator similar to Ratliff and the Provine boys?   2. Like "That Evening Sun," this story contains many memorable characters — the narrator of the "prologue," Ratliff, Major de Spain, Lucius Provine, Old Man Ash, Uncle Ike McCaslin, John Basket. Compare or contrast these characters with the people of "That Evening Sun."   3. In *The Collected Stories of William Faulkner*, "A Bear Hunt" appears under the category of "The Country"; "That Evening Sun" under the category of "The Village." Compare or contrast these two different worlds. What differences, for example, exist in the white-black relationships suggested or embodied in these stories?   4. Compare or contrast the complicated narrative method of this story with that of a relatively simple story such as "Chickamauga."

Although "A Bear Hunt" is confusing upon first reading, the author's purpose and direction are never confused. The trigger of the subsequent action is the incident in which the Provine gang burns the Negroes' collars on the night of the country dance; if you bear this in mind, the reappearance of Old Man Ash later in the story is like a signpost pointing to the ultimate climax; in terms of this, Ratliff's comments such as "But still I never suspected nothing" whet the reader's interest and prepare the way for the story's ending. What other devices does Faulkner employ?   5. Contrast the rough good humor of this story with the somber and foreboding tone of "That Evening Sun." On the basis of this story, would you agree that Faulkner — contrary to the judgment of many early critics who overemphasized or misunderstood his thematic use of decay, violence, and abnormality — is an important figure in the development of native American humor?

ERNEST HEMINGWAY

Indian Camp

AT THE lake shore there was another rowboat drawn up. The two Indians stood waiting.

Nick and his father got in the stern of the boat and the Indians shoved it off and one of them got in to row. Uncle George sat in the stern of the camp rowboat. The young Indian shoved the camp boat off and got in to row Uncle George.

The two boats started off in the dark. Nick heard the oarlocks of the other boat quite a way ahead of them in the mist. The Indians rowed with quick choppy strokes. Nick lay back with his father's arm around him. It was cold on the water. The Indian who was rowing them was working very hard, but the other boat moved further ahead in the mist all the time.

"Where are we going, Dad?" Nick asked.

"Over to the Indian camp. There is an Indian lady very sick."

"Oh," said Nick.

Across the bay they found the other boat beached. Uncle George was smoking a cigar in the dark. The young Indian pulled the boat way up on the beach. Uncle George gave both the Indians cigars.

They walked up from the beach through a meadow that was soaking wet with dew, following the young Indian who carried a lantern. Then they went into the woods and followed a trail that led to the logging road that ran back into the hills. It was

INDIAN CAMP   Reprinted from *In Our Time* by Ernest Hemingway, copyright 1925 Charles Scribner's Sons; renewal copyright 1953 Ernest Hemingway. Used by permission of Charles Scribner's Sons.

was much lighter on the logging road as the timber was cut away on both sides. The young Indian stopped and blew out his lantern and they all walked on along the road.

They came around a bend and a dog came out barking. Ahead were the lights of the shanties where the Indian bark-peelers lived. More dogs rushed out at them. The two Indians sent them back to the shanties. In the shanty nearest the road there was a light in the window. An old woman stood in the doorway holding a lamp.

Inside on a wooden bunk lay a young Indian woman. She had been trying to have her baby for two days. All the old women in the camp had been helping her. The men had moved off up the road to sit in the dark and smoke out of range of the noise she made. She screamed just as Nick and the two Indians followed his father and Uncle George into the shanty. She lay in the lower bunk, very big under a quilt. Her head was turned to one side. In the upper bunk was her husband. He had cut his foot very badly with an ax three days before. He was smoking a pipe. The room smelled very bad.

Nick's father ordered some water to be put on the stove, and while it was heating he spoke to Nick.

"This lady is going to have a baby, Nick," he said.

"I know," said Nick.

"You don't know," said his father. "Listen to me. What she is going through is called being in labor. The baby wants to be born and she wants it to be born. All her muscles are trying to get the baby born. That is what is happening when she screams."

"I see," Nick said.

Just then the woman cried out.

"Oh, Daddy, can't you give her something to make her stop screaming?" asked Nick.

"No. I haven't any anæsthetic," his father said. "But her screams are not important. I don't hear them because they are not important."

The husband in the upper bunk rolled over against the wall.

The woman in the kitchen motioned to the doctor that the water was hot. Nick's father went into the kitchen and poured about half of the water out of the big kettle into a basin. Into the water left in the kettle he put several things he unwrapped from a handkerchief.

"Those must boil," he said, and began to scrub his hands in the basin of hot water with a cake of soap he had brought from the camp. Nick watched his father's hands scrubbing each other with the soap. While his father washed his hands very carefully and thoroughly, he talked.

"You see, Nick, babies are supposed to be born head first but sometimes they're not. When they're not they make a lot of trouble for everybody. Maybe I'll have to operate on this lady. We'll know in a little while."

When he was satisfied with his hands he went in and went to work.

"Pull back that quilt, will you, George?" he said. "I'd rather not touch it."

Later when he started to operate Uncle George and three Indian men held the woman still. She bit Uncle George on the arm and Uncle George said, "Damn squaw bitch!" and the young Indian who had rowed Uncle George over laughed at him. Nick held the basin for his father. It all took a long time.

His father picked the baby up and slapped it to make it breathe and handed it to the old woman.

"See, it's a boy, Nick," he said. "How do you like being an interne?"

Nick said, "All right." He was looking away so as not to see what his father was doing.

"There. That gets it," said his father and put something into the basin.

Nick didn't look at it.

"Now," his father said, "there's some stitches to put in. You can watch this or not, Nick, just as you like. I'm going to sew up the incision I made."

Nick did not watch. His curiosity had been gone for a long time.

His father finished and stood up. Uncle George and the three Indian men stood up. Nick put the basin out in the kitchen.

Uncle George looked at his arm. The young Indian smiled reminiscently.

"I'll put some peroxide on that, George," the doctor said.

He bent over the Indian woman. She was quiet now and her eyes were closed. She looked very pale. She did not know what had become of the baby or anything.

"I'll be back in the morning," the doctor said, standing up. "The nurse should be here from St. Ignace by noon and she'll bring everything we need."

He was feeling exalted and talkative as football players are in the dressing room after a game.

"That's one for the medical journal, George," he said. "Doing a Cæsarian with a jack-knife and sewing it up with nine-foot, tapered gut leaders."

Uncle George was standing against the wall, looking at his arm.

"Oh, you're a great man, all right," he said.

"Ought to have a look at the proud father. They're usually the worst sufferers in these little affairs," the doctor said. "I must say he took it all pretty quietly."

He pulled back the blanket from the Indian's head. His hand came away wet. He mounted on the edge of the lower bunk with the lamp in one hand and looked in. The Indian lay with his face toward the wall. His throat had been cut from ear to ear. The blood had flowed into a pool where his body sagged the bunk. His head rested on his left arm. The open razor lay, edge up, in the blankets.

"Take Nick out of the shanty, George," the doctor said.

There was no need of that. Nick, standing in the door of the kitchen, had a good view of the upper bunk when his father, the lamp in one hand, tipped the Indian's head back.

It was just beginning to be daylight when they walked along the logging road back toward the lake.

"I'm terribly sorry I brought you along, Nickie," said his father, all his post-operative exhilaration gone. "It was an awful mess to put you through."

"Do ladies always have such a hard time having babies?" Nick asked.

"No, that was very, very exceptional."

"Why did he kill himself, Daddy?"

"I don't know, Nick. He couldn't stand things, I guess."

"Do many men kill themselves, Daddy?"

"Not very many, Nick."

"Do many women?"

"Hardly ever."

"Don't they ever?"

"Oh, yes. They do sometimes."

"Daddy?"

"Yes."

"Where did Uncle George go?"

"He'll turn up all right."

"Is dying hard, Daddy?"

"No, I think it's pretty easy, Nick. It all depends."

They were seated in the boat, Nick in the stern, his father rowing. The sun was coming up over the hills. A bass jumped, making a circle in the water. Nick trailed his hand in the water. It felt warm in the sharp chill of the morning.

In the early morning on the lake sitting in the stern of the boat with his father rowing, he felt quite sure that he would never die.

Ernest Hemingway (1898-   )   World traveler, sportsman, international celebrity, and Nobel prize-winning author, Ernest Hemingway is one of the rare human beings who become legends during their own lifetimes. The son of a doctor, Hemingway was born in Oak Park, Illinois. After leaving high school, he worked for the Kansas City *Star;* was wounded and decorated during World War I; knew Ezra Pound, Sherwood Anderson, Gertrude Stein, and other American expatriates in Paris; and, with the publication of his first novel, *The Sun Also Rises* (1926), came to be regarded as a kind of unofficial spokesman for the so-called "Lost Generation." He had already published some poetry and short stories (*Three Stories and Ten Poems,* 1923; *In Our Time,* 1924), and he continued to work with increasing skill in both the shorter and the longer narrative forms; among his five volumes of short stories are *Men Without Women* (1927) and *Winner Take Nothing* (1933). In recent years, following activities in World War II which included supplying the Navy with intelligence in connection with submarine warfare and organizing "papa's irregulars," he has lived in Cuba, while making only infrequent visits to the United States. In 1954 he was awarded the Nobel Prize for literature.

Hemingway has changed the direction of contemporary fiction; few writers in history have had more imitators than he. His terse, staccato dialogue and the studied simplicity of his language; the economy of his narrative methods; and his favorite subjects and themes (the struggle of the individual against forces ranging from the mores of society to the purely physical obstacles to survival, the importance of sex, the physical joys of the "strenuous life", the virtue of courage and loyalty);—these are unmistakably and completely his own, whether he writes of a boy in Northern Michigan, American expatriates in Europe, or big game hunters in Africa.

"Indian Camp" is one of several stories based on Hemingway's experiences on hunting and fishing trips with his father, a well-known Chicago physician. His mastery of the "single incident story," his effective use of dialogue, and his highly economical narrative method are seldom better displayed than in this powerful and moving depiction of a boy's initiation into a world of violence and death. The seemingly effortless, almost reportorial nature of the story is, to the beginner, misleading; this apparently "simple story" is the result of the technical mastery and artistic discipline which make the work of many of Hemingway's contemporaries seem amateurish by comparison.

Forty-nine of Hemingway's short stories were for years available in a Modern Library edition; unfortunately at present no inexpensive, easily accessible volume exists.

Questions   1. At first glance, few writers seem to offer a more marked contrast than Hemingway and Faulkner; for example, compare the compressed action, limited time-span, and simple language of "Indian Camp" with the equivalent elements in "A Bear Hunt" or "That Evening Sun." There is, however, a deeper similarity between the two authors than is immediately apparent. What traits in common, for example, do Nick's father and some of the men in "A Bear Hunt" possess? Would Nick's father have been out of place around Major de Spain's campfire? Can you conceive of the Provine boys hunting or fishing with Nick and his father? Are there any similarities between the attitude of Nick's father towards the Indians, and that of Quentin's father towards the Negroes; or between these father's attitudes toward their children?   2. Hemingway's fiction is frequently concerned with rituals: the ritual of the bullfight, the ritual of the hunter, the ritual of the soldier, and the like. Such rituals, he suggests, establish a kind of kinship between men of all times, countries, races, and persuasions — as the correspondent in Stephen Crane's "The Open Boat" discovered. In this connection do you see any kinship between Hemingway and Faulkner? Between Hemingway and Crane?   3. Compare Hemingway's detached, unmelodramatic treatment of such incidents as the birth of the baby or the suicide of the male Indian with the treatment of similar materials in other stories you have read or in television shows or motion pictures you have seen.   4. Notice the effectiveness of Hemingway's characters — the father, Nick himself, the Indians. Compare or contrast Hemingway's methods of characterization with those of other authors in the text.   5. What is the significance of Nick's last thoughts ("In the early morning on the lake sitting in the stern of the boat with his father rowing, he felt quite sure that he would never die")?

V. S. PRITCHETT

The Sailor

HE WAS LIFTING his knees high and putting his hand up when I first saw him, as if, crossing the road through that stinging rain, he were breaking through the bead curtain of a Pernambuco bar. I knew he was going to stop me. This part of the Euston Road is a beat of the men who want a cup of tea or their fare to a job in Luton or some outlying town.

"Beg pardon, chum," he said in an anxious hot-potato voice. "Is that Whitechapel?"

He pointed to the traffic clogged in the rain farther down where the electric signs were printing off the advertisements and daubing them on the wet road. Coatless, with a smudged trilby hat on the back of his head so that a curl of boot-polish black hair glistered with raindrops over his forehead, he stood there squeezing the water in his boots and looking at me, from his bilious eyes, like a man drowning and screaming for help in two feet of water and wondering why the crowd is laughing.

"That's St. Pancras," I said.

"Oh, Gawd," he said, putting his hand to his jaw like a man with toothache. "I'm all messed up." And he moved on at once, gaping at the lights ahead.

"Here, wait," I said. "Which part of Whitechapel do you want? Where have you come from?"

THE SAILOR Reprinted from *The Sailor, Sense of Humour and Other Stories* by V. S. Pritchett, by permission of Alfred A. Knopf, Inc. Copyright 1953 by V. S. Pritchett.

"Surrey Docks," he said. "They said it was near Surrey Docks, see, but they put me wrong. I bin on the road since ten this morning."

"Acton," he read a bus sign aloud, recalling the bottom of the day's misery. "I bin there," and, fascinated, watched the bus out of sight.

The man's worried mouth dropped open. He was sodden. His clothes were black with damp. The smell of it came off him. The rain stained from the shoulders of his suit past the armpits over the ribs to the waist. It spread from dark blobs over his knees to his thighs. He was a greasy-looking man, once fat, and the fat had gone down unevenly like a deflating bladder. He was calming as I spoke to him.

A sailor, of course, and lost. Hopelessly, blindly lost. I calculated that he must have wandered twenty miles that day exhausting a genius for misdirection.

"Here," I said. "You're soaked. Come and have a drink."

There was a public-house nearby. He looked away at once.

"I never touch it," he said. "It's temptation."

I think it was that word which convinced me the sailor was my kind of man. I am, on the whole, glad to say that I am a puritan and the word "temptation" went home, painfully, pleasurably, excitingly and intimately familiar. A most stimulating and austerely gregarious word, it indicates either the irresistible hypocrite or the fellow struggler with sin. I couldn't let him go after that.

Presently we were in a café drinking acrid Indian tea.

"Off a ship?" I said.

He looked at me as if I were a magician would could read his soul.

"Thank Gawd I stopped you," he said. "I kep' stopping people all day and they messed me up, but you been straight."

He gave me his papers, his discharge paper, his pension form, official letters, as he said this, like a child handing himself over. Albert Edward Thompson, they said, cook, born '96, invalided out of the service two years before. So he was not just off a ship.

"They're clean," he said suspiciously when I asked him about this. "I got ulcers, riddled with ulcers for fourteen years."

He had no job and that worried him, because it was the winter. He had ganged on the road, worked in a circus, had been a waiter in an Italian restaurant. But what worried him much more was getting to Whitechapel. He made it sound to me as though for two years he had been threshing about the country, dished by one job and another, in a less and less successful attempt to get there.

"What job are you going to do?" I said.

"I don't know," he said.

"It's a bad time," I said.

"I fall on my feet," he said, "like I done with you."

We sat opposite to each other at the table. He stared at the people in the café with his appalled eyeballs. He was scared of them and they looked scared too. He looked as though he was going to give a yell and spring at them; in fact, he was likelier to have gone down on his knees to them and to have started sobbing. They couldn't know this. And then he and I looked at each other and the look discovered that we were the only two decent, trustworthy men in a seedy and grabbing world. Within the next two hours I had given him a job. I was chum no longer, but "sir." "Chum" was anarchy and the name of any twisty bleeder you knocked up against, but "sir" for Thompson (out of the naval nursery), was hierarchy, order, pay-day, and peace.

I was living alone in the country in those days. I had no one to look after me. I gave Albert Thompson some money; I took him to Whitechapel and wrote down the directions for his journey to my house.

The bungalow where I lived was small and stood just under the brow of a hill. The country was high and stony there. The roads broke up into lanes, the lanes sank into woods, and cottages were few. The oak woods were naked and as green as canker. They stood like old men, and below them were sweet plantations of larch where the clockwork pheasants went off like toys in the rainy afternoons. At night you heard a farm dog bark like a pistol and the oceanic sound of the trees and sometimes, over an hour and half's walk away, the whistle of a train. But that was all. The few people looked as though they had grown out of the land, sticks and stones in cloth; they were old people chiefly. In the one or two bigger houses they were childless. It was derelict country; frost with its teeth fast in the ground, the wind running finer than sand through a changeless sky or the solitary dribble of water in the butts and the rain legging it over the grass — that was all one heard or saw there.

Place isolated + cheerless

"Gawd!" said Thompson when he got there. "I thought I'd never strike the place." Pale, coatless again in the wet, his hat tipped back from a face puddingy and martyred, he came up the hill with the dancing step of a man treading on nails. He had been lost again. He had travelled by the wrong train, even by the wrong line, he had assumed that, as in towns, it was safest to follow the crowd. But country crowds soon scatter. He had been following people — it sounded to me — to half the cottages for miles around.

"Then I come to the Common," he said. "I didn't like the look of that. I kept round it."

At last some girl had shown him the way.

I calmed him down. We got to my house and I took him to his room. He sat down on the bed and told me the story again. He took off his boots and socks and looked at his blistered feet, murmuring to them as if they were a pair of orphans. There was a woman in the train with a kid, he said, and to amuse the kid he had taken out his jack-knife. The woman called the guard.

After we had eaten and I had settled in, I went for a walk that afternoon. The pleasure of life in the country for me is in its monotony. One understands how much of living is habit, a long war to which people, plants, and animals have settled down. In the country one expects nothing of people; they are themselves, not bringers of gifts. In towns one asks too little or too much of them.

The drizzle had stopped when I went out, the afternoon was warmer and inert, and the dull stench of cattle hung over the grass. On my way down the hill I passed the bungalow that was my nearest neighbour. I could see the roof as pink as a slice of salt ham, from the top of my garden. The bungalow was ten years old. A chicken man had built it. Now the woodwork was splitting and shrinking, the garden was rank, two or three larches, which the rabbits had been at, showed above the dead grass, and there was a rosebush. The bush had one frozen and worm-eaten flower which would stick there half the winter. The history of the bungalow was written in the tin bath by the side door. The bath was full of gin, beer, and whisky bottles, discarded after the weekend parties of many tenants. People took the place forever and then, after a month or two, it changed hands. A business man, sentimental about the country, an in-

valid social worker, a couple with a motor bicycle, an inseparable
pair of school-teachers with big legs and jumping jumpers; and
now there was a woman I hardly saw, a colonel's daughter, but
the place was said to belong to a man in the Northampton boot
trade.

A gramophone was playing when I walked by. Whenever I
passed, the colonel's daughter was either playing the gramophone or digging in the garden. She was a small girl in her late
twenties, with a big knowledgeable-looking head under tobacco-
brown curls, and the garden fork was nearly as big as herself.
Her gardening never lasted long. It consisted usually in digging
up a piece of the matted lawn in order to bury tins; but she
went at it intensely, drawing back the fork until her hair fell
over her face and the sweat stood on her brow. She always had
a cigarette in her mouth, and every now and then the carnation
skin of her face, with its warm, dark-blue eyes, would be distorted and turned crimson by violent bronchial coughing. When
this stopped she would straighten up, the delicacy came back
to her skin, and she would say: "Oh, Christ. Oh, bloody hell,"
and you noticed at the end of every speech the fine right eyebrow
would rise a little, and the lid of the eye below it would quiver.
This wink, the limpid wink of the colonel's daughter, you noticed
at once. You wondered what it meant and planned to find out.
It was as startling and enticing as a fish rising, and you discovered
when you went after it that the colonel's daughter was the hard-
est-drinking and most blasphemous piece of apparent childish
innocence you had ever seen. Old men in pubs gripped their
sticks, went scarlet, and said someone ought to take her drawers
down and give her a tanning. I got a sort of fame from being a
neighbour of the colonel's daughter. "Who's that piece we saw
down the road?" people asked.

"Her father's in the Army."

"Not," two or three of them said, for this kind of wit spreads
like measles, "the Salvation Army." They said I was a dirty dog.
But I hardly knew the colonel's daughter. Across a field she
would wave, utter her obscenity, perform her wink, and edge off
on her slight legs. Her legs were not very good. But if we met
face to face on the road she became embarrassed and nervous;
this was one of her dodges. "Still alone?" she said.

"Yes. And you?"

"Yes. What do you do about sex?"

"I haven't got any."

"Oh, God, I wish I'd met you before."

When I had friends she would come to the house. She daren't come there when I was alone, she said. Every night, she said, she locked and bolted up at six. Then the wink — if it was a wink. The men laughed. She did not want to be raped, she said. Their wives froze and some curled up as if they had got the blight and put their hands hard on their husbands' arms. But the few times she came to the house when I was alone, the colonel's daughter stood by the door, the full length of the room away, with a guilty look on her face.

When I came back from my walk the gramophone had stopped. The colonel's daughter was standing at the door of her bungalow with her sleeves rolled up, a pail of water beside her, and a scrubbing-brush in her hand.

"Hullo," she said awkwardly.

"Hullo," I said.

"I see you've got the Navy down here. I didn't know you were that way."

"I thought you would have guessed that straight away," I said.

"I found him on the Common crying this morning. You've broken his heart." Suddenly she was taken by a fit of coughing.

"Well," she said, "every day brings forth something."

When I got to the gate of my bungalow I saw that at any rate if Thompson could do nothing else he could bring forth smoke. It was travelling in thick brown funnel puffs from the short chimney of the kitchen. The smoke came out with such dense streaming energy that the house looked like a destroyer racing full steam ahead into the wave of hills. I went down the path to the kitchen and looked inside. There was Thompson, not only with his sleeves rolled up but his trousers also, and he was shovelling coal into the kitchener with the garden spade, the face of the fire was roaring yellow, the water was throbbing and sighing in the boiler, the pipes were singing through the house.

"Bunkering," Thompson said.

I went into the sitting-room. I thought I had come into the wrong house. The paint had been scrubbed, the floors polished like decks, the reflections of the firelight danced in them, the windows gleamed, and the room was glittering with polished metal. Doorknobs, keyholes, fire-irons, window-catches, were polished; metal that I had no idea existed flashed with life.

"What time is supper piped — er, ordered," said Thompson, appearing in his stocking feet. His big round eyes started out of their dyspeptic shadows and became enthusiastic when I told him the hour.

A change came over my life after this. Before Thompson everything had been disorganized and wearying. He drove my papers and clothes back to their proper places. He brought the zest and routine of the Royal Navy into my life. He kept to his stocking feet out of tenderness for those orphans, a kind of repentance for what he had done to them; he was collarless and he served food with a splash as if he allowed for the house to give a pitch or a roll that didn't come off. His thumbs left their marks on the plates. But he was punctual. He lived for "orders." "All ready, sir," he said, planking down the dish and looking up at the clock at the same moment. Burned, perhaps, spilling over the side, invisible beneath Bisto — but on time!

The secret of happiness is to find a congenial monotony. My own housekeeping had suffered from the imagination. Thompson put an end to this tiring chase of the ideal. "What's orders for lunch, sir?"

"Do you a nice fried chop and chips?" he said. That was settled. He went away, but soon he came back.

"What pudding's ordered, sir?" That stumped both of us, or it stumped me. Thompson watched me to time his own suggestion.

"Do you a nice spotted dick?" So it was. We had this on the second day and the third, we changed on the fourth, but on the fifth we came back to it. Then Thompson's mind gave a leap.

"Do you grilled chop, chips, spotted dick *and custard?*" he said. That became almost our fixed menu. There were bouts of blancmange, but spotted dick came back.

Thompson had been sinking towards semi-starvation, I to the insidious Oblomovism of the country. Now we were reformed and happy.

"I always fall on my feet," he said, "like I done with you." It was his refrain.

The winter dripped like a tap, the fog hardly left our hill. Winter in England has the colourless, steaming look of a fried-fish-shop window. But we were stoking huge fires, we bunkered, the garden spade went through coal by the hundredweight. We began to talk a more tangy dialect. Things were not put away; they were "stowed." String appeared in strange knots to make things "fast," plants were "lashed" in the dying garden, washing was "hoist" on the lines, floors were "swabbed." The kitchen became the "galley." The postman came "alongside," all meals were "piped," and at bedtime we "piped down." At night, hearing the wind bump in the chimneys and slop like ocean surf in the woods, looking out at the leather darkness, I had the sensation that we were creeping down the Mersey in a fog or lumping about in the Atlantic swell off Ushant.

I was happy. But was Thompson happy? He seemed to be. In the mornings we were both working, but in the afternoons there was little more to do. He sat on a low chair with his knees close to the bars of the range or on the edge of his bed, darning his clothes. (He lived in a peculiar muddle of his own and he was dirty in his own quarters.) In the evenings he did the same and sometimes we talked. He told me about his life. There was nothing in it at all. It was buried under a mumble of obscurity. His memories were mainly of people who hadn't "behaved right," a dejecting moral wilderness with Thompson mooching about in it, disappointed with human nature. He didn't stay to talk with me much. He preferred the kitchen, where, the oil-lamp smoking, the range smoking, and himself smoking, he sat chewing it all over, gazing into the fire.

"You can go out, you know," I said, "whenever you want. Do what you like."

"I'm O.K.," he said.

"See some of the people," I said. Thompson said he'd just as lief stand by.

Everyone knows his own business best. But I was interested one night when I heard the sound of voices in the kitchen. Someone had come in. The voices went on on other nights. Who was it? The milker from the farm probably or the cowman who cleaned out cesspits by lantern light at night and talked with nostalgia about burying bodies during the war. "If there hadn't been a war," this man used to say, "I wouldn't have seen nothing. It was an education."

I listened. Slow in question, slow in answer, the monotonous voices came. The woodcutter, the postman? I went into the kitchen to see who the profound and interminable crony was.

There was no one. There was only Thompson in the kitchen. Sitting close to the fire with all windows closed, a shallow, stupe-fied, oil-haired head in his own fug, Thompson was spelling out a story from a *Wild West Magazine*. It was old and dirty and his coal-blackened finger was moving from word to word.

So far Thompson had refused to go out of the house except as far as the coal-shed, but I was determined after this discovery that he should go out. I waited until pay-day.

"Here's your money," I said. "Take the afternoon off."

Thompson stepped back from the money.

"You keep it," he said, in a panic. "You keep it for me."

"You may need it," I said. "For a glass of beer or cigarettes or something."

"If I have it I'll lose it," he said. "They'll pinch it."

"Who?" I said.

"People," Thompson said. I could not persuade him.

"All right, I'll keep it for you," I said.

"Yes," he said eagerly. "If I want a bob I'll ask you. Money's temptation," he said.

"Well, anyway," I said, "take the afternoon off. It's the first sunny afternoon we've had. I'll tell you where to go. Turn to the right in the lane . . ."

"I don't like them lanes," said Thompson, looking suspiciously out of the window. "I'll stay by you."

"Well, take a couple of hours," I said. "We all need fresh air."

He looked at me as if I had suggested he should poison him-self; indeed as if I were going to do the poisoning.

"What if I do an hour?" he began to bargain.

"No, the afternoon," I said.

"Do you half an hour?" he pleaded.

"All right, I don't want to force you," I said. "This is a free country. Go for an hour."

It was like an auction.

"Tell you what," he said, looking shifty. "I'll do you twenty minutes." He thought he had tricked me, but I went back into the kitchen and drove him to it. I had given him an overcoat and shoes, and it was this appeal to his vanity that got him. Out he went for his twenty minutes. He was going straight down the

lane to where it met the main road and then straight back; it
would take a smart walker about twelve minutes on a winter's
day.

When an hour passed, I was pleased with myself. But when
four hours had gone by and darkness came, I began to wonder.
I went out to the gate. The land and the night had become one
thing. I had just gone in again when I heard loud voices and
saw the swing of a lamp. There came Thompson with a labourer.
The labourer, a little bandy man known as Fleas, stood like a
bent bush with a sodden sack on his shoulders, snuffling in the
darkness, and he grinned at me with the malevolence of the land.

"He got astray," he said, handing Thompson over.

"Gawd," exclaimed Thompson, exhausted. His face was the
familiar pale suety agony. He was full of explanations. He was
sweating like a scared horse and nearly hysterical. He'd been on
the wrong course. He didn't know where to steer. One thing
looked like another. Roads and lanes, woods and fields, mixed
themselves together.

"Woods I seen," he said in horror. "And that Common! It
played me up proper."

"But you weren't anywhere near the Common," I said.

"Then what was it?" he said.

That night he sat by the fire with his head in his hands.

"I got a mood," he said.

The next morning cigarette smoke blew past my window and I
heard coughing. The colonel's daughter was at the kitchen door
talking to Thompson. "Cheero," I heard her say and then she
came to my door and pushed it open. She stood there gravely
and her eye winked. She was wearing a yellow jersey and looked
as neat as a bird.

"You're a swine," she said.

"What have I done?"

"Raping women on the Common," she said. "Deserting your
old friends, aren't you?"

"It's been too wet on the Common," I said.

"Not for me," she said. "I'm always hopeful. I came across
last night. There was the minister's wife screaming in the middle
of it. I sat on her head and calmed her down, and she said a
man had been chasing her. 'Stop screaming,' I said. 'You flatter
yourself, dear.' It was getting dark and I carried her shopping-

bag and umbrella for her and took her to her house. I often go
and see her in the evenings. I've got to do something, haven't I?
I can't stick alone in that bungalow all day and all night. We sit
and talk her about her son in China. When you're old you'll be
lonely too."

"What happened on the Common?"

"I think I'm drunk," said the colonel's daughter, "but I believe
I've been drunk since breakfast. Well, where was I? I'm losing
my memory too. Well, we hadn't gone five minutes before I
heard someone panting like a dog behind us and jumping over
bushes. Old Mrs. Stour started screaming again. 'Stand still,' I
said, and I looked and then a man came out of a tree about ten
yards away. 'What the hell do you want?' I said. A noise came
back like a sheep. 'Ma'am, ma'am, ma'am, ma'am,' it said."

"So that's where Thompson was," I said.

"I thought it was you," the colonel's daughter said. " 'There's
a woman set about me with a stick on the Common,' he said. 'I
didn't touch her, I was only following her,' he said. 'I reckoned
if I followed her I'd get home.'

"When they got to the wood, Thompson wouldn't go into it
and she had to take his hand; that was a mistake. He took
his hand away and moved off. So she grabbed his coat. He
struggled after this, she chased him into the thicket and told him
not to be a fool but he got away and disappeared, running on to
the Common.

"You're a damn swine," the colonel's daughter said to me.
"How would you like to be put down in the middle of the sea?"

She walked away. I watched her go up the path and lean on
the gate opposite to stroke the nose of a horse. She climbed into
the field and the horses, like hairy yokels, went off. I heard her
calling them, but they did not come.

When she was out of sight, the door opened behind me and
Thompson came in.

"Beg pardon, sir," he said. "That young lady, sir. She's been
round my kitchen door."

"Yes," I said.

He gaped at me and then burst out: "I didn't touch her, straight
I didn't. I didn't lay a finger on her."

"She didn't say you did. She was trying to help you."

He calmed down. "Yes, sir," he said.

When he came back into the room to lay the table I could see he was trying to catch my eye.

"Sir," he said at last, standing at attention. "Beg pardon, sir, the young lady . . ."

His mouth was opening and shutting, trying to shape a sentence.

"The young lady — she'd had a couple, sir," he said in a rush.

"Oh," I said, "don't worry about that. She often has."

"It's ruination, sir," said Thompson evangelically.

She did not come to the house again for many days, but when she came I heard him lock both kitchen doors.

Orders at the one extreme, temptation at the other, were the good and evil of Thompson's life. I no longer suggested that he go out. I invented errands and ordered him to go. I wanted, in that unfortunate way one has, to do good to Thompson. I wanted him to be free and happy. At first he saw that I was not used to giving orders and he tried to dodge. His ulcers were bad, he said. Once or twice he went about barefoot, saying the sole was off one of his boots. But when he saw I meant what I said, he went. I used to watch him go, tilted forward on his toes in his half-running walk, like someone throwing himself blindly upon the mercy of the world. When he came back he was excited. He had the look of someone stupefied by incomprehensible success. It is the feeling a landsman has when he steps off a boat after a voyage. You feel giddy, canny, surprised at your survival after crossing that bridge of deep, loose water. You boast. So did Thompson — morally.

"There was a couple of tramps on the road," Thompson said. "I steered clear. I never talked to them," he said.

"Someone asked me who I was working for." He described the man. "I never told him," he said shrewdly. "I just said 'A gentleman.' Meaning you," he said.

There was a man in an allotment who had asked him for a light and wanted to know his business.

"I told him I didn't smoke," said Thompson. "You see my meaning — you don't know what it's leading up to. There warn't no harm, but that's how temptation starts."

What was temptation? Almost everything was temptation to Thompson. Pubs, cinemas, allotments, chicken-runs, tobacconists

— in these, everywhere, the tempter might be. Temptation, like Othello's jealousy, was the air itself.

"I expect you'd like to go to church," I said. He seemed that kind.

"I got nothing *against* religion," Thompson said. "But best keep clear. They see you in church and the next thing they're after you."

"Who?" I asked.

"People," he said. "It's not like a ship."

I was like him, he said, I kept myself to myself. I kept out of temptation's way. He was glad I was like that, he said.

It was a shock to me that while I observed Thompson, Thompson observed me. At the same time one prides oneself, the moment one's character is defined by someone else, on defeating the definition, I kept myself to myself? I avoided temptation? That was all Thompson knew! There was the colonel's daughter. I might not see her very often; she might be loud, likable, dreary or alarming by turns, but she was Temptation itself. How did he know I wasn't tempted? Thompson's remark made me thrill. I began to see rather more of the colonel's daughter.

And so I discovered how misleading he had been about his habits and how, where temptation was concerned, he made a difference between profession and practice. So strong was Thompson's feeling about temptation that he was drawn at once to every tempter he saw. He stopped them on the road and was soon talking about it. The postman was told. The shopkeepers heard all his business and mine. He hurried after tramps, he detained cyclists, he sat down on the banks with road-makers and ditchers, telling them the dangers of drink, the caution to be kept before strangers. And after he had done this he always ended by telling them he kept himself to himself, avoided drink, ignored women, and, patting his breast pocket, said that was where he kept his money and his papers. He behaved to them exactly as he had behaved with me two months before in the Euston Road. The colonel's daughter told me. She picked up all the news in that district.

"He's a decent, friendly soul," muttered the colonel's daughter thickly. "You're a prig. Keep your hair on. You can't help it. I expect you're decent, too, but you're like all my bloody so-called friends."

"Oh," I said hopefully, "are prigs your special line?"

I found out, too, why Thompson was always late when he came home from his errands. I had always accepted that he was lost. And so he was in a way, but he was lost through wandering about with people, following them to their doorsteps, drifting to their allotments, back yards, and all the time telling them, as he clung to their company, about the dangers of human intercourse. "I never speak to nobody" — it was untrue, but it was not a lie. It was simply a delusion.

"He lives in two worlds at once," I said to the colonel's daughter one morning. I had sent Thompson to the town to buy the usual chops, and I was sitting in her bungalow. This was the first time I had ever been in it. The walls were of varnished matchboarding like the inside of a gospel hall, and the room was heated by a kerosene stove which smelled like armpits. There were two rexine-covered chairs, a rug, and a table in the room. She was sorting out gramophone records as I talked and the records she did not like she dropped to the floor and broke. She was listening very little to what I said but walked to the gramophone, put on a record, stopped it after a few turns, and then, switching it off, threw the record away.

"Oh, you know a hell of a lot, don't you?" she said. "I don't say you're not an interesting man, but you don't get on with it, do you?"

"How old are you? Twenty-five?" I said.

Her sulking, ironical expression went. She was astonished.

"Good God!" she exclaimed with a smile of sincerity. "Don't be a damn fool." Then she frowned. "Or are you being professionally clever.

"Here," she said. "I was damn pretty when I was twenty-five. I'm thirty-nine. I've still got a good figure."

"I would have put you at twenty-seven at the most," I said truthfully.

She walked towards me. I was sitting on the armchair and she stood very close. She had never been as close to me before. I had thought her eyes were dark blue, but now I saw they were green and grey, with a moist lascivious haze in them and yet dead and clock-like, like a cat's on a sunless day. And the skin, which had seemed fresh to me, I saw in its truth for the first time. It was clouded and flushed, clouded with that thickened pimpled ruddiness which the skin of heavy drinkers has and which in middle age becomes bloated and mottled. I felt: "This is why she has always stood the length of the room away before."

She saw what was in my mind and she sat down on the chair opposite me. The eye winked.

"Keep control of yourself," she said. "I came down here for a rest and now you've started coming round."

"Only in the mornings," I said.

She laughed. She went to a bookshelf and took down a bottle of whisky and poured out half a tumblerful.

"This is what you've done coming in here, early bird," she said. "Exciting me on an empty stomach. I haven't touched it for ten days. I had a letter this morning. From my old man."

"Your father?"

I had always tried to imagine the colonel. She gave a shout of cheerful laughter and it ended in coughing till tears came to her eyes.

"That's rich. God, that's rich. Keen observer of women! No, from my husband, darling. He's not my husband, damn him, of course, but when you've lived with someone for ten years and he pays the rent and keeps you, he is your husband, isn't he? Or ought to be. Ten years is a long time and his family thought he ought to be married. He thought so too. So he picked up a rich American girl and pushed me down here to take it easy in the country. I'm on the dole like your sailor boy. Well, I said, if he felt that way, he'd better have his head. In six months he'll tire of the new bitch. So I left him alone. I didn't want to spoil his fun. Well, now, he writes me, he wants to bring his fiancée down because she's heard so much about me and adores the country. . . ."

I was going to say something indignant.

"He's nice too," she said casually. "He sells gas heaters. You'd like him all the same. But blast that bloody woman," she said, raising her cool voice. "She's turned him into a snob. I'm just his whore now.

"Don't look so embarrassed," she said. "I'm not going to cry.

"For ten years," she said, "I read books, I learned French, educated myself, learned to say 'How d'you do?' instead of 'Pleased to meet you,' and look down my nose at everything in his sort of way. And I let him go about saying my father was in the

Army too, but they were such bloody fools they thought he must be a colonel. They'd never heard of sergeant majors having children. Even my old man, bless his heart," she smiled affectionately, "thought or let himself think as they did. I was a damn silly little snob."

"I don't know him," I said. "But he doesn't sound much good to me."

"That's where you're wrong," she said sharply. "Just weak, poor kid, that's all. You don't know what it is to be ashamed your mother's a housemaid. I got over it — but he didn't, that's all."

She paused and the wink gave its signal.

"This is more embarrassing than I thought," she said.

"I am very sorry," I said. "Actually I am in favour of snobbery, it is a sign of character. It's a bad thing to have, but it's a bad thing not to have had. You can't help having the diseases of your time."

"There you go," she said.

The suffering of others is incredible. When it is obscure it seems like a lie; when it is garish and raw, it is like boasting. It is a challenge to oneself. I got up from my chair and went towards her. I was going to kiss her.

"You are the sentimental type," she said.

So I didn't kiss her.

Then we heard someone passing the bungalow and she went to the window. Thompson was going by. The lock of black hair was curling over his sweating forehead and he gave a hesitant staggering look at the bungalow. There was a lump of fear on his face.

"He'd better not know where you've been," she said. She moved her lips to be kissed, but I walked out.

I was glad of the steady sense of the fresh grey air when I got outside. I was angry and depressed. I stood at the window of my house. Thompson came in and was very talkative. He'd been lost, of course. He'd seen people. He'd seen fields. He'd heard trees. He'd seen roads. I hardly listened. I was used to the jerky wobbling voice. I caught the words "legion" and "temptation," and thought he was quoting from the Bible. Presently I realized he was talking about the British Legion. The postman had asked him to go to a meeting of the British Legion that night. How simple other people's problems are! Yet "No" Thompson was saying. He was not going to the British Legion. It was temptation.

I ought to have made love to her and kissed her I was thinking. She was right, I was a prig.

"You go," I said to Thompson, "if you want to. You'd enjoy it."

But how disgusting, obvious, stupid, to have made love to her then, I thought.

"Do as you like," I said.

"I'm best alongside you," said Thompson.

"You can't always be by me," I said. "In a month, perhaps less, as you know, I'll be leaving here and you'll have to go."

"Yes," he said. "You tol' me. You been straight. I'll be straight with you. I won't go to the Legion."

We ate our meal and I read.

"In every branch of our spiritual and material civilization we seem to have reached a turning-point," I read. "This spirit shows itself not only in the actual state of public affairs. . . ."

"Well," I thought, "I can ask her over tonight. I needn't be a fool twice." I went out for an hour. When I returned, Thompson was fighting Temptation hard. If he went to the Legion how would he get back? No, best not. He took the Legion on in its strength. ("She is a type," I thought.) At four he was still at it. At five he asked me for his money. ("Well, we are all types," I was thinking.) Very shortly he brought the money back and asked me to keep his pension papers. At half past six I realized this meant that Thompson was losing and the Legion and all its devils winning. (What is a prig, anyway?) He was looking out at the night. Yet, just when I thought he had lost, he had won. There was the familiar sound of the Wild West monologue in the kitchen. It was half past eight. The Legion was defeated.

I was disappointed in Thompson. Really, not to have had more guts than that! Restlessly I looked out of the window. There was a full moon spinning on the tail of a dying wind. Under the moonlight the fields were like wide-awake faces, the woods like womanish heads of hair upon them. I put on my hat and coat and went out. I was astonished by the circle of stars. They were as distinct as figures on a clock. I took out my watch and compared the small time in my hand with the wide time above. Then I walked on. There was a sour smell at the end of the wood, where, no doubt, a dead rabbit or pigeon was rotting.

I came out of the wood on to the metalled road. Suddenly my
heart began to beat quickly as I hurried down the road, but it
was a long way round now. I cut across fields. There was a
cottage and a family were listening to a dance-band on the
wireless. A man was going the rounds of his chickens. There
was a wheelbarrow and there were spades and steel bars where a
water mill was being built.

Then I crossed the last fields and saw the bungalow. My
heart throbbed heavily and I felt all my blood slow down and my
limbs grow heavy. It was only when I got to the road that I saw
there were no lights in the bungalow. The colonel's daughter,
the sergeant's daughter, had gone to bed early like a child. While
I stood I heard men's voices singing across the fields. It must
have gone ten o'clock and people were coming out of the public-
house. In all the villages of England, at this hour, loud-voiced
groups were breaking up and dispersing into the lanes.

I got to my house and lit a candle. The fire was low. I was
exhausted and happy to be in my house among my own things,
as if I had got into my own skin again. There was no light in
the kitchen. Thompson had gone to bed. I grinned at the
thought of the struggles of poor Thompson. I picked up a book
and read. I could hear still the sound of that shouting and singing. The beer was sour and flat in this part of the country, but it
made people sing.

The singing voices came nearer. I put down the book. An
argument was going on in the lane. I listened. The argument
was nearing the cottage. The words got louder. They were going
on at my gate. I heard the gate go and the argument was on my
path. Suddenly — there could be no doubt — people were coming to the door. I stood up, I could recognize no voice. Loud
singing, stumbling feet, then bang! The door broke open and
crashed against the wall. Tottering, drunk, with their arms round
each other, Thompson and the colonel's daughter nearly fell
into the room.

Thompson stared at me with terror.

"Stand up, sailor," said the colonel's daughter, clinging to him.

"He was lonely," she said unsteadily to me. "We've been playing gramophone records. Sing," she said.

Thompson was still staring.

"Don't look at him. Sing," she said. Then she gave a low laugh and they fell, bolt upright on the sofa like prim, dishevelled dolls.

A look of wild love of all the world came into Thompson's eyes and he smiled as I had never seen him smile before. He suddenly opened his twitching mouth and bawled:

> *"You've robbed every tailor,*
> *And you've skinned every sailor,*
> *But you won't go walking Paradise Street no more."*

"Go on. That's not all," the colonel's daughter cried and sang: "Go on — something — something, deep and rugged shore."

She put her arms round his neck and kissed him. He gaped at her with panic and looked at her skirt. It was undone.

He pointed at her leg in consternation. The sight sobered him. He pulled away his arms and rushed out of the room. He did not come back. She looked at me and giggled. Her eyes were warm and shining. She picked leaves off her skirt.

"Where's he gone? Where's he gone?" she kept asking.

"He's gone to bed," I said.

She started a fit of coughing. It strained her throat. Her eyes were dilated like an animal's caught in a trap, and she held her hand to her chest.

"I wish," she cried hysterically, pointing at me in the middle of her coughing, "I wish you could see your bloody face."

She got up and called out: "Thompson! Thompson!" And when he did not answer she sang out: "Down by the deep and rugged shore — ore-ore-ore."

"What's the idea?" I said.

"I want Thompson," she said. "He's the only man up here."

Then she began to cry. She marched out to his room, but it was locked. She was wandering through the other rooms calling him and then she went out, away up the path. She went calling him all the way down to her bungalow.

In the morning Thompson appeared as usual. He brought the breakfast. He came in for "orders." Grilled chop, did I think? And what about spotted dick? He seemed no worse. He behaved as though nothing had happened. There was no guilty look in his eyes and no apprehension. He made no apology. Lunch passed, teatime, and the day. I finished my work and went into the kitchen.

"Tell me," I said, "about last night."

Thompson was peeling potatoes. He used to do this into a bucket on the floor, as if he were peeling for a whole crew. He put down the clasp-knife and stood up. He looked worried.

"That was a terrible thing," Thompson said, as if it was something he had read about in the papers. "Terrible, sir. A young lady like that, sir. To come over here for me, an educated lady like that. Someone oughter teach her a lesson. Coming over and saying she wanted to play some music. I was took clean off my guard. It wasn't right," said Thompson. "Whichever way you look at it, it wasn't right. I told her she'd messed me up."

"I'm not blaming you. I want to know."

"And she waited till you was out," Thompson said. "That's not straight. She may class herself as an educated young lady, but do you know what I reckon she is? I reckon she's a jane."

I went down to the bungalow. I was beginning to laugh now. She was in the garden digging. Her sleeves were rolled up and she was sweating over the fork. The beds were thick with leaves and dead plants. I stood there watching her. She looked at me nervously for a moment. "I'm making the garden tidy," she said. "For Monday. When the bitch comes down."

She was shy and awkward. I walked on and, looking back, saw her go into the house. It was the last I ever saw of her. When I came back, the fork she had been using was stuck in the flower bed where she had left it. She went to London that night and did not return.

"Thank Gawd," Thompson said.

There was a change in Thompson after this and there was a change in me. Perhaps the change came because the dirty February days were going, the air softer and the year moving. I was leaving soon. Thompson mentioned temptation no more. Now he went out every day. The postman was his friend. They used to go to the pub. He asked for his money. In the public-house the labourers sat around muttering in a language Thompson didn't understand. He stood them drinks. At his first pint he would start singing. They encouraged him. He stood them more drinks. The postman ordered them for him and then tapped him on the pocket book. They emptied his pockets every night. They despised him and even brought complaints to me about him after they had emptied his pockets.

Thompson came back across the Common alone, wild, enthusiastic, and moaning with suspicion by turns. The next day he
would have a mood. All the countryside for ten miles around
knew the sailor. He became famous.

Our last week came. He quietened down.

"What are you going to do," I asked.

"I'll stay by you."

"You can't," I said. "I'll be going abroad."

"You needn't pay me," he said. "I'll stay by you." It was hard
to make him understand he could not stay with me. He was
depressed.

"Get me out of here safe," he pleaded at last. "Come with me
to the station." He could not go on his own because all the people
he knew would be after him. He had told them he was going.
He had told them I was saving his pension and his last fortnight's
pay. They would come creeping out of cottage doors and ditches
for him. So I packed his things and got a taxi to call for us. How
slowly we had lived and moved in these fields and lanes! Now
we broke through it all with a rush as the car dropped down the
hill and the air blew in at the window. As we passed the bungalow with the sun on its empty windows, I saw the fork standing in
the neglected bed. Then we swept on. Thompson sat back in
the car so that no one should see him, but I leaned forward to
see everything for the last time and forget it.

We got to the town. As the taxi slowed down in the streets,
people looked out of shop doors; a potman nodded from the
pub.

"Whatcha, Jack," the voices called.

The police, the fishmonger, boys going to school, dozens of
people waved to him. I might have been riding with royalty.
At the station a large woman sweeping down the steps of the
bank straightened up and gave a shout.

"Hi, Jacko!" she called, bending double, went into shrieks of
laughter and called across to a friend at a first-floor window. It
was a triumph. But Thompson ignored them all. He sat back
out of sight.

"Thank Gawd I've got you," he said. "They skin you of everything."

We sat in the train. It was a two-hour journey.

"Once I strike Whitechapel," he said in the voice of one naming

Singapore, "I'll be O.K." He said this several times, averting his
face from the passing horror of the green fields.

"Don't you worry," he said. "Don't fret yourself for me. Don't
you worry." His optimism increased as mine dwindled as we got
nearer London. By the time we reached London he was almost
shouting. "I'll fall on my feet, don't you worry. I'll send you my
address."

We stood on the curb and I watched him walk off into the yellow rain and the clogged, grunting, and mewing traffic. He
stepped right into it without looking. Taxis braked to avoid him.
He was going to walk to Whitechapel. He reckoned it was safer.

V(ictor) S(awdon) Pritchett (1900-)   V. S. Pritchett was
born in Ipswich, England, and educated at Alleyn's School in London.
Like his countrymen A. E. Coppard and Walter de la Mare, he deserted business to be a writer. He has been a newspaper correspondent, in Spain and Morocco; literary editor of *The New Statesman and
Nation;* a broadcaster and frequent contributor to British and American
magazines; and is generally regarded as one of the most distinguished
living British writers of fiction. Besides several collections of short
stories and novels, he is the author of three books of criticism. Mr.
Pritchett lives with his wife and two children at Andover, in Hamp-
shire.

Many of Pritchett's stories are, like "The Sailor," concerned with
the ambivalence of human experience and what the author has termed
the "double lives" of middle-class Britishers undone by their own
shortcomings and bewildered by changing social and moral values of
the world in which they live. Although he is a sound, often engrossing
story teller in a long and great tradition of British writers beginning
with Henry Fielding in the mid-eighteenth century, Pritchett's main
interest is with people rather than with plot, with character rather
than events, with personality rather than incidents. "The Sailor," with
its lonely, schizoid human beings playing out their roles in a drama
of which they themselves are hardly aware, is characteristic; the comments of the narrator — "He lives in two worlds at once" — is applicable to many of the author's people. The colonel's alcoholic
daughter, the lonely sailor with his penchant for getting lost, and the
withdrawn and inhibited narrator all dwell, in the author's own
words, "in a solitude which they alone can populate."

Twenty-five of V. S. Pritchett's stories, composed over a quarter of a century, appear in *The Sailor, Sense of Humour, and Other Stories* (Knopf).

Questions   1. *Whose* story is this, that of the narrator, of the sailor, or of the colonel's daughter? What, if anything, do these characters have in common with the "grotesques" of Sherwood Anderson's *Winesburg, Ohio?* Who is the most sympathetic of the three major characters? The least sympathetic? What traits do these three characters have in common? In what ways do they bear out the author's own comment that in his short stories the "drama has lain in the portrait, in the unconscious self-revelation of people. . . . It strikes me that the story lies in their double lives, . . . the drama, the event, the plot, is the person; and the more fantastic, the more certain to be true." 2. Mr. Pritchett has stated that he originally wrote several versions of this story narrated in the third person. What do you think he may have gained by switching to the point of view of the narrating "I"? This character, "I," is extremely conscious of the shortcomings of the people around him; is he aware of his own limitations and shortcomings? 3. Pritchett, like Charles Dickens, is a master of character-portrayal and caricature; among numerous other devices, he often employs "taglines" which help sum up or epitomize a character. For example, with the sailor, the "tag" is "It's temptation." Are there any more such examples in the story? What other devices are used?   4. What is the purpose of such a line as "There was a sour smell at the end of the wood, where, no doubt, a dead rabbit or pigeon was rotting"? Do you find any other examples of this sort of thing in the story?

FRANK O'CONNOR

Legal Aid

DELIA CARTY came of a very respectable family. It was going as
maid to the O'Gradys of Pouladuff that ruined her. That whole
family was slightly touched. The old man, a national teacher, was
hardly ever at home, and the daughters weren't much better.
When they weren't away visiting, they had people visiting them,
and it was nothing to Delia to come in late at night and find one
of them plastered round some young fellow on the sofa.

That sort of thing isn't good for any young girl. Like mistress
like maid; inside six months she was smoking, and within a year
she was carrying on with one Tom Flynn, a farmer's son. Her
father, a respectable, hard-working man, knew nothing about it,
for he would have realized that she was no match for one of the
Flynns, and even if Tom's father, Ned, had known, he would
never have thought it possible that any labourer's daughter could
imagine herself a match for Tom.

Not, God knows, that Tom was any great catch. He was a big
uncouth galoot who was certain that lovemaking, like drink,
was one of the simple pleasures his father tried to deprive him
of, out of spite. He used to call at the house while the O'Gradys
were away, and there would be Delia in one of Eileen O'Grady's
frocks and with Eileen O'Grady's lipstick and powder on, doing
the lady over the tea things in the parlour. Throwing a glance

LEGAL AID   Reprinted from *The Stories of Frank O'Connor, by permission*
of Alfred A. Knopf, Inc. Copyright 1951, 1952 by Frank O'Connor.

over his shoulder in case anyone might spot him, Tom would heave himself onto the sofa with his boots over the end.

"Begod, I love sofas," he would say with simple pleasure.

"Put a cushion behind you," Delia would say.

"Oh, begod," Tom would say, making himself comfortable, "if ever I have a house of my own 'tis unknown what sofas and cushions I'll have. Them teachers must get great money. What the hell do they go away at all for?"

Delia loved making the tea and handing it out like a real lady, but you couldn't catch Tom out like that.

"Ah, what do I want tay for?" he would say with a doubtful glance at the cup. "Haven't you any whisky? Ould O'Grady must have gallons of it. . . . Leave it there on the table. Why the hell don't they have proper mugs with handles a man could get a grip on? Is that taypot silver? Pity I'm not a teacher!"

It was only natural for Delia to show him the bedrooms and the dressing-tables with the three mirrors, the way you could see yourself from all sides, but Tom, his hands under his head, threw himself with incredulous delight on the low double bed and cried: "Springs! Begod, 'tis like a car!"

What the springs gave rise to was entirely the O'Gradys' fault since no one but themselves would have left a house in a lonesome part to a girl of nineteen to mind. The only surprising thing was that it lasted two years without Delia showing any signs of it. It probably took Tom that time to find the right way.

But when he did he got into a terrible state. It was hardly in him to believe that a harmless poor devil like himself whom no one ever bothered his head about could achieve such unprecedented results on one girl, but when he understood it he knew only too well what the result of it would be. His father would first beat hell out of him and then throw him out and leave the farm to his nephews. There being no hope of conciliating his father, Tom turned his attention to God, who, though supposed to share Ned Flynn's views about fellows and girls, had some nature in Him. Tom stopped seeing Delia, to persuade God that he was reforming and to show that anyway it wasn't his fault. Left alone he could be a decent, good-living young fellow, but the Carty girl was a forward, deceitful hussy who

had led him on instead of putting him off the way any well-bred
girl would do. Between lipsticks, sofas, and tay in the parlour,
Tom put it up to God that it was a great wonder she hadn't got
him into worse trouble.

Delia had to tell her mother, and Mrs. Carty went to Father
Corcoran to see could he induce Tom to marry her. Father
Corcoran was a tall, testy old man who, even at the age of sixty-
five, couldn't make out for the life of him what young fellows
saw in girls, but if he didn't know much about lovers he knew a
lot about farmers.

"Wisha, Mrs. Carty," he said crankily, "how could I get him to
marry her? Wouldn't you have a bit of sense? Some little financial arrangement, maybe, so that she could leave the parish
and not be a cause of scandal — I might be able to do that."

He interviewed Ned Flynn, who by this time had got Tom's
version of the story and knew financial arrangements were going
to be the order of the day unless he could put a stop to them. Ned
was a man of over six foot with a bald brow and a smooth un-
lined face as though he never had a care except his general concern for the welfare of humanity which made him look so
abnormally thoughtful. Even Tom's conduct hadn't brought a
wrinkle to his brow.

"I don't know, father," he said, stroking his bald brow with a
dieaway air, "I don't know what you could do at all."

"Wisha, Mr. Flynn," said the priest who, when it came to the
pinch, had more nature than twenty Flynns, "wouldn't you do the
handsome thing and let him marry her before it goes any farther?"

"I don't see how much farther it could go, father," said Ned.

"It could become a scandal."

"I'm afraid 'tis that already, father."

"And after all," said Father Corcoran, forcing himself to put in
a good word for one of the unfortunate sex whose very existence
was a mystery to him, "is she any worse than the rest of the girls
that are going? Bad is the best of them, from what I see, and
Delia is a great deal better than most."

"That's not my information at all, father," said Ned, looking
like "The Heart Bowed Down."

"That's a very serious statement, Mr. Flynn," said Father Corcoran, giving him a challenging look.

"It can be proved, father," said Ned gloomily. "Of course I'm not denying the boy was foolish, but the cleverest can be caught."

"You astonish me, Mr. Flynn," said Father Corcoran who was beginning to realize that he wasn't even going to get a subscription. "Of course I can't contradict you, but 'twill cause a terrible scandal."

"I'm as sorry for that as you are, Father," said Ned, "but I have my son's future to think of."

Then, of course, the fun began. Foolish to the last, the O'Gradys wanted to keep Delia on till it was pointed out to them that Mr. O'Grady would be bound to get the blame. After this, her father had to be told. Dick Carty knew exactly what became a devoted father, and he beat Delia till he had to be hauled off her by the neighbours. He was a man who loved to sit in his garden reading his paper; now he felt he owed it to himself not to be seen enjoying himself, so instead he sat over the fire and brooded. The more he brooded the angrier he became. But seeing that, with the best will in the world, he could not beat Delia every time he got angry, he turned his attention to the Flynns. Ned Flynn, that contemptible bosthoon, had slighted one of the Cartys in a parish where they had lived for hundreds of years with unblemished reputations; the Flynns, as everyone knew, being mere upstarts and outsiders without a date on their gravestones before 1850 — nobodies!

He brought Delia to see Jackie Canty, the solicitor in town. Jackie was a little jenny-ass of a man with thin lips, a pointed nose, and a pince-nez that wouldn't stop in place, and he listened with grave enjoyment to the story of Delia's misconduct. "And what happened then, please?" he asked in his shrill singsong, looking at the floor and trying hard not to burst out into a giggle of delight. "The devils!" he thought. "The devils!" It was as close as Jackie was ever likely to get to the facts of life, an opportunity not to be missed.

"Anything in writing?" he sang, looking at her over the pince-nez. "Any letters? Any documents?"

"Only a couple of notes I burned," said Delia, who thought him a very queer man, and no wonder.

"Pity!" Jackie said with an admiring smile. "O smart man! Oh, a very smart man!"

"Ah, 'tisn't that at all," said Delia uncomfortably, "only he had no occasion for writing."

"Ah, Miss Carty," cried Jackie in great indignation, looking at her challengingly through the specs while his voice took on a steely ring, "a gentleman in love always finds plenty of occasion for writing. He's a smart man; your father might succeed in an action for seduction, but if 'tis defended 'twill be a dirty case."

"Mr. Canty," said her father solemnly, "I don't mind how dirty it is so long as I get justice." He stood up, a powerful man of six feet, and held up his clenched fist. "Justice is what I want," he said dramatically. "That's the sort I am. I keep myself to myself and mind my own business, but give me a cut, and I'll fight in a bag, tied up."

"Don't forget that Ned Flynn has the money, Dick," wailed Jackie.

"Mr. Canty," said Dick with a dignity verging on pathos, "you know me?"

"I do, Dick, I do."

"I'm living in this neighbourhood, man and boy, fifty years, and I owe nobody a ha-penny. If it took me ten years, breaking stones by the road, I'd pay it back, every penny."

"I know, Dick, I know," moaned Jackie. "But there's other things as well. There's your daughter's reputation. Do you know what they'll do? They'll go into court and swear someone else was the father."

"Tom could never say that," Delia cried despairingly. "The tongue would rot in his mouth."

Jackie had no patience at all with this chit of a girl, telling him his business. He sat back with a weary air, his arm over the back of his chair.

"That statement has no foundation," he said icily. "There is no record of any such thing happening a witness. If there was, the inhabitants of Ireland would have considerably less to say for themselves. You would be surprised the things respectable people will say in the witness box. Rot in their mouths indeed! Ah, dear me, no. With documents, of course, it would be different, but it is only our word against theirs. Can it be proved that you weren't knocking round with any other man at this time, Miss Carty?"

"Indeed, I was doing nothing of the sort," Delia said indignantly. "I swear to God I wasn't, Mr. Canty. I hardy spoke to a fellow the whole time, only when Tom and myself might have a row and I'd go out with Timmy Martin."

"Timmy Martin!" Canty cried dramatically, pointing an accusing finger at her. "There is their man!"

"But Tom did the same with Betty Daly," cried Delia on the point of tears, "and he only did it to spite me. I swear there was nothing else in it, Mr. Canty, nor he never accused me of it."

"Mark my words," chanted Jackie with a mournful smile, "he'll make up for lost time now."

In this he showed considerably more foresight than Delia gave him credit for. After the baby was born and the action begun, Tom and his father went to town to see their solicitor, Peter Humphreys. Peter, who knew all he wanted to know about the facts of life, liked the case much less than Jackie. A crosseyed, full-blooded man who had made his money when law was about land, not love, he thought it a terrible comedown. Besides, he didn't think it nice to be listening to such things.

"And so, according to you, Timmy Martin is the father?" he asked Tom.

"Oh, I'm not swearing he is," said Tom earnestly, giving himself a heave in his chair and crossing his legs. "How the hell could I? All I am saying is that I wasn't the only one, and what's more she boasted about it. Boasted about it, begod!" he added with a look of astonishment at such female depravity.

"Before witnesses?" asked Peter, his eyes doing a double cross with hopelessness.

"As to that," replied Tom with great solemnity, looking over his shoulder for an open window he could spit through, "I couldn't swear."

"But you understood her to mean Timmy Martin?"

"I'm not accusing Timmy Martin at all," said Tom in great alarm, seeing how the processes of law were tending to involve him in a row with the Martins, who were a turbulent family with ways of getting their own back unknown to any law. "Timmy

Martin is one man she used to be round with. It might be Timmy
Martin or it might be someone else, or what's more," he added
with the look of a man who has had a sudden revelation, "it
might be more than one." He looked from Peter to his father and
back again to see what effect the revelation was having, but like
other revelations it didn't seem to be going down too well.
"Begod," he said, giving himself another heave, "it might be
any God's number. . . . But, as to that," he added cautiously, "I
wouldn't like to swear."

"Nor indeed, Tom," said his solicitor with a great effort at
politeness, "no one would advise you. You'll want a good counsel."

"Begod, I suppose I will," said Tom with astonished resignation
before the idea that there might be people in the world bad
enough to doubt his word.

There was great excitement in the village when it became
known that the Flynns were having the Roarer Cooper as counsel. Even as a first-class variety turn Cooper could always command attention, and everyone knew that the rights and wrongs
of the case would be relegated to their proper position while the
little matter of Eileen O'Grady's best frock received the attention
it deserved.

On the day of the hearing the court was crowded. Tom and
his father were sitting at the back with Peter Humphreys, waiting
for Cooper, while Delia and her father were talking to Jackie
Canty and their own counsel, Ivers. He was a well-built young
man with a high brow, black hair, and half-closed, red-tinged
sleepy eyes. He talked in a bland drawl.

"You're not worrying, are you?" he asked Delia kindly. "Don't
be a bit afraid. . . . I suppose there's no chance of them settling,
Jackie?"

"Musha, what chance would there be?" Canty asked scoldingly.
"Don't you know yourself what sort they are?"

"I'll have a word with Cooper myself," said Ivers. "Dan isn't
as bad as he looks." He went to talk to a coarse-looking man in
wig and gown who had just come in. To say he wasn't as bad
as he looked was no great compliment. He had a face that was
almost a square, with a big jaw and blue eyes in wicked little slits
that made deep dents across his cheekbones.

"What about settling this case of ours, Dan?" Ivers asked gently.

Cooper didn't even return his look; apparently he was not responsive to charm.

"Did you ever know me to settle when I could fight?" he growled.

"Not when you could fight your match," Ivers said, without taking offence. "You don't consider that poor girl your match?"

"We'll soon see what sort of girl she is," replied Cooper complacently as his eyes fell on the Flynns. "Tell me," he whispered, "what did she see in my client?"

"What you saw yourself when you were her age, I suppose," said Ivers. "You don't mean there wasn't a girl in a tobacconist's shop that you thought came down from heaven with the purpose of consoling you?"

"She had nothing in writing," Cooper replied gravely. "And, unlike your client, I never saw double."

"You don't believe that yarn, do you?"

"That's one of the things I'm going to inquire into."

"I can save you the trouble. She was too fond of him."

"Hah!" snorted Cooper as though this were a good joke. "And I suppose that's why she wants the cash."

"The girl doesn't care if she never got a penny. Don't you know yourself what's behind it? A respectable father. Two respectable fathers! The trouble about marriage in this country, Dan Cooper, is that the fathers always insist on doing the coorting."

"Hah!" grunted Cooper, rather more uncertain of himself. "Show me this paragon of the female sex, Ivers."

"There in the brown hat beside Canty," said Ivers without looking round. "Come on, you old devil, and stop trying to pretend you're Buffalo Bill. It's enough going through what she had to go through. I don't want her to go through any more."

"And why in God's name do you come to me?" Cooper asked in sudden indignation. "What the hell do you take me for? A Society for Protecting Fallen Women? Why didn't the priest make him marry her?"

"When the Catholic Church can make a farmer marry a labourer's daughter the Kingdom of God will be at hand," said Ivers. "I'm surprised at you, Dan Cooper, not knowing better at your age."

"And what are the neighbours doing here if she has nothing to hide?"

"Who said she had nothing to hide?" Ivers asked lightly, throwing in his hand. "Haven't you daughters of your own? You know she played the fine lady in the O'Gradys' frocks. If 'tis any information to you she wore their jewellery as well."

"Ivers, you're a young man of great plausibility," said Cooper, "but you can spare your charm on me. I have my client's interests to consider. Did she sleep with the other fellow?"

"She did not."

"Do you believe that?"

"As I believe in my own mother."

"The faith that moves mountains," Cooper said despondently. "How much are ye asking?"

"Two hundred and fifty," replied Ivers, shaky for the first time.

"Merciful God Almighty," moaned Cooper, turning his eyes to the ceiling. "As if any responsible Irish court would put that price on a girl's virtue. Still, it might be as well. I'll see what I can do."

He moved ponderously across the court and with two big arms outstretched like wings shepherded out the Flynns.

"Two hundred and fifty pounds?" gasped Ned, going white. "Where in God's name would I get that money?"

"My dear Mr. Flynn," Cooper said with coarse amiability, "that's only half the yearly allowance his Lordship makes the young lady that obliges him, and she's not a patch on that girl in court. After a lifetime of experience I can assure you that for two years' fornication with a fine girl like that you won't pay a penny less than five hundred."

Peter Humphrey's eyes almost grew straight with the shock of such reckless slander on a blameless judge. He didn't know what had come over the Roarer. But that wasn't the worst. When the settlement was announced and the Flynns were leaving he went up to them again.

"You can believe me when I say you did the right thing, Mr. Flynn," he said. "I never like cases involving good-looking girls. Gentlemen of his Lordship's age are terribly susceptible. But tell me, why wouldn't your son marry her now as he's about it?"

"Marry her?" echoed Ned, who hadn't yet got over the shock of having to pay two hundred and fifty pounds and costs for a little matter he could have compounded for with Father Corcoran for fifty. "A thing like that!"

"With two hundred and fifty pounds, man?" snarled Cooper. " 'Tisn't every day you'll pick up a daughter-in-law with that. . . . What do you say to the girl yourself?" he asked Tom.

"Oh, begod, the girl is all right," said Tom.

Tom looked different. It was partly relief that he wouldn't have to perjure himself, partly astonishment at seeing his father so swiftly overthrown. His face said: "The world is wide."

"Ah, Mr. Flynn, Mr. Flynn," whispered Cooper scornfully, "sure you're not such a fool as to let all that good money out of the family?"

Leaving Ned gasping, he went on to where Dick Carty, aglow with pride and malice, was receiving congratulations. There were no congratulations for Delia who was standing near him. She felt a big paw on her arm and looked up to see the Roarer.

"Are you still fond of that boy?" he whispered.

"I have reason to be, haven't I?" she retorted bitterly.

"You have," he replied with no great sympathy. "The best. I got you that money so that you could marry him if you wanted to. Do you want to?"

Her eyes filled with tears as she thought of the poor broken china of an idol that was being offered her now.

"Once a fool, always a fool," she said sullenly.

"You're no fool at all, girl," he said, giving her arm an encouraging squeeze. "You might make a man of him yet. I don't know what the law in this country is coming to. Get him away to hell out of this till I find Michael Ivers and get him to talk to your father."

The two lawyers made the match themselves at Johnny Desmond's pub, and Johnny said it was like nothing in the world so much as a mission, with the Roarer roaring and threatening hell-fire on all concerned, and Michael Ivers piping away about the joys of heaven. Johnny said it was the most instructive evening he ever had. Ivers was always recognized as a weak man so the marriage did him no great harm, but of course it was a terrible comedown for a true Roarer, and Cooper's reputation has never been the same since then.

Frank O'Connor (1903-   )   A younger member of the Irish
Literary Renaissance and a onetime director of Dublin's renowned
Abbey Theatre, Frank O'Connor (Michael O'Donovan) was born and
educated in Cork, Ireland. Like Sean O'Faolain, Liam O'Flaherty,
Michael McLaverty, Brian MacMahon, and others of his countrymen,
O'Connor is as prolific as he is talented. He has written plays, literary
essays, verse, and biographies in addition to several novels and seven
volumes of short stories. In recent years, Frank O'Connor has lived
in the United States and has taught at such American universities as
Harvard and Northwestern.

Many of O'Connor's best stories are in marked contrast to the work
of a group of earlier Irish writers whom he has termed "romanticists
acting on a supercharged nationalism." A witty, urbane, and unwink-
ing recorder of what he has called the "Irish middleclass Catholic way
of life with its virtues and its faults without any of the picturesqueness
of earlier Irish writing which concentrated on colour and extravagance," Frank O'Connor achieves a significant individual contribution
to the short fiction of our time.

The Stories of Frank O'Connor and *More Stories by Frank O'Connor* (Knopf) are full, representative collections; from these, eighteen
of the author's favorites are included in *Stories by Frank O'Connor*
(Vintage).

Questions   1. In what ways does "Legal Aid" remind you of
Joyce's "Araby" or "A Little Cloud"? In what ways does it differ from
these stories? Are the differences more pronounced than the similarities? What attitudes towards Ireland and the Irish, for example, are
displayed in these stories?   2. Do you find that the large number of
people in this story tends to confuse you? Are the characters sharply
individualized? Compare or contrast various attitudes towards Delia
— Tom Flynn's, for example, or Father Corcoran's, or the Roarer
Cooper's? Is Delia a sympathetic character? A realistic, convincing
one?   3. Compare or contrast O'Connor's treatment of the theme of
marriage with that of O. Henry in "Mammon and the Archer." Are
you prepared for the ending of "Legal Aid"? Could you call this a
trick-ending story? Why or why not?

WILLIAM SAROYAN

Snake

WALKING THROUGH the park in May, he saw a small brown snake slipping away from him through grass and leaves, and he went after it with a long twig, feeling as he did so the instinctive fear of man for reptiles.

Ah, he thought, our symbol of evil, and he touched the snake with the twig, making it squirm. The snake lifted its head and struck at the twig, then shot away through the grass, hurrying fearfully, and he went after it.

It was very beautiful, and it was amazingly clever, but he intended to stay with it for a while and find out something about it.

The little brown snake led him deep into the park, so that he was hidden from view and alone with it. He had a guilty feeling that in pursuing the snake he was violating some rule of the park, and he prepared a remark for anyone who might discover him. I am a student of contemporary morality, he thought he would say, or, I am a sculptor and I am studying the structure of reptiles. At any rate, he would make some sort of reasonable explanation.

He would not say that he intended to kill the snake.

He moved beside the frightened reptile, leaping now and then to keep up with it, until the snake became exhausted and could not go on. Then he squatted on his heels to have a closer view

SNAKE From *The Daring Young Man on the Flying Trapeze and Other Stories,* by William Saroyan. Copyright 1934 by The Modern Library, Inc. Reprinted by permission of Random House, Inc.

of it, holding the snake before him by touching it with the twig. He admitted to himself that he was afraid to touch it with his hands. To touch a snake was to touch something secret in the mind of man, something one ought never to bring out into the light. That sleek gliding, and that awful silence, *was* once man, and now that man had come to this last form, here were snakes still moving over the earth as if no change had ever taken place.

The first male and female, biblical; and evolution. Adam and Eve, and the human embryo.

It was a lovely snake, clean and graceful and precise. The snake's fear frightened him and he became panic stricken thinking that perhaps all the snakes in the park would come quietly to the rescue of the little brown snake, and surround him with their malicious silence and the unbearable horror of their evil forms. It was a large park and there must be thousands of snakes in it. If all the snakes were to find out that he was with this little snake, they would easily be able to paralyse him.

He stood up and looked around. All was quiet. The silence was almost the biblical silence of *in the beginning*. He could hear a bird hopping from twig to twig in a low earthbush near by, but he was alone with the snake. He forgot that he was in a public park, in a large city. An airplane passed overhead, but he did not see or hear it. The silence was too emphatic and his vision was too emphatically focused on the snake before him.

In the garden with the snake, unnaked, in the beginning, in the year 1931.

He squatted on his heels again and began to commune with the snake. It made him laugh, inwardly and outwardly, to have the form of the snake so substantially before him, apart from his own being, flat on the surface of the earth instead of subtly a part of his own identity. It was really a tremendous thing. At first he was afraid to speak aloud, but as time went on he became less timid, and began to speak in English to it. It was very pleasant to speak to the snake.

All right, he said, here I am, after all these years, a young man living on the same earth, under the same sun, having the same passions. And here you are before me, the same. The situation is the same. What do you intend to do? Escape? I will not let you escape. What have you in mind? How will you defend yourself? I intend to destroy you. As an obligation to man.

The snake twitched before him helplessly, unable to avoid the twig. It struck at the twig several times, and then became too tired to bother with it. He drew away the twig, and heard the snake say, Thank you.

He began to whistle to the snake, to see if the music would have any effect on its movements, if it would make the snake dance. You are my only love, he whistled; Schubert made into a New York musical comedy; *my only love, my only love;* but the snake would not dance. Something Italian perhaps, he thought, and began to sing *la donna è mobile,* intentionally mispronouncing the words in order to amuse himself. He tried a Brahms lullaby, but the music had no effect on the snake. It was tired. It was frightened. It wanted to get away.

He was amazed at himself suddenly; it had occurred to him to let the snake flee, to let it glide away and be lost in the lowly worlds of its kind. Why should he allow it to escape?

He lifted a heavy boulder from the ground and thought: Now I shall bash your head with this rock and see you die.

To destroy that evil grace, to mangle that sinful loveliness.

But it was very strange. He could not let the rock fall on the snake's head, and began suddenly to feel sorry for it. I am sorry, he said, dropping the boulder. I beg your pardon. I see now that I have only love for you.

And he wanted to touch the snake with his hands, to hold it and understand the truth of its touch. But it was difficult. The snake was frightened and each time he extended his hands to touch it, the snake turned on him and charged. I have only love for you, he said. Do not be afraid. I am not going to hurt you.

Then, swiftly, he lifted the snake from the earth, learned the true feel of it, and dropped it. There, he said. Now I know the truth. A snake is cold, but it is clean. It is not slimy, as I thought.

He smiled upon the little brown snake. You may go now, he said. The inquisition is over. You are yet alive. You have been in the presence of man, and you are yet alive. You may go now.

But the snake would not go away. It was exhausted with fear.

He felt deeply ashamed of what he had done, and angry with himself. Jesus, he thought, I have scared the little snake. It will never get over this. It will always remember me squatting over it.

For God's sake, he said to the snake, go away. Return to your kind. Tell them what you saw, you yourself, with your own eyes. Tell them what you felt. The sickly heat of the hand of man. Tell them of the presence you felt.

Suddenly the snake turned from him and spilled itself forward, away from him. Thank you, he said. And it made him laugh with joy to see the little snake throwing itself into the grass and leaves, thrusting itself away from man. Splendid, he said; hurry to them and say that you were in the presence of man and that you were not killed. Think of all the snakes that live and die without ever meeting man. Think of the distinction it will mean for you.

It seemed to him that the little snake's movements away from him were the essence of joyous laughter, and he felt greatly pleased. He found his way back to the path, and continued his walk.

In the evening, while she sat at the piano, playing softly, he said: A funny thing happened.

She went on playing. A funny thing? she asked.

Yes, he said. I was walking through the park and I saw a little brown snake.

She stopped playing and turned on the bench to look at him. A snake? she said. How ugly!

No, he said. It was beautiful.

What about it?

Oh, nothing, he said. I just caught it and wouldn't let it go for a while.

But why?

For no good reason at all, he said.

She walked across the room and sat beside him, looking at him strangely.

Tell me about the snake, she said.

It was lovely, he said. Not ugly at all. When I touched it, I felt its cleanliness.

I am so glad, she said. What else?

I wanted to kill the snake, he said. But I couldn't. It was too lovely.

I'm so glad, she said. But tell me everything.

That's all, he said.

But it isn't, she said. I know it isn't. Tell me everything.

It is very funny, he said. I was going to kill the snake, and not come here again.

Aren't you ashamed of yourself? she said.

Of course I am, he said.

What else? she said. What did you think, of me, when you had the snake before you?

You will be angry, he said.

Oh, nonsense. It is impossible for me to be angry with you. Tell me.

Well, he said, I thought you were lovely but evil.

Evil?

I told you you would be angry.

And then?

Then I touched the snake, he said. It wasn't easy, but I picked it up with my hands. What do you make of this? You've read a lot of books about such things. What does it mean, my picking up the snake?

She began to laugh softly, intelligently. Why, she laughed, it means, it simply means that you are an idiot. Why, it's splendid.

Is that according to Freud? he said.

Yes, she laughed. According to Freud.

Well, anyway, he said, it was very fine to let the snake go free.

Have you ever told me you loved me? she asked.

You ought to know, he said. I do not remember one or two things I have said to you.

No, she said. You have never told me.

She began to laugh again, feeling suddenly very happy about him. You have always talked of other things, she said. Irrelevant things. At the most amazing times. She laughed.

This snake, he said, was a little brown snake.

And that explains it, she said. You have never intruded.

What the hell are you talking about? he said.

I'm so glad you didn't kill the snake, she said.

She returned to the piano, and placed her hands softly upon the keys.

I whistled a few songs to the snake, he said. I whistled a fragment from Schubert's Unfinished Symphony. I would like to hear that. You know, the melody that was used in a musical comedy called *Blossom Time.* The part that goes, *you are my only love, my only love,* and so on.

She began to play softly, feeling his eyes on her hair, on her hands, her neck, her back, her arms, feeling him studying her as he had studied the snake.

William Saroyan (1908-   )   The son of an Armenian minister-turned-grape-rancher, William Saroyan was born in Fresno, California, where he was educated in the public schools and where, except for occasional invasions of New York and Hollywood, he has lived most of his life. He commenced writing avidly while a boy, and continued during the Depression while drifting from one job to another. After considerable economic privation, and after receiving "countless" rejection slips, he achieved sudden notoriety with the publication in *Story* magazine (1934) of "The Daring Young Man on the Flying Trapeze" and the subsequent publication of his first volume of short stories. Since then he has become the widely known and controversial author of a great many novels, plays, and collections of short stories including *Dear Baby* (1944), *The Assyrian and Other Stories* (1950), and *The Whole Voyald* (1956).

Saroyan has stated that as a boy he discovered that all the "classic rules" about writing short stories were wrong; at the age of eleven or twelve, he says in his preface to *The Daring Young Man on the Flying Trapeze* (1934), he decided that the best advice a writer could follow was to "Forget everybody who ever wrote anything." Since that early declaration, Saroyan has made — and lost — a fortune, and is still a rebel: "the writer who is a writer is a rebel who never stops," he avers in the preface to his most recent collection of stories. Saroyan's contributions to the American short story are considerable. He brought to the American literary scene simplicity, freshness of vision, and gaiety. His sympathetic understanding of "little" people and his warm-hearted love of the American way of life give his stories a warmth lacking in most of the grimly militant literary protests of the Depression era. He exerted a beneficial influence against the pretentious, elaborately contrived story of many of his contemporaries. Like Mark Twain, it has been said, he "opened the windows and aired the room at a time when fresh air was badly needed."

Questions   1. "Snake" is the kind of story that cannot be read on a strictly literal level; it is a story constructed in terms of symbols, the most important and obvious of which is the snake itself. Notice that in the second paragraph of the story Saroyan "points the way" to the story's meanings: "Ah, he thought, our symbol of evil, and he touched the snake with the twig, making it squirm." Notice the changing attitudes of the young man towards the snake, and try to relate them to the changing attitudes between the young man and the young woman at the conclusion of the story. What is the significance of such lines as "Is that according to Freud?", "Yes, . . . According to Freud."? Why does the young man conclude that it was "very fine to let the snake go free"?   2. Notice the important part that dialogue plays in this story; compare or contrast with Hemingway's use of dialogue in "Indian Camp." Which do you think the more effective? Saroyan refers frequently to Hemingway in the story "Seventy Thousand Assyrians," which like "Snake" was published in *The Daring Young Man on the Flying Trapeze;* he concludes by saying that "Even when Hemingway is a fool, he is at least an accurate fool." Do you think this conclusion is sound? Judging by "Snake," do you think it could be applied to Saroyan or his work?   3. What is your opinion of the characters in this story? Would it be fair or accurate to think of the young man as "neurotic"? Why or why not? Is the young woman convincing? What is the significance of the final scene between the two?

EUDORA WELTY

A Piece of News

SHE HAD BEEN out in the rain. She stood in front of the cabin fireplace, her legs wide apart, bending over, shaking her wet yellow head crossly, like a cat reproaching itself for not knowing better. She was talking to herself — only a small fluttering sound, hard to lay hold of in the sparsity of the room.

"The pouring-down rain, the pouring-down rain" — was that what she was saying over and over, like a song? She stood turning in little quarter turns to dry herself, her head bent forward and the yellow hair hanging out streaming and tangled. She was holding her skirt primly out to draw the warmth in.

Then, quite rosy, she walked over to the table and picked up a little bundle. It was a sack of coffee, marked "Sample" in red letters, which she unwrapped from a wet newspaper. But she handled it tenderly.

"Why, how come he wrapped it in a newspaper!" she said, catching her breath, looking from one hand to the other. She must have been lonesome and slow all her life, the way things would take her by surprise.

She set the coffee on the table, just in the center. Then she dragged the newspaper by one corner in a dreamy walk across the floor, spread it all out, and lay down full length on top of it in front of the fire. Her little song about the rain, her cries of surprise, had been only a preliminary, only playful pouting with which she amused herself when she was alone. She was pleased with herself now. As she sprawled close to the fire, her hair began to slide out of its damp tangles and hung all displayed down her back like a piece of bargain silk. She closed her eyes. Her mouth fell into a deepness, into a look of unconscious cunning. Yet in her very stillness and pleasure she seemed to be hiding there, all alone. And at moments when the fire stirred and tumbled in the grate, she would tremble, and her hand would start out as if in impatience or despair.

Presently she stirred and reached under her back for the newspaper. Then she squatted there, touching the printed page as if it were fragile. She did not merely look at it — she watched it, as if it were unpredictable, like a young girl watching a baby. The paper was still wet in places where her body had lain. Crouching tensely and patting the creases away with small cracked red fingers, she frowned now and then at the blotched drawing of something and big letters that spelled a word underneath. Her lips trembled, as if looking and spelling so slowly had stirred her heart.

All at once she laughed.

She looked up.

"Ruby Fisher!" she whispered.

An expression of utter timidity came over her flat blue eyes and her soft mouth. Then a look of fright. She stared about. . . . What eye in the world did she feel looking in on her? She pulled her dress down tightly and began to spell through a dozen words in the newspaper.

The little item said:

"Mrs. Ruby Fisher had the misfortune to be shot in the leg by her husband this week."

As she passed from one word to the next she only whispered; she left the long word, "misfortune," until the last, and came back to it, then she said it all over out loud, like conversation.

"That's me," she said softly, with deference, very formally.

The fire slipped and suddenly roared in the house already deafening with the rain which beat upon the roof and hung full of lightning and thunder outside.

"You Clyde!" screamed Ruby Fisher at last, jumping to her feet. "Where are you, Clyde Fisher?"

She ran straight to the door and pulled it open. A shudder of cold brushed over her in the heat, and she seemed striped with anger and bewilderment. There was a flash of lightning, and she stood waiting, as if she half thought that would bring him in, a gun leveled in his hand.

She said nothing more and, backing against the door, pushed it closed with her hip. Her anger passed like a remote flare of elation. Neatly avoiding the table where the bag of coffee stood, she began to walk nervously about the room, as if a teasing indecision, an untouched mystery, led her by the hand. There was one window, and she paused now and then, waiting, looking out at the rain. When she was still, there was a passivity about her, or a deception of passivity, that was not really passive at all. There was something in her that never stopped.

At last she flung herself onto the floor, back across the newspaper, and looked at length into the fire. It might have been a mirror in the cabin, into which she could look deeper and deeper as she pulled her fingers through her hair, trying to see herself and Clyde coming up behind her.

"Clyde?"

But of course her husband, Clyde, was still in the woods. He kept a thick brushwood roof over his whisky still, and he was mortally afraid of lightning like this, and would never go out in it for anything.

And then, almost in amazement, she began to comprehend her predicament: it was unlike Clyde to take up a gun and shoot her.

She bowed her head toward the heat, onto her rosy arms, and began to talk and talk to herself. She grew voluble. Even if he heard about the coffee man, with a Pontiac car, she did not think he would shoot her. When Clyde would make her blue, she would go out onto the road, some car would slow down, and if it had a Tennessee license, the lucky kind, the chances were that she would spend the afternoon in the shed of the empty gin. (Here she rolled her head about on her arms and stretched her legs tiredly behind her, like a cat.) And if Clyde got word, he would slap her. But the account in the paper was wrong. Clyde had never shot her, even once. There had been a mistake made.

A spark flew out and nearly caught the paper on fire. Almost in fright she beat it out with her fingers. Then she murmured and lay back more firmly upon the pages.

There she stretched, growing warmer and warmer, sleepier and sleepier. She began to wonder out loud how it would be if Clyde shot her in the leg. . . . If he were truly angry, might he shoot her through the heart?

At once she was imagining herself dying. She would have a nightgown to lie in, and a bullet in her heart. Anyone could tell, to see her lying there with that deep expression about her mouth, how strange and terrible that would be. Underneath a brand-new nightgown her heart would be hurting with every beat, many times more than her toughened skin when Clyde slapped at her. Ruby began to cry softly, the way she would be crying from the extremity of pain; tears would run down in a little stream over the quilt. Clyde would be standing there above her, as he once looked, with his wild black hair hanging to his shoulders. He used to be very handsome and strong!

He would say, "Ruby, I done this to you."

She would say — only a whisper — "That is the truth, Clyde — you done this to me."

Then she would die; her life would stop right there.

She lay silently for a moment, composing her face into a look which would be beautiful, desirable, and dead.

Clyde would have to buy her a dress to bury her in. He would have to dig a deep hole behind the house, under the cedar, a grave. He would have to nail her up a pine coffin and lay her inside. Then he would have to carry her to the grave, lay her down and cover her up. All the time he would be wild, shouting, and all distracted, to think he could never touch her one more time.

She moved slightly, and her eyes turned toward the window. The white rain splashed down. She could hardly breathe, for thinking that this was the way it was to fall on her grave, where Clyde would come and stand, looking down in the tears of some repentance.

A whole tree of lightning stood in the sky. She kept looking out the window, suffused with the warmth from the fire and with the pity and beauty and power of her death. The thunder rolled.

Then Clyde was standing there, with dark streams flowing over the floor where he had walked. He poked at Ruby with the butt of his gun, as if she were asleep.

"What's keepin' supper?" he growled.

She jumped up and darted away from him. Then, quicker than lightning, she put away the paper. The room was dark, except for the firelight. From the long shadow of his steamy presence she spoke to him glibly and lighted the lamp.

He stood there with a stunned, yet rather good-humored look of delay and patience in his face, and kept on standing there. He stamped his mud-red boots, and his enormous hands seemed weighted with the rain that fell from him and dripped down the barrel of the gun. Presently he sat down with dignity in the chair at the table, making a little tumult of his rightful wetness and hunger. Small streams began to flow from him everywhere.

Ruby was going through the preparations for the meal gently. She stood almost on tiptoe in her bare, warm feet. Once as she knelt at the safe, getting out the biscuits, she saw Clyde looking at her and she smiled and bent her head tenderly. There was some way she began to move her arms that was mysteriously sweet and yet abrupt and tentative, a delicate and vulnerable manner, as though her breasts gave her pain. She made many unnecessary trips back and forth across the floor, circling Clyde where he sat in his steamy silence, a knife and fork in his fists.

"Well, where you been, anyway?" he grumbled at last, as she set the first dish on the table.

"Nowheres special."

"Don't you talk back to me. You been hitch-hikin' again, ain't you?" He almost chuckled.

She gave him a quick look straight into his eyes. She had not even heard him. She was filled with happiness. Her hand trembled when she poured the coffee. Some of it splashed on his wrist.

At that he let his hand drop heavily down upon the table and made the plates jump.

"Some day I'm goin' to smack the livin' devil outa you," he said.

Ruby dodged mechanically. She let him eat. Then, when he had crossed his knife and fork over his plate, she brought him the newspaper. Again she looked at him in delight. It excited her even to touch the paper with her hand, to hear its quiet secret noise when she carried it, the rustle of surprise.

"A newspaper!" Clyde snatched it roughly and with a grabbing disparagement. "Where 'd you git that? Hussy."

"Look at this-here," said Ruby in her small singsong voice. She opened the paper while he held it and pointed gravely to the paragraph.

Reluctantly, Clyde began to read it. She watched his damp bald head slowly bend and turn.

Then he made a sound in his throat and said, "It's a lie."

"That's what's in the newspaper about me," said Ruby, standing up straight. She took up his plate and gave him that look of joy.

He put his big crooked finger on the paragraph and poked at it.

"Well, I'd just like to see the place I shot you!" he cried explosively. He looked up, his face blank and bold.

But she drew herself in, still holding the empty plate, faced him straightened and hard, and they looked at each other. The moment filled full with their helplessness. Slowly they both flushed, as though with a double shame and a double pleasure. It was as though Clyde might really have killed Ruby, and as though Ruby might really have been dead at his hand. Rare and wavering, some possibility stood timidly like a stranger between them and made them hang their heads.

Then Clyde walked over in his water-soaked boots and laid the paper on the dying fire. It floated there a moment and then burst into flame. They stood still and watched it burn. The whole room was bright.

"Look," said Clyde suddenly. "It's a Tennessee paper. See 'Tennessee'? That wasn't none of you it wrote about." He laughed, to show that he had been right all the time.

"It was Ruby Fisher!" cried Ruby. "My name is Ruby Fisher!" she declared passionately to Clyde.

"Oho, it was another Ruby Fisher — in Tennessee," cried her husband. "Fool me, huh? Where 'd you get that paper?" He spanked her good-humoredly across her backside.

Ruby folded her still trembling hands into her skirt. She stood stooping by the window until everything, outside and in, was quieted before she went to her supper.

It was dark and vague outside. The storm had rolled away to faintness like a wagon crossing a bridge.

Eudora Welty (1909-)   Of many talented American women who have been writing short stories over the past two or three decades (including Katherine Anne Porter, Caroline Gordon, Jean Stafford, and Flannery O'Connor), perhaps the most significant is Eudora Welty. Born in Jackson, Mississippi, she attended Mississippi State College for Women, was graduated from the University of Wisconsin, and, after further academic work at Columbia University and a brief stint with an advertising agency, returned to Mississippi, the locale which provides the material for most of her best work. She is now living in Jackson. Miss Welty's stories were first published in such magazines as *The Southern Review* during the late 1930's; with their appearance in book form, *A Curtain of Green* (1941), she was recognized as a highly individualistic writer and a superb artist. Later collections include *The Wide Net* (1943), *The Golden Apples* (1949), and *The Bride of the Innisfallen* (1955). Miss Welty is also an accomplished novelist (*Delta Wedding*, 1946, and *The Ponder Heart*, 1953).

A story like "A Piece of News" is not unlike an iceberg — there is much more to it than is immediately apparent to the untrained observer. Upon first reading, it may seem a simple or meaningless account of a young woman who reads a newspaper story about the shooting of a woman who bears her name; the reader may be tempted to ask, "Well, so what?" Around this trivial, if unusual coincidence, however, Miss Welty has written a perceptive commentary on human relationships. When Ruby Fisher sees in the newspaper what she thinks to be her own name, she is at first pleased, then shocked, and ultimately excited; after the reverie in which she fancies herself bedecked in a nightgown, she is sensuously attracted to Clyde when, with gun in hand, he returns home from the still, with "dark streams flowing over the floor where he had walked" — more like a character from folklore, romance, or myth, than a bald, semi-literate, often brutal bootlegger. She "gently" prepares the meal, standing almost on tiptoe in her "bare, warm feet"; she circles around Clyde many times, almost like a priestess performing a ritual. She is emotionally and physically excited with her fantasy. The coincidence of the newspaper story has made her intuitively more aware of her own identity. The basic facts of her existence — where she lives, her often dismal marriage to a clod of a man, even her own body — suddenly seem new and different. Ruby at the conclusion of the story is different from Ruby at the beginning; whether she will be quite the same again, is for the reader to determine. The paradoxical quality of this story is characteristic of much of Miss Welty's short fiction. Only when the clear, lucid exterior of her impeccably wrought stories is once penetrated, does the reader become aware of the depths beneath.

A Curtain of Green and *The Wide Net*, two of Miss Welty's finest collections, are included in *The Selected Stories of Eudora Welty* (Modern Library).

Questions   **1.** This story begins during a storm; at the conclusion, the storm has "rolled away to faintness like a wagon crossing a bridge." What is the significance of this? Compare or contrast with the depiction of nature and atmospheric conditions in "The Fall of the House of Usher" and in "The Open Boat."   **2.** Compare or contrast the use of symbols in this story with that in such stories as "Snake," "The Riddle," and "Arabesque — The Mouse." What is suggested by the newspaper, by Clyde's gun, and the like?   **3.** Notice the effective similes and metaphors in this story; for example, Ruby's hair "hung all displayed down her back like a piece of bargain silk"; she watches the newspaper "like a young girl watching a baby." What are some of the other figures of speech in the story? What is their function in the story?   **4.** In what ways does Clyde resemble some of the men in Faulkner's "A Bear Hunt"? In what ways is he different? Does any change, comparable to that which occurs to Ruby, take place in Clyde's personality during the story?

JOHN CHEEVER

The Enormous Radio

JIM and IRENE WESTCOTT were the kind of people who seem to strike that satisfactory average of income, endeavor, and respectability that is reached by the statistical reports in college alumni bulletins. They were the parents of two young children, they had been married nine years, they lived on the twelfth floor of an apartment house near Sutton Place, they went to the theatre on an average of 10.3 times a year, and they hoped someday to live in Westchester. Irene Westcott was a pleasant, rather plain girl with soft brown hair and a wide, fine forehead upon which nothing at all had been written, and in the cold weather she wore a coat of fitch skins dyed to resemble mink. You could not say that Jim Westcott looked younger than he was, but you could at least say of him that he seemed to feel younger. He wore his graying hair cut very short, he dressed in the kind of clothes his class had worn at Andover, and his manner was earnest, vehement, and intentionally naïve. The Westcotts differed from their friends, their classmates, and their neighbors only in an interest they shared in serious music. They went to a great many concerts — although they seldom mentioned this to anyone — and they spent a good deal of time listening to music on the radio.

THE ENORMOUS RADIO From *The Enormous Radio and Other Stories,* by John Cheever; reprinted by permission of the publishers, Funk & Wagnalls Company.

Their radio was an old instrument, sensitive, unpredictable, and beyond repair. Neither of them understood the mechanics of radio — or of any of the other appliances that surrounded them — and when the instrument faltered, Jim would strike the side of the cabinet with his hand. This sometimes helped. One Sunday afternoon, in the middle of a Schubert quartet, the music faded away altogether. Jim struck the cabinet repeatedly, but there was no response; the Schubert was lost to them forever. He promised to buy Irene a new radio, and on Monday when he came home from work he told her that he had got one. He refused to describe it, and said it would be a surprise for her when it came.

The radio was delivered at the kitchen door the following afternoon, and with the assistance of her maid and the handyman Irene uncrated it and brought it into the living room. She was struck at once with the physical ugliness of the large gumwood cabinet. Irene was proud of her living room, she had chosen its furnishings and colors as carefully as she chose her clothes, and now it seemed to her that the new radio stood among her intimate possessions like an aggressive intruder. She was confounded by the number of dials and switches on the instrument panel, and she studied them thoroughly before she put the plug into a wall socket and turned the radio on. The dials flooded with a malevolent green light, and in the distance she heard the music of a piano quintet. The quintet was in the distance for only an instant; it bore down upon her with a speed greater than light and filled the apartment with the noise of music amplified so mightily that it knocked a china ornament from a table to the floor. She rushed to the instrument and reduced the volume. The violent forces that were snared in the ugly gumwood cabinet made her uneasy. Her children came home from school then, and she took them to the Park. It was not until later in the afternoon that she was able to return to the radio.

The maid had given the children their suppers and was supervising their baths when Irene turned on the radio, reduced the volume, and sat down to listen to a Mozart quintet that she knew and enjoyed. The music came through clearly. The new instrument had a much purer tone, she thought, than the old one. She decided that tone was most important and that she could conceal the cabinet behind a sofa. But as soon as she had made her

peace with the radio, the interference began. A crackling sound
like the noise of a burning powder fuse began to accompany the
singing of the strings. Beyond the music, there was a rustling
that reminded Irene unpleasantly of the sea, and as the quintet
progressed, these noises were joined by many others. She tried
all the dials and switches but nothing dimmed the interference,
and she sat down, disappointed and bewildered, and tried to
trace the flight of the melody. The elevator shaft in her building
ran beside the living-room wall, and it was the noise of the elevator that gave her a clue to the character of the static. The
rattling of the elevator cables and the opening and closing of the
elevator doors were reproduced in her loudspeaker, and, realizing
that the radio was sensitive to electrical currents of all sorts, she
began to discern through the Mozart the ringing of telephone
bells, the dialing of phones, and the lamentation of a vacuum
cleaner. By listening more carefully, she was able to distinguish
doorbells, elevator bells, electric razors, and Waring mixers,
whose sounds had been picked up from the apartments that surrounded hers and transmitted through her loudspeaker. The
powerful and ugly instrument, with its mistaken sensitivity to
discord, was more than she could hope to master, so she turned
the thing off and went into the nursery to see her children.

When Jim Westcott came home that night, he went to the
radio confidently and worked the controls. He had the same
sort of experience Irene had had. A man was speaking on the
station Jim had chosen, and his voice swung instantly from the
distance into a force so powerful that it shook the apartment.
Jim turned the volume control and reduced the voice. Then, a
minute or two later, the interference began. The ringing of tele-
phones and doorbells set in, joined by the rasp of the elevator
doors and the whir of cooking appliances. The character of the
noise had changed since Irene had tried the radio earlier; the
last of the electric razors was being unplugged, the vacuum
cleaners had all been returned to their closets, and the static reflected that change in pace that overtakes the city after the sun
goes down. He fiddled with the knobs but couldn't get rid of
the noises, so he turned the radio off and told Irene that in the
morning he'd call the people who had sold it to him and give
them hell.

The following afternoon, when Irene returned to the apartment from a luncheon date, the maid told her that a man had come and fixed the radio. Irene went into the living room before she took off her hat or her furs and tried the instrument. From the loudspeaker came a recording of the "Missouri Waltz." It reminded her of the thin, scratchy music from an old-fashioned phonograph that she sometimes heard across the lake where she spent her summers. She waited until the waltz had finished, expecting an explanation of the recording, but there was none. The music was followed by silence, and then the plaintive and scratchy record was repeated. She turned the dial and got a satisfactory burst of Caucasian music — the thump of bare feet in the dust and the rattle of coin jewelry — but in the background she could hear the ringing of bells and a confusion of voices. Her children came home from school then, and she turned off the radio and went to the nursery.

When Jim came home that night, he was tired, and he took a bath and changed his clothes. Then he joined Irene in the living room. He had just turned on the radio when the maid announced dinner, so he left it on, and he and Irene went to the table.

Jim was too tired to make even a pretense of sociability, and there was nothing about the dinner to hold Irene's interest, so her attention wandered from the food to the deposits of silver polish on the candlesticks and from there to the music in the other room. She listened for a few moments to a Chopin prelude and then was surprised to hear a man's voice break in. "For Christ's sake, Kathy," he said, "do you always have to play the piano when I get home?" The music stopped abruptly. "It's the only chance I have," a woman said. "I'm at the office all day." "So am I," the man said. He added something obscene about an upright piano, and slammed a door. The passionate and melancholy music began again.

"Did you hear that?" Irene asked.

"What?" Jim was eating his dessert.

"The radio. A man said something while the music was still going on — something dirty."

"It's probably a play."

"I don't think it is a play," Irene said.

They left the table and took their coffee into the living room. Irene asked Jim to try another station. He turned the knob. "Have you seen my garters?" a man asked. "Button me up," a woman said. "Have you seen my garters?" the man said again. "Just button me up and I'll find your garters," the woman said. Jim shifted to another station. "I wish you wouldn't leave apple cores in the ashtrays," a man said. "I hate the smell."

"This is strange," Jim said.

"Isn't it?" Irene said.

Jim turned the knob again. "'On the coast of Coromandel where the early pumpkins blow,'" a woman with a pronounced English accent said, "'in the middle of the woods lived the Yonghy-Bonghy-Bò. Two old chairs, and half a candle, one old jug without a handle . . .'"

"My God!" Irene cried. "That's the Sweeneys' nurse."

"'These were all his worldly goods,'" the British voice continued.

"Turn that thing off," Irene said. "Maybe they can hear *us*." Jim switched the radio off. "That was Miss Armstrong, the Sweeneys' nurse," Irene said. "She must be reading to the little girl. They live in 17-B. I've talked with Miss Armstrong in the Park. I know her voice very well. We must be getting other people's apartments."

"That's impossible," Jim said.

"Well, that was the Sweeneys' nurse," Irene said hotly. "I know her voice. I know it very well. I'm wondering if they can hear us."

Jim turned the switch. First from a distance and then nearer, nearer, as if borne on the wind, came the pure accents of the Sweeneys' nurse again: "'*Lady Jingly! Lady Jingly!*'" she said, "'*Sitting where the pumpkins blow, will you come and be my wife*, said the Yonghy-Bonghy-Bò . . .'"

Jim went over to the radio and said "Hello" loudly into the speaker.

"'*I am tired of living singly,*'" the nurse went on, "'*on this coast so wild and shingly, I'm a-weary of my life; if you'll come and be my wife, quite serene would be my life . . .*'"

"I guess she can't hear us," Irene said. "Try something else."

Jim turned to another station, and the living room was filled with the uproar of a cocktail party that had overshot its mark. Someone was playing the piano and singing the Whiffenpoof Song, and the voices that surrounded the piano were vehement and happy. "Eat some more sandwiches," a woman shrieked.

There were screams of laughter and a dish of some sort crashed to the floor.

"Those must be the Fullers, in 11-E," Irene said. "I knew they were giving a party this afternoon. I saw her in the liquor store. Isn't this too divine? Try something else. See if you can get those people in 18-C."

The Westcotts overheard that evening a monologue on salmon fishing in Canada, a bridge game, running comments on home movies of what had apparently been a fortnight at Sea Island, and a bitter family quarrel about an overdraft at the bank. They turned off their radio at midnight and went to bed, weak with laughter. Sometime in the night, their son began to call for a glass of water and Irene got one and took it to his room. It was very early. All the lights in the neighborhood were extinguished, and from the boy's window she could see the empty street. She went into the living room and tried the radio. There was some faint coughing, a moan, and then a man spoke. "Are you all right, darling?" he asked. "Yes," a woman said wearily. "Yes, I'm all right, I guess," and then she added with great feeling, "but, you know, Charlie, I don't feel like myself any more. Sometimes there are about fifteen or twenty minutes in the week when I feel like myself. I don't like to go to another doctor, because the doctor's bills are so awful already, but I just don't feel like myself, Charlie. I just never feel like myself." They were not young, Irene thought. She guessed from the timbre of their voices that they were middle-aged. The restrained melancholy of the dialogue and the draft from the bedroom window made her shiver, and she went back to bed.

The following morning, Irene cooked breakfast for the family — the maid didn't come up from her room in the basement until ten — braided her daughter's hair, and waited at the door until her children and her husband had been carried away in the elevator. Then she went into the living room and tried the radio. "I don't want to go to school," a child screamed. "I hate school. I won't go to school. I hate school." "You will go to school," an enraged woman said. "We paid eight hundred dollars to get you into that school and you'll go if it kills you." The next number on the dial produced the worn record of the "Missouri Waltz." Irene shifted the control and invaded the privacy of several breakfast tables. She overheard demonstrations of indigestion, carnal love, abysmal vanity, faith, and despair. Irene's life was nearly as simple and sheltered as it appeared to be, and the forthright and sometimes brutal language that came from the loudspeaker that morning astonished and troubled her. She continued to listen until her maid came in. Then she turned off the radio quickly, since this insight, she realized, was a furtive one.

Irene had a luncheon date with a friend that day, and she left her apartment at a little after twelve. There were a number of women in the elevator when it stopped at her floor. She stared at their handsome and impassive faces, their furs, and the cloth flowers in their hats. Which one of them had been to Sea Island, she wondered. Which one had overdrawn her bank account? The elevator stopped at the tenth floor and a woman with a pair of Skye terriers joined them. Her hair was rigged high on her head and she wore a mink cape. She was humming the "Missouri Waltz."

Irene had two Martinis at lunch, and she looked searchingly at her friend and wondered what her secrets were. They had intended to go shopping after lunch, but Irene excused herself and went home. She told the maid that she was not to be disturbed; then she went into the living room, closed the doors, and switched on the radio. She heard, in the course of the afternoon, the halting conversation of a woman entertaining her aunt, the hysterical conclusion of a luncheon party, and a hostess briefing her maid about some cocktail guests. "Don't give the best Scotch to anyone who hasn't white hair," the hostess said. "See if you can get rid of that liver paste before you pass those hot things, and could you lend me five dollars? I want to tip the elevator man."

As the afternoon waned, the conversations increased in intensity. From where Irene sat, she could see the open sky above the East River. There were hundreds of clouds in the sky, as though the south wind had broken the winter into pieces and were blowing it north, and on her radio she could hear the arrival of cocktail guests and the return of children and businessmen from their schools and offices. "I found a good-sized diamond on the bathroom floor this morning," a woman said. "It must have fallen out of that bracelet Mrs. Dunston was wearing last night." "We'll sell it," a man said. "Take it down to the jeweller on Madison Avenue and sell it. Mrs. Dunston won't know the difference, and we could use a couple of hundred bucks . . ." "'Oranges and lemons, say the bells of St. Clement's,'" the Sweeneys' nurse sang. "'Half-pence and farthings, say the bells of St. Martin's. When will you pay me? say the bells at old Bailey . . .'" "It's not a hat," a woman cried, and at her back roared a cocktail party. "It's not a hat, it's a love affair. That's what Walter Florell said. He said it's not a hat, it's a love affair," and then, in a lower voice, the same woman added, "Talk to somebody, for Christ's sake, honey, talk to somebody. If she catches you standing here not talking to anybody, she'll take us off her invitation list, and I love these parties."

The Westcotts were going out for dinner that night, and when Jim came home, Irene was dressing. She seemed sad and vague, and he bought her a drink. They were dining with friends in the neighborhood, and they walked to where they were going. The sky was broad and filled with light. It was one of those splendid spring evenings that excite memory and desire, and the air that touched their hands and faces felt very soft. A Salvation Army band was on the corner playing "Jesus Is Sweeter." Irene drew on her husband's arm and held him there for a minute, to hear the music. "They're really such nice people, aren't they?" she said. "They have such nice faces. Actually, they're so much nicer than a lot of the people we know." She took a bill from her purse and walked over and dropped it into the tambourine. There was in her face, when she returned to her husband, a look of radiant melancholy that he was not familiar with. And her conduct at the dinner party that night seemed strange to him, too. She interrupted her hostess rudely and stared at the people across the table from her with an intensity for which she would have punished her children.

It was still mild when they walked home from the party, and Irene looked up at the spring stars. "'How far that little candle throws its beams,'" she exclaimed. "'So shines a good deed in a naughty world.'" She waited that night until Jim had fallen asleep, and then went into the living room and turned on the radio.

Jim came home at about six the next night. Emma, the maid, let him in, and he had taken off his hat and was taking off his coat when Irene ran into the hall. Her face was shining with tears and her hair was disordered. "Go up to 16-C, Jim!" she screamed. "Don't take off your coat. Go up to 16-C. Mr. Osborn's beating his wife. They've been quarrelling since four o'clock, and now he's hitting her. Go up there and stop him."

From the radio in the living room, Jim heard screams, obscenities, and thuds. "You know you don't have to listen to this sort of thing," he said. He strode into the living room and turned the switch. "It's indecent," he said. "It's like looking in windows. You know you don't have to listen to this sort of thing. You can turn it off."

"Oh, it's so horrible, it's so dreadful," Irene was sobbing. "I've been listening all day, and it's so depressing."

"Well, if it's so depressing, why do you listen to it? I bought this damned radio to give you some pleasure," he said. "I paid a great deal of money for it. I thought it might make you happy. I wanted to make you happy."

"Don't, don't, don't, don't quarrel with me," she moaned, and laid her head on his shoulder. "All the others have been quarrelling all day. Everybody's been quarrelling. They're all worried about money. Mrs. Hutchinson's mother is dying of cancer in Florida and they don't have enough money to send her to the Mayo Clinic. At least, Mr. Hutchinson says they don't have enough money. And some woman in this building is having an affair with the handyman — with that hideous handyman. It's too disgusting. And Mrs. Melville has heart trouble and Mr. Hendricks is going to lose his job in April and Mrs. Hendricks is horrid about the whole thing, and that girl who plays the 'Missouri Waltz' is a whore, a common whore, and the elevator man has tuberculosis and Mr. Osborn has been beating Mrs. Osborn." She wailed, she trembled with grief and checked the stream of tears down her face with the heel of her palm.

"Well, why do you have to listen?" Jim asked again. "Why do you have to listen to this stuff if it makes you so miserable?"

"Oh, don't, don't, don't," she cried. "Life is too terrible, too sordid and awful. But we've never been like that, have we, darling? Have we? I mean we've always been good and decent and loving to one another, haven't we? And we have two children, two beautiful children. Our lives aren't sordid, are they, darling? Are they?" She flung her arms around his neck and drew his face down to hers. "We're happy, aren't we, darling? We are happy, aren't we?"

"Of course we're happy," he said tiredly. He began to surrender his resentment. "Of course we're happy. I'll have that damned radio fixed or taken away tomorrow." He stroked her soft hair. "My poor girl," he said.

"You love me, don't you?" she asked. "And we're not hypercritical or worried about money or dishonest, are we?"

"No, darling," he said.

A man came in the morning and fixed the radio. Irene turned it on cautiously and was happy to hear a California-wine commercial and a recording of Beethoven's Ninth Symphony, including Schiller's "Ode to Joy." She kept the radio on all day and nothing untoward came from the speaker.

A Spanish suite was being played when Jim came home. "Is everything all right?" he asked. His face was pale, she thought. They had some cocktails and went in to dinner to the "Anvil Chorus" from "Il Trovatore." This was followed by Debussy's "La Mer."

"I paid the bill for the radio today," Jim said. "It cost four hundred dollars. I hope you'll get some enjoyment out of it."

"Oh, I'm sure I will," Irene said.

"Four hundred dollars is a good deal more than I can afford," he went on. "I wanted to get something that you'd enjoy. It's the last extravagance we'll be able to indulge in this year. I see that you haven't paid your clothing bills yet. I saw them on your dressing table." He looked directly at her. "Why did you tell me you'd paid them? Why did you lie to me?"

"I just didn't want you to worry, Jim," she said. She drank some water. "I'll be able to pay my bills out of this month's allowance. There were the slipcovers last month, and that party."

"You've got to learn to handle the money I give you a little more intelligently, Irene," he said. "You've got to understand that we won't have as much money this year as we had last. I had a very sobering talk with Mitchell today. No one is buying anything. We're spending all our time promoting new issues, and you know how long that takes. I'm not getting any younger, you know. I'm thirty-seven. My hair will be gray next year. I haven't done as well as I'd hoped to do. And I don't suppose things will get any better."

"Yes, dear," she said.

"We've got to start cutting down," Jim said. "We've got to think of the children. To be perfectly frank with you, I worry about money a great deal. I'm not at all sure of the future. No one is. If anything should happen to me, there's the insurance, but that wouldn't go very far today. I've worked awfully hard to give you and the children a comfortable life," he said bitterly. "I don't like to see all of my energies, all of my youth, wasted in fur coats and radios and slipcovers and — "

"Please, Jim," she said. "Please. They'll hear us."

"*Who'll hear us?* Emma can't hear us."

"The radio."

"Oh, I'm sick!" he shouted. "I'm sick to death of your apprehensiveness. The radio can't hear us. Nobody can hear us. And what if they can hear us? Who cares?"

Irene got up from the table and went into the living room. Jim went to the door and shouted at her from there. "Why are you so Christly all of a sudden? What's turned you overnight into a convent girl? You stole your mother's jewelry before they probated her will. You never gave your sister a cent of that money that was intended for her — not even when she needed it. You made Grace Howland's life miserable, and where was all your piety and your virtue when you went to that abortionist? I'll never forget how cool you were. You packed your bag and went off to have that child murdered as if you were going to Nassau. If you'd had any reasons, if you'd had any good reasons — "

Irene stood for a minute before the hideous cabinet, disgraced and sickened, but she held her hand on the switch before she extinguished the music and the voices, hoping that the instrument might speak to her kindly, that she might hear the Sweeneys' nurse. Jim coninued to shout at her from the door. The voice on the radio was suave and noncommittal. "An early-morning railroad disaster in Tokyo," the loudspeaker said, "killed twenty-nine people. A fire in a Catholic hospital near Buffalo for the care of blind children was extinguished early this morning by nuns. The temperature is forty-seven. The humidity is eighty-nine."

John Cheever (1912-   )   John Cheever was born in Quincy, Massachusetts, and educated at Thayer Academy in South Braintree, from which he was expelled at the age of seventeen. Since then, except for service during World War II and relatively brief periods of teaching and writing for one of the major broadcasting systems, he has been a professional writer whose work has maintained consistently high standards. Although his only novel, *The Wapshot Chronicle*, won a National Book Award, Mr. Cheever is essentially a writer of short stories. More than a hundred of his stories have appeared in American magazines, many of them in *The New Yorker*. The best of these have been collected in *The Way Some People Live* (1943), *The Enormous Radio* (1953), and *The Housebreaker of Shady Hill* (1958); four are included in *Stories* (1956), and one of these, "The Country Husband," won first prize in the O. Henry Awards for 1956.

Like John Galsworthy, Mr. Cheever is an urbane and highly civilized social satirist. Few writers have depicted more skilfully than he the loneliness and emptiness of certain segments of contemporary society. He possesses great talent for transforming an essentially commonplace incident — such as a husband's purchase of a new radio for his wife — into something which is at once significant and sinister. Many of his earlier stories, like "The Enormous Radio," are concerned with the corrosive effect of metropolitan life upon essentially decent people who are isolated, defeated, or deprived of their individuality in the vastness of a great city. Recently he has shifted his locale to suburbia-within-commuting-distance-of-New-York. In either setting he views his subjects with both understanding and dislike, with compassionate irony. There are few individual villains in John Cheever's fiction; the villain, if there be one, is "society" itself, with its hunger for economic security, its irresistible drift towards conformity, its avid desire to "keep up with the Joneses."

The Enormous Radio is available in a paperback edition (Berkeley).

Questions   1. One of the recurring themes in contemporary literature is the search of the individual for his real identity, or the quest for self-realization. In what ways is this theme implicit in "The Enormous Radio"? Could this be said to be the theme, or part of the theme, of Eudora Welty's "A Piece of News"? Are these two stories — so very different in many ways — similar in any other ways? Do you see any similarities — grotesque as the comparison may seem at first

— between "The Enormous Radio" and Hawthorne's "Young Goodman Brown"?   2. Are the descriptions of the radio ("physical ugliness," "aggressive intruder," "malevolent green light") effective? What purpose do they serve? Are they overdone?   3. What are the reasons underlying Jim Westcott's final outburst against his wife? Are you prepared for it?   4. Do you agree with Irene Westcott's cry that "we've never been like that, have we? . . . I mean we've always been good and decent and loving to one another, haven't we?" Compare the revelations about Irene which Jim discloses at the end of the story with the characterization of her at the very beginning (her "wide, fine forehead upon which nothing at all had been written"); with her growing preoccupation with the radio and its secrets; and with her reaction, while having lunch with her friend, when she finds herself wondering what the friend's "secrets" are.   5. Contrast the women in the elevator with their "handsome and impassive faces, their furs, and the cloth flowers on their hats" with the radio's harsh revelations of their "indigestion, carnal love, abysmal vanity, faith, and despair."

PIERRE GASCAR

The Horses

THE NIGHT was overcast with threatening storm clouds that had
been seen gathering in the east at dusk an hour previously. The
foliage that Peer guessed at overhead was still, or stirred only at
long intervals as a slow breath rippled over the countryside like
a scale, rousing an emotion that was almost detached from earthly
reality, akin to the apprehension of music or the quivering excitement of inspiration. The thought that thousands of creatures were
at that moment listening to the first whispers of the imminent
storm gave an added solemnity to the scene — to the dimly felt
presence of the natural world which, now suddenly sighing, lay
submissively awaiting its fate, cruel or beneficent, but still
shrouded in darkness.

A gentle landscape, a gathering storm: war had been declared
two days earlier and, during the last few hours of a life that had
not yet quite lost the aspect of peace, human beings, still rapt
with surprise, lingered in a state of simple emotion and of silence,
soon — tomorrow, maybe — to be replaced by a passion for facts
and an urge to fight.

Peer did not feel alone in the heart of the night; after so many
storms that he had made his own, that he had brought crashing
down on his lonely tower, he was at last seeing a storm break
over the world, a storm towards which the faces of all his fellow
men, and the face of the whole earth, were upturned. Only he

could not help thinking that before long this widespread communion of feeling would be aroused by less pure symbols, demanding a less passive response.

He followed the way that had been pointed out to him along a sort of avenue, at the far end of which he could now make out streaks of light from the ill-darkened windows of some building and, here and there, a beacon at some indefinite distance, beyond gulfs of darkness on the edge of which the trees seemed to stop short until a fresh sigh set their leaves rustling again all around, like the sound of water over shallows. At last he came to the place where the vault of trees ended, and crossed a road that surprised him by its paleness; no doubt a change had come over the sky. Peer could make out a large hut looming up on his right. He paused.

He knew that, now he had reached the place, he would inevitably have to speak to somebody, introduce himself, go through the usual formalities; and he still could not make up his mind to do so, as though the prospect of these simple actions, which he would be obliged to perform and which, indeed, he was anxious to perform, had scared an unfamiliar self in him. Once he had pushed open this door, once he had spent the necessary quarter of an hour with a man sitting in front of a pile of papers, his fate would move forward under fresh colors, his position would be clear, his future unhindered. He anticipated this with a certain obscure delight; only an instinct of shyness held him back for an instant on the brink. That which was so suddenly to become his past deserved a moment's pause; was he never to enjoy a truce?

So he had gone past the entrance of the hutment, and now he was standing before a vast, darker space on the edge of which the trees began again, forming a pattern he could not guess at. For the last few minutes, as he drew nearer to this plantation, he had been aware of a strange sound which presently swelled, became recognizable and made him halt in astonishment. It was as though a moving, murmuring sea were stretched out before him. Deep breaths, rustling noises, sobbing neighs mingled with the clatter of chains, while the sound of hoofs rapidly pawing the summer-baked earth in many places allowed him to identify the smell that hung under the trees in the heavy, slow-moving air.

The guests of wind, which had just begun to grow more frequent and made a high run through the black foliage, kept stirring up this vague mass, this sea of animal life which otherwise might have settled down, if not into stillness, at least in a reassuringly peaceful rhythm. And then fresh and more violent sounds arose, sounds of huge invisible bodies in collision, the creaking of countless chains like cables in a storm-swept harbor; desperate neighings rang out, and the smell, for a while, was dissipated and lost. And it seemed then as though some force mightier and more mysterious than the presence of a hundred horses were pent up under the trees, thudding against the trunks and rattling the pebbles in its inexplicable anguish.

The first lightning flash showed Peer a confused mass of gleaming cruppers and horses' heads, in the tense contorted attitude and with that violent backward look over the shoulder by which damned souls in the Inferno, as Dante and his guide went by, expressed their hopeless curiosity, their bitter longing. A sharper whinny rang out and was answered by one still shriller, suggestive of the nervous excitement of the race-course or the kindred ecstasy of sexual pleasure. The wind, which had now risen to a full gale, was tossing the leaves, and its slow unbroken roar sounded above the horses' Inferno like the suppressed fury of fire or ocean — the atmosphere of damnation. Bluish white flashes lit up a mob of bare-backed horses. The thunder rumbled in the sky, accompanying the clamor for a moment, and in the far distance some horses wailed. Drops of rain started falling. In the direction from which the storm was coming, Peer could hear the sound of galloping hoofs and men's shouts.

Then he turned, ran back to the hut, and went in. The light dazzled him, and the silence into which he suddenly stepped brought him sharply back to reality. A soldier was sitting at a table. He looked questioningly at Peer: "Hullo? . . . B2? The N.C.O.'s next door. You're just in time to dodge the rain."

It was pouring down now, pattering against the thin roof. Peer imagined the panic it must be arousing among the animals; then he remembered those cart-horses that are left standing in the rain fully harnessed, like shiny statues with drooping heads. Now he was standing in front of two N.C.O.'s bent over a pile of papers.

"Your form . . . You're two days late . . ." said the one who had taken the green paper from Peer's hand, without giving him a glance.

He had seized his pen. Peer tried to explain things, out of pure courtesy, seeing that no account was being taken of the fact that he had set about going to war with the calm deliberation appropriate to big business undertakings.

"Besides," he added, "there's been some mistake."

The man stopped writing to look at him for a moment and then went back to his task.

"Yes," Peer said, "I shouldn't be attached to this unit." (He had done his compulsory service driving.)

The man was quite aware of this; he kept nodding his head as he wrote. Peer tried to explain how the mistake had arisen, but his speech was constantly interrupted by the sharp ringing of the telephone bell, which kept the N.C.O. dashing to lift the receiver that hung on the wall. Almost invariably, with his fingers curled round the mouthpiece, his eyes intently staring, he would answer with eager delight as though he had been waiting all his life for this conversation.

"I'll put you through to the captain's office," he would shout. Then he would fiddle about with various plugs and come back to his seat, sucking his teeth with a satisfied air. And in the distance, through the noise of the rain, a deep voice could be heard speaking, pausing repeatedly and then speaking again even deeper. No! Peer could not understand why they insisted on attaching him to units in which he could be of no use.

At these words the N.C.O. made a slight gesture expressive of indifference mingled with irritation. "There are certain phrases that a soldier must never use: a private must observe traditional humility — his value is laid down for him and he must not form his own opinion of it, for this would upset the rules of the game. At this level — at your level, Peer — the spirit of discipline and the spirit of sacrifice are maintained by an unvarying feeling of unworthiness or, better still, by a complete absence of feeling." The N.C.O. did not say all this. He said: "We'll see about this later." Somebody would be written to, somewhere; meanwhile, he'd be attached to the Eighth Section. Sensing the irrevocability of this assignment, Peer tried to protest. Couldn't they take into account his false position and give him a place where he would still retain his "temporary" quality?

The other N.C.O., hitherto silent, lifted his head and asked angrily: "Have you nearly finished?"

"Well, good Lord, I've a right . . ." went on Peer.

"A right? A right? To what?" shouted the man, getting out of his chair. Peer realized that it was a physical relief to him to stand up and let himself go in anger.

"Individual rights are finished with now. Haven't you grasped that yet?"

And Peer was obliged to answer and could only find clumsy words. The other N.C.O. had thrust aside his papers and was staring malevolently at Peer, expressing approval of his colleague's words. Suddenly a door in the wall that Peer had not noticed opened, and there stood the captain. He stopped and looked at Peer, who happened to be speaking.

"Go on, shout," he said softly. "Shout louder still! You're so very important. You're the only one that matters, aren't you? And we'd forgotten you." His gaze hardened. "Listen," he went on in the same quiet voice, "Ive got eight hundred head of horses here or more. . . . I've got . . . but what's the use? Punish this man," he said, turning to the N.C.O. "Look! I'm short of fodder, short of equipment, short of men, and here's this fellow asserting his rights and shouting . . . shouting," he repeated mechanically.

And then, through the rustling noise of the rain, Peer heard the clatter of galloping hoofs and the broken shouts of men running. The officer dashed to the door with a curse; he left it open behind him, letting in a great gust of cool air, and the light from the room shone onto a screen of darkness scored with slanting lines of rain. Peer, the two N.C.O.'s and the orderly stood on the threshold. A horse galloped past quite close, and rushed out of the patch of light cast on the ground by the office lamps.

"How many of them are there?" shouted an N.C.O. to a man who had been running after the beast but had given it up and was slowing down, raising his arms with a helpless gesture.

He didn't know; a whole ropeful, fifteen or twenty maybe. Farther off, the shouts that rang out dismally here and there in the vast darkness and the sporadic scurry of hoofs suggested that the horses were being driven round in a circle: a desperate merry-go-round. A sound of trotting came towards them:

"There's one coming back." The four men with one accord ran to line up in the rain and vanished from sight. Peer did not stir. He heard them, at some distance away, scaring the creature and driving it involuntarily in his direction. A few seconds later he saw a horse, its head hanging, come up towards the light; it stared at Peer, who stood motionless. "Off you go," Peer thought, and clicked his tongue. "Escape!"

Just then one of the four men ran up towards the horse. It tossed its glistening head and dashed off into the night.

"Couldn't you have caught it?" cried the man angrily. "It still had its halter on."

Peer did not answer. He went off in the rain; that evening, it seemed to him, he was not to enjoy friendly relations with men, although he knew now that he would die unless this favor was granted him. It would be better to put off till next day any contact with his fellow creatures, who had come into his hitherto lonely life in the shape, unfortunately, of fighting men. He walked along parallel to the horses' enclosure, hoping to find the men's living quarters in that direction.

The agitation set up by the animals' flight, the shouts and sounds of galloping that could still be heard in the distance, had increased the hubbub in the paddock. Peer was walking alongside an abyss that was loud with neighs. The night was so dark that he could no longer make out the trees as he passed by. After walking for what seemed to him a long time he found he must make a further detour to avoid colliding with some tethered horses that blocked his way. He felt he ought to go back to the office, find out where he was to sleep and ask for a lamp, but remembering the scene he had just had with the officer and the latter's hostile attitude, he gave up this idea.

He walked on cautiously, stretching out his arms occasionally to ward off the obstacles which he imagined confronting him in the darkness. The sodden earth sank under his feet. Suddenly he realized that he could no longer hear the noise of the horses which had been guiding him. Soon he was treading on plowed land that seemed to stretch out to infinity under the hissing rain. Deeply depressed, he turned round and hurried back towards the living presence of the horses. He thought he would be unable to find them again, and then he discovered that he was

almost in the midst of them. At one time he touched a wet
crupper in the darkness as he wandered aimlessly by.

Later on, much later, when he was leaning against a tree
soaked to the skin, he caught sight of the gleam through an
opening door. He hurried up and discovered a stable with men
inside.

"Can I sleep here?" he asked, noticing a heap of straw in the
doorway.

"Surely."

They started asking him questions, but he could not understand
what they were saying and lay down without answering. They
thought he must be drunk.

Next morning Peer joined the Eighth Section. He had woken
up shivering in his wet clothes, in the midst of a mob of horses
that were being taken off to drink. Directed by the soldier in
charge of them, he had located his unit and settled down in a
corner of one of the three big rooms of which its quarters consisted, after speaking to a corporal who had merely asked his
name for the roll. Straw was strewn on the floor along each
wall, and some men still lay sleeping there, sullen-faced in the
gray morning light, with their tunics buttoned at the waist and
rumpled up under their arms so that they looked puffed out,
like corpses.

Others, squatting Eastern fashion, were eating in almost complete silence, staring in front of them as they munched their
hard bread as though weighed down by their animal function
and, perhaps, by some secret despair. From their speech, which
he could hardly understand, Peer recognized Southerners (who
are reputed to be brutal) and, after an exchange of greetings,
he deliberately moved away from them. Through the windows,
on which intermittent rain sprayed a few drops of bluish translu-
cency, he could see the horses pass, led by the men — each in a
different way, with an individual attitude, forming an unfamiliar
picture as though in the neutral morning light the whole range of
equine types was filing past in an incoherent procession: as if,
in some timeless sphere, the vast and prolific imagination of some
supernatural horse-trainer were bodying forth countless shapes,
now with concentrated violence, now with careless freedom.

One horse seemed like a figure from ancient art, with its head thrown back and its mouth tugging at the bit, while its leader, with feet close together, arched back and uplifted arms, reared his head in the same attitude of silent pride; then came a horse from the plains, its mane flowing over its low-arched neck, led by a slow-moving man chained to the bridle; an upright white mare advanced with perfect smoothness, at the same level as the man whose profile appeared behind her own, so that they seemed to be physically united as in some old myth; a heavy horse walked along, showing all the movements of its muscles under the skin, especially at the shoulder, and ceaselessly tossing its head and ears as if it really found it hard to control all those tiny ripples of flesh; some were trotting in a stilted way, others galloping in a manner that seemed timeless and universal, being the supreme answer to one's need for violence, for escape.

The men had gone up to the window.

"Some more of them have escaped. . . ."

"How many horses are there?" Peer asked.

"Seven or eight hundred." They could not tell him the exact number; there were horses everywhere; people brought more in every day. Every day some of them died; most of them were short of food, and, frantic with hunger, gnawed the ropes with which, for lack of chains, they were now fastened. Some soldiers had had their faces mauled, others had been kicked to death. Peer explained how, the night before, he had got lost in the paddock.

"What paddock?"

They could not make out what place he was speaking of: "trees, a lot of horses outside in the darkness"? Moreover their attention was now focused on an exciting scene taking place in the flat landscape where the horses had been filing past like lost souls. Some men astride their mounts galloped after the fugitives; others on foot, with outstretched arms and mouths distended in a shout, had lined up to form a barrier, darting about so swiftly that, despite the inordinate distances between them, there seemed to be a real fence joining their spread-eagled, fanatically resolute figures; so that the animals turned round abruptly and then, finding themselves confronted by their pursuers, reared their heads with a desperate neigh and let themselves be captured, their eyes staring and blood-flecked. Now, held close by the mounted men, they gradually straggled home, shaking their heads gently in a broken rhythm expressive of grief. Little by little the tumult died down.

"Where's the new fellow?" asked a voice behind Peer, that of an N.C.O. who had just entered the room.

When he had been told of the order that condemned him to stable duties until his conduct should have atoned for the previous night's misdemeanor, Peer thought it wise to consult the men, who might be able to give him useful advice. They merely exhorted him to use violence, and as they judged him incapable of this they spoke with an indifference that was near contempt.

Peer withdrew and began to work out a line of conduct. He was fond of animals; and horses, whose forms evoked the old tradition of man's mastery and of great journeys, were particularly dear to his easygoing nature. The shock of war, the sudden absence of certain faces, the unfamiliar surroundings, inclined him to a Franciscan gentleness which was always the inward expression of his troubles, when he brooded over these. And so he imagined a peaceful mastery, a sudden power that would curb beasts and men. But soon, at the back of his mind, there grew a feeling that overruled these thoughts — a sense that, despite misleading appearances, despite manifold similarities, the race of animals that lived here was one with which he had no connection, as though the war had actually brought into being an unfamiliar animal and human kingdom, a state of visible, permanent damnation, the implacable invasion of a set of forms that had hitherto been lying in wait up above. So he left things to fate. He waited till night fell and then went off to the stable to which he had been assigned.

Under the dim yellow lamplight, as far as the eye could see, horses were drawn up neck to tail. The confused throng of animals, standing there amidst a haze of irritant dust, was astir with ceaseless movements like the scattered eddies produced by underwater currents. Innumerable varied sounds revealed their unavailing efforts, their frustrated impetus, their curbed frenzy; as if some hydra lay suffering the pangs of childbirth, a head would be reared high from time to time and then swiftly dropped as though struck down. Peer was shown what he had to do. The details of his duties mattered little to him; what he had to do

was, primarily and almost solely, to penetrate into that seething
mass of animal life, quivering with sudden shocks.

To reach the alley over which muzzles were bent as over a
manger, he had to force his way between the cruppers of two
reliably placid beasts. That was easy. The hard part only began
when one stood between those two rows of excited heads and
pawing hoofs, often mingled in the course of a scuffle or a slow
mass movement. Clutching a sack of oats under one arm, one
had to strike out with a stick carried in the other hand and force
those goggle-eyed heads to draw back and let one pass. The
grain was scattered haphazard as the open-mouthed sack was
jerked about in the struggle. One dared not stop. The horses,
wild with excitement at the sight of the spilled oats, closed in
behind the man; and these soldiers, these violent men, were
horribly afraid of some injury to their loins, the seat of supple
movement and of all their virile power. In every one of their
gestures they betrayed this sense of vulnerability.

As Peer was slipping between two horses that had been pointed
out to him, a wave ran through the whole row, pressing the
bodies against one another, and he had that sensation of being
slowly crushed between two living masses that he had hitherto
experienced only in dreams. He could still breathe, however; he
pressed his fists and elbows against his emaciated sides and
leaned heavily forward. The animals happened to move apart
and Peer fell down in the alley. Then he took fright, and when
a horse jerked its head towards him as he was rising, once on
his feet he struck out with all his might. The stick quivered,
making his hand ache; he had set the world reeling, and he was
suddenly cured of his fright. More than cured. A shrill neigh
sounded; the creature had leaped backward, tugging at the rope
that fastened the others; more neighs rang out; the whole row
wavered; hoofs beat the air, which was thick with dark clouds
of dust. Peer had picked up the sack of oats and was dragging
it along the ground, dropping it at intervals to let the grain run
out. A horse bit the sack as it passed; Peer turned round and
hit out, walked on and hit out again. After each step he hit out;
he struck fine cart-horses' heads, solemn as sextons' under their
hanging forelocks; he struck nostrils still bloodstained from last
night's blows; he struck dying horses that stared down between

their forelegs, seeming every moment to sink closer to the earth; and he struck creatures full of fire and fury that drew back their lips over sharp square teeth, baring their jaws up to the moist red base of the nostrils so that the sight of the living flesh enhanced the dreadful menace of their expression. Gone, now, were the mild oblong equine faces, full of patience and bony good nature, with great round eyes blinking with weariness; instead, here were faces like the four-stroke sketches in old Oriental drawings, the upreared heads, distorted by their own strength, of horses in antique battle scenes; with great hollow sockets where there is no eye, only a shadow, since darkness is swift-moving like violence or death, and the slit mouth breaking into flower, silently, under the terribly smooth steel of the bit.

Peer struck without aiming now. One last blow. He had reached the end of the row, and his sack had long been empty. A man looked at him in astonishment: "Well!" Peer sat down. The din went on in other parts of the stable, where the orderlies were engaged in struggles like that from which he had just emerged. Some of the men were deliberately shouting, clamorously hymning their conflict with the animals. They interspersed these strains with comic improvisations or grotesque expressions of anger; they uttered their "Hoo-oo!" with the shrillness of a bird's whistle or with dreadful explosive yells. The general impression was quite hellish.

Thenceforward Peer's life consisted of hours like these, spent in the midst of uproar, anger and danger, alternating with periods of sleep and brief moments of leisure made gloomy by the ceaseless rain. The appalling reverses that the troops were suffering at the front brought about a general disorganization which affected even this remote station. The consignments of fodder, already meager, dwindled still further; news was lacking; the men ran short of food.

Peer, having woken in the late afternoon, stood leaning against a window watching the men come and go through the camp with ever slower steps. It seemed as though a process of universal leveling were taking place, a slow osmosis tending to the total merging of every variety of color, shape and time. The rainy sky piled up its darkening shades of gray above the sodden earth where countless puddles reflected its dubious light; white mists rose from the nearby woods and blurred the foliage; horses and

men, bogged ankle-deep and weary of the gray dusk and the
confusion, moved forward through the downpour with extreme
slowness, as though affected by the immobility of the landscape
and dangerously bewitched by its rainy stillness; the rain, falling
on roofs, into pools, beating against their garments, was like the
onset of tranquillity, the subjection of all rhythms, the advance
guard of silence. . . .

"Peer!" It was time once more.

Ten minutes later, Peer was back among the turmoil and the
blows.

Occasionally, if it was still daylight when he went on duty, he
was sent to help the burial squad for a little. How many horses
died each day? Nobody knew. Groups of men armed with
spades, dispersed through the camp, would dig ditches into which
the corpses, brought thither in carts, were tipped; dreadfully
flaccid, with their forelegs drawn up daintily; and a black fly,
like a tireless ghost, would hover for hours above the loose earth
that was thrown by spadefuls over the bodies. Peer enjoyed the
work because it was not concerned with living creatures full of
instincts and passions and unpredictable things. He might have
asked to be transferred to it permanently but for the captain's
animosity, which still pursued him at a distance. He had to
resign himself. When night fell he went back to the stable, the
warmth of which, for a few minutes, was welcome after the chilly
dankness of dusk outside.

The nights were variously spent, but before the orderlies took
up their individual duties there were certain general tasks which
they performed together. These involved only familiar, well-nigh
foreseeable accidents. Sometimes only the usual restlessness pre-
vailed, sometimes a sudden scuffle would throw one corner of the
stable into confusion; at other times some horse would break
loose and charge into the mob of its fellows. Then the soldiers
had to guard all the exits and surround the animal, which finally,
to dodge their blows, would slip between two others from the
rear. In the ensuing chaos it was impossible to try to catch it;
one could merely stand and keep watch over it — or them, if
there was more than one — with one's whip dangling, motionless
as a sentry, the harsh lamplight blinding one's eyes, in utter
weariness.

The horses' irritability often spread to the men, who were

worn out by the heat and the lack of sleep. Soldiers would exchange blows, without a word, and then dropping their ferocious expression would begin to argue, passing one another flasks of brandy. Peer was left out of it. They were astonished at his savagery towards the animals, or rather at the nature of that savagery. He was no more violent than the rest, but he was violent in a hopeless, utterly silent way that surprised these men whose anger always seemed in some degree the ecstatic expression of their strength.

In order to conceal the terror and dismay that found vent in his assault on the horses, Peer had striven to gain control over his gestures, to give them an appearance of redoubtable calm, and he had soon discovered that while this made his blows more impressive it also increased their effectiveness and accuracy. They were an intellectual's blows, bruising blows struck in cold panic, aimed with clumsy cunning, as though some pernicious strength lay behind his feebleness. Of this he was not aware. He only knew that each of his blows plunged him a little deeper into a hideously grimacing universe where the horses were all ferocity, the men all hate. He was forging his own demons. Whip in hand, he seemed to be lashing his own weary days into a long-repressed gallop, towards a charge which he knew beforehand would be their last.

One day when pandemonium reigned among the horses, finding himself driven back against a wall by a frenzied animal rearing and bucking in wild terror, he seized a huge stake and hurled it at the beast's head. It neighed and dashed off, shaking its head; he had pierced its eye. An N.C.O. killed the horse and the stable orderlies carved it into great chunks of meat. Peer ate none of it, but this fastidiousness, far from winning him their esteem again, only confirmed their opinion of him as a weakling.

But he no longer noticed the growing contempt in which his companions held him. The war had begun catastrophically and the officers of the station, deprived of orders, of cadres, and of man power, could no longer hope to maintain a service which, moreover, the lack of equipment and supplies rendered increasingly difficult. The litter rotted, the atmosphere in the stables grew asphyxiating, the beasts died by dozens. The men sprawled in the straw, drinking the spirits that three riders on specially pampered mounts had gone forty miles to fetch. In the general slackening of discipline Peer was no longer obliged to live in the midst of his companions.

Meanwhile, however, the rain was still falling and the cold winds of sudden autumn drove him from the drafty room in which he might have lingered at leisure. Besides, did not some hidden force impel him to cling to those difficult duties which nobody demanded of him?

He soon found a home in a shed used for storing straw adjoining the stable, whence the now welcome warmth of the animals reached him. He had become less sensitive to noise, and in the midst of the unending uproar he was liable to fall into a long sleep, troubled with trying dreams which lingered like an echo after his wakening, bestowing on the actual world something of the stifling atmosphere and faded light of the unconscious world.

Gradually his health began to deteriorate, owing to the combination of overwork and lonely boredom involved in his confined existence together with undernourishment and, above all, the effect of the extreme foulness of the air he breathed. He himself aggravated the moral effect of this physical weakening by personal neglect; cleanliness seemed futile now. His reflection in the mirror confirmed that disgust which his whole body, by countless indirect and indefinable sensations, had already aroused in him. And as though up till now he had been protected by his ordinary outward decency, his normal blood pressure and his moderate slumbers, misfortune struck him. It has its own devious ways. An overlong sleep with a troubled wakening, physical fatigue that can reduce one to the level of despair, or a rainy sky foreboding every sort of treachery — and misfortune descends, or unfolds.

Peer's home town was taken by the enemy, after a battle that left it in ruins; in that wan town, under its rags of smoke, where are your loved ones now?

The horses danced under his blows; their terrifying emaciation, since it was not yet that of death, could only mean madness. They were not the same horses at all! Famine and Peer's blows had given them the aspect of stray dogs, of restive skeletons. One or two of them died; then they died two by two, in some corners; but the stable was not yet empty — far from it. "Two by two, my God, two by two!" Peer wondered sometimes, as he lay in the straw tormented by its prickly blades and by his prickly misery.

Meanwhile the officers were planning a reorganization, a general move down to the valley, where there was still grass to be found. Cadres were needed; somebody came to tell Peer he was promoted to corporal.

The times were past when even such a routine promotion as this might have meant a tangible improvement in the material conditions of the soldier concerned or, at any rate, release from the more unpleasant aspects of military duty and communal life. Peer stayed on his heap of straw. He heard his companions grumbling as they learned the news. When they were so short of staff in the stables, to go and make one of them a boss! And what a choice!

Peer rose, went up to them, and told them that he would still keep on with his stable duties. Why did he do this? From a sense of solidarity? No; he had long lost all contact with that atmosphere of manly integrity in which such fine words have a meaning. Out of fear? Perhaps, and also because he did not want to emerge from that humble, battered way of life that sheltered his misery like a dark night, with the relaxation and protection which, after all, night provides. Although this life, together with a torpor that was becoming habitual to him, had gradually come to numb his feelings, he could still frame thoughts: "What were the horses, and why did he beat them?"

Sometimes, when these questions grew urgent, he would get up and stand in front of the nearest animal. Its eyes drew him first of all; this is a deep-seated instinct that recurs both in savage combat and in love. And here? Here, he made a great effort: "Poor beast, poor beast." And the eyes were like a calm sea, and the words soon died away in its silence. He could not help thinking that when he struck the horses, when he let loose their frenzy, the world began to take a shape. A horse that neighs, leaps and bucks has its place in some sort of social order; Peer's own misfortunes, his loneliness, the war, that perpetual nightmare, were about to assume a meaning, they were on the verge of it. You lashed out . . . and creatures died at the very moment when these lunatic gestures, this state of damnation were about to reveal the truth about this desolate world. He would come back again, unsatisfied.

"Corporal . . . !" The others had got into the habit of calling him when one of the animals was beyond their control. Not that they acknowledged his superior power, but they enjoyed watching his strange acts of violence. He dared not refuse, and moreover he could not believe that his companions were really acting out of malice, since no failure on his part ever justified such an attitude.

Weeks passed, and still the descent into the valley did not take place; it was constantly postponed on account of fresh plans, bad weather, or the hope of reinforcements of men and material. By the onset of winter the idea seemed to have been abandoned. It was at about this period that Peer started to have dreams.

These dreams followed the recognized pattern so closely that he immediately blamed himself, thinking that he must be affected by the force of suggestion of early memories, of the moral tales of his childhood. But was it really strange that, living continually amongst the horses, whose uproar battered his mind even in sleep, like waves, he should be haunted by tossing hoofs, writhing necks, equestrian terrors? Often he was surrounded by countless thronging beasts; he struggled, he fell, he was crushed underfoot. Then sometimes he felt all his sufferings suddenly vanish. He became a rider then, dashing over empty spaces where not even a breath of wind impeded his career or deprived him of the inspiring sensation of airy flight that was terrifying at first and then brought total release.

But soon he was back amidst the scenes of his torment; he was shut up with the animals as in an ark obstinately surviving on the calm extent of waters, and he would wake up moaning, profoundly bewildered. That trot that recurred as a leitmotiv through his dreams, that escape into space with which they all ended, might have taught him the reasons for the bitterness which he wreaked upon the animals and allowed him to identify one aspect at least of his misery. But it was too late.

Sometimes he saw spots dancing in the light before his eyes, and he was half aware that he would soon belong to that world towards which he was slowly gravitating, which drew him somewhat as one can fascinate a child and awaken his longing by juggling, at a little distance from him, with some fruit that hitherto he has scarcely desired.

Peer had grown considerably thinner. He sometimes caught

his fellows looking at him with that critical curiosity amounting almost to suspicion aroused by those in whom madness lies latent. The stable orderlies watched him with the same cold scrutiny with which they observed the behavior of a young unbroken animal. Peer had already begun to grow frightened, driven faster towards his doom by that terror inevitably aroused by the grim and earnest faces of psychiatrists and horse trainers. Suppose one of them were to come up and twist his arm; he would weep with shame and weakness!

And in the stable the trampling grew wilder, as though thousands of furies were chained up there. Despite their enfeebled condition, the animals were in a state of extreme nervous tension. One sharp crack of a whip was enough to make the whole mass catch fire, to set all the manes fluttering. Peer recognized here the familiar incidents of his dreams. Was this dream about to open out, as sometimes happened in the night? To expand into a wide clear sky, the haunt of infinite invisible riders? Was a bright birth about to crown the somber centuries of gestation?

"Corporal, the straw's moldy. Corporal, one horse has broken its foot. Corporal, one horse has died. Corporal . . ."

There was one short period during which the men took a delight in harassing him, trying to turn his anger against themselves. They hoped thus to become acquainted with that semi-madness of his that found vent only against the animals or retired into a mute solitude that irritated them.

Peer would lift his hand slowly with a gesture of indifference, as though to exorcise the irreparable, a lingering gesture that sometimes left his hand raised forgetfully in the air. The men grew tired of the game; besides, the sadness of their condition left them little heart for such things. It was winter. All life had taken refuge in the stables where, if the air was unbreathable, movement impossible and rest disturbed by rats and vermin, the men could yet find warmth and noise, the one relaxing their bodies, the other dissipating their anxiety. And even this refuge was a precarious one, for they were exposed not only to the discomfort of their surroundings but to hunger and the repeated echo of disastrous news.

The cold snowy weather had slowed down the march of the hostile armies, but the South, where were most of the men's families and homes, had already been overrun. And it was prob-

able that the region where they were stationed would soon be in
danger. Nobody knew whether these facts made any impression
on Peer.

When people passed by the heap of straw where he was usually
lying they were surprised to meet his gaze, wide open in the
darkness; at the sight of this stare, their questions died on their
lips because they read in it the tremendous answer that every
man carries secretly in his heart, postponed no doubt but inevitable. And then, out of a distant sky, came the moment which
was to bring to a conclusion all the long-drawn-out torments of
this lonely spot.

It was on a winter's day, a little brighter than the previous
days. Towards noon the sound of throbbing engines reached
them from the west.

They were surprised at first; since the beginning of the war
they had barely seen three aircraft pass. Then they grew uneasy.
The planes, which they could now make out and which bore
enemy markings, were wheeling round in the sky looking for
their objective with such an even speed and so smooth a sound
that they seemed merely to form part of a sidereal movement.

Then, very far off behind the trees, explosions shook the soil,
without affecting the calm of the sky. At the time, nobody knew
what had happened: the column of a company of the Army
Service Corps, loaded with equipment and provisions, had been
blown up five miles from the camp, to which it was bringing relief and — with its fresh troops and modern trucks — the token
of the country's first victorious reaction, showing the war in a
new and more hopeful light. The aircraft were still wheeling.

"Our turn next," thought the men, and they did not move,
unconsciously preferring the familiar shelter of the walls that for
six months had housed their untroubled way of life, their un-
eventful past, to the open spaces where they would run, carrying
their own fate, exposed to their own unpredictable swerves and
conflicting instincts — and where they would be utterly, nakedly
alone.

Fear had begun to grip them, however, and almost simultaneously they all thought of Peer, no doubt because he, with his
semimadness which seemed to them something surpassing reason,
belonged to that occult world where in the next ten minutes they
were going to die or to live; in short, because he carried a secret,

the only thing that could be opposed to that obscure, insistent throbbing up in the sky.

"Corporal!" they shouted, this time in earnest. Peer had gone out. They soon saw him come running back.

"Captain's orders! All the horses to be untied, all the doors to be opened. Quick, quick!"

He seemed calmer and more dignified than usual.

The men carried out the order, which had come from no captain but from a very different power — one which had suffered deeply hitherto. They hacked through the taut ropes to which the horses' bridles were fastened.

There was a moment's hesitation. The men were backing against the walls. Then one of the animals that was standing near the wide-open door moved towards the open air, snorted and neighed. And the stampede began.

The order had been passed to every corner of the camp. Columns of horses rushed towards freedom, so close-pressed as they passed through the doors that the heads of some lay on the cruppers of others, tossing jerkily as though they were trying to bite the air, like the little fringed waves that crest the sea.

The drone in the depths of the sky was covered now by the sound of a thousand hoofs; the whole earth was pulsating with the noise. Sometimes a horse that from chance or habit had strayed apart from the rest would begin to prance on the spot as though driven against an invisible shore, would bite at imaginary foliage in the air and then drift back into the stream.

All individuality, all precision of form had vanished; there were no longer any thin horses, lame or blind horses, dying horses; there was only a great rushing stream of equine life, at first seeming lightly furrowed, from a close view, by the myriad folds of skin at groin and neck, but soon becoming wholly smooth and flowing with a noise of subterranean thunder towards the untroubled prospect where storms were past and miracles accomplished.

Not a single horse was ever brought back. Peer was listed as a deserter after a week's absence.

❁

Pierre Gascar (1916-   )   Pierre Gascar (born Pierre Fournier) served on the Maginot Line and in Norway during World War II; from 1940 to 1945 he was a prisoner of war. *Beasts and Men*, a collection of seven haunting stories of death, slaughter, and warfare, received two of France's highest literary awards, the Prix Goncourt and the Prix des Critiques, and has been translated into German, Swedish, Italian, Japanese, and English; it and a novel, *The Seed*, are his only works thus far available in American editions. M. Gascar, with his wife and two children, currently lives in Paris.

Few writers have depicted more painfully than M. Gascar the searing effects of war upon the individual. Like Peer of "The Horses," many of his characters are like somnambulists in some blood-drenched nightmare. Their terrible actions grow out of neither reason nor hatred, but, like Peer's, are set in motion by forces beyond their control.

The strength of M. Gascar's memorable and disturbing stories, apart from the author's extreme technical skill and compassion, lies in his ability to transform the elements of horror and violence into a moving parable of man's fate in a world from which reason and love have been banished.

Questions   1. In "The Horses" the question is asked: "What were the horses, and why did he beat them?" Does Peer ever find the answer to this question?   2. Is Peer, in your opinion, representative of the so-called "typical" or "ordinary" man? Why or why not?   3. What are we told about Peer before the outbreak of the war which makes his "forging [of] his own demons" appear convincing. ("He only knew that each of his blows plunged him a little deeper into a hideously grimacing universe where the horses were all ferocity, the men all hate. He was forging his own demons.")   4. The statement is made that Pierre's blows are those of an "intellectual," but of this "he was not aware." What is the significance of this comment?   5. In what ways does the story remind you of other war stories you may have read? Is it a thematic story? If so, what is the theme? Is the theme implicit in the action?   6. In another story by Pierre Gascar the central character comments that "There's a certain stage, in cruelty, where all flesh smells alike." Could this remark apply to "The Horses"?

NADINE GORDIMER

Six Feet of
the Country

MY WIFE and I are not real farmers — not even Lerice, really.
We bought our place, ten miles out of Johannesburg on one of
the main roads, to change something in ourselves, I suppose; you
seem to rattle about so much within a marriage like ours. You
long to hear nothing but a deep satisfying silence when you sound
a marriage. The farm hasn't managed that for us, of course, but
it has done other things, unexpected, illogical. Lerice, who I
thought would retire there in Chekhovian sadness for a month or
two, and then leave the place to the servants while she tried yet
again to get a part she wanted and become the actress she would
like to be, has sunk into the business of running the farm with all
the serious intensity with which she once imbued the shadows in
a playwright's mind. I should have given it up long ago if it had
not been for her. Her hands, once small and plain and well kept
— she was not the sort of actress who wears red paint and diamond rings — are hard as a dog's pads.

I, of course, am there only in the evenings and on week-ends.
I am a partner in a luxury-travel agency, which is flourishing —
needs to be, as I tell Lerice, in order to carry the farm. Still,
though I know we can't afford it, and though the sweetish smell

of the fowls Lerice breeds sickens me, so that I avoid going past their runs, the farm is beautiful in a way I had almost forgotten — especially on a Sunday morning when I get up and go out into the paddock and see not the palm trees and fishpond and imitation-stone bird bath of the suburbs but white ducks on the dam, the lucerne field brilliant as window dresser's grass, and the little, stocky, mean-eyed bull, lustful but bored, having his face tenderly licked by one of his ladies. Lerice comes out with her hair uncombed, in her hand a stick dripping with cattle dip. She will stand and look dreamily for a moment, the way she would pretend to look sometimes in those plays. "They'll mate tomorrow," she will say. "This is their second day. Look how she loves him, my little Napoleon." So that when people come out to see us on Sunday afternoon, I am likely to hear myself saying as I pour out the drinks, "When I drive back home from the city every day, past those rows of suburban houses, I wonder how the devil we ever did stand it. . . . Would you care to look around?" And there I am, taking some pretty girl and her young husband stumbling down to our riverbank, the girl catching her stockings on the mealie-stooks and stepping over cow turds humming with jewel-green flies while she says, ". . . the *tensions* of the damned city. And you're near enough to get into town to a show, too! I think it's wonderful. Why, you've got it both ways!"

And for a moment I accept the triumph as if I *had* managed it — the impossibility that I've been trying for all my life — just as if the truth was that you could get it "both ways," instead of finding yourself with not even one way or the other but a third, one you you had not provided for at all.

But even in our saner moments, when I find Lerice's earthy enthusiasms just as irritating as I once found her histrionical ones, and she finds what she calls my "jealousy" of her capacity for enthusiasm as big a proof of my inadequacy for her as a mate as ever it was, we do believe that we have at least honestly escaped those tensions peculiar to the city about which our visitors speak. When Johannesburg people speak of "tension," they don't mean hurrying people in crowded streets, the struggle for money, or the general competitive character of city life. They mean the guns under the white men's pillows and the burglar bars on the white men's windows. They mean those strange moments on city pavements when a black man won't stand aside for a white man.

Out in the country, even ten miles out, life is better than that. In the country, there is a lingering remnant of the pretransitional stage; our relationship with the blacks is almost feudal. Wrong, I suppose, obsolete, but more comfortable all around. We have no burglar bars, no gun. Lerice's farm boys have their wives and their piccanins living with them on the land. They brew their sour beer without the fear of police raids. In fact, we've always rather prided ourselves that the poor devils have nothing much to fear, being with us; Lerice even keeps an eye on their children, with all the competence of a woman who has never had a child of her own, and she certainly doctors them all — children and adults — like babies whenever they happen to be sick.

It was because of this that we were not particularly startled one night last winter when the boy Albert came knocking at our window long after we had gone to bed. I wasn't in our bed but sleeping in the little dressing-room-*cum*-linen-room next door, because Lerice had annoyed me and I didn't want to find myself softening toward her simply because of the sweet smell of the talcum powder on her flesh after her bath. She came and woke me up. "Albert says one of the boys is very sick," she said. "I think you'd better go down and see. He wouldn't get us up at this hour for nothing?"

"What time is it?"

"What does it matter?" Lerice is maddeningly logical.

I got up awkwardly as she watched me — how is it I always feel a fool when I have deserted her bed? After all, I know from the way she never looks at me when she talks to me at breakfast the next day that she is hurt and humiliated at my not wanting her — and I went out, clumsy with sleep.

"Which of the boys is it?" I asked Albert as we followed the dance of my torch.

"He's too sick. Very sick, *Baas*," he said.

"But who? Franz?" I remembered Franz had had a bad cough for the past week.

Albert did not answer; he had given me the path, and was walking along beside me in the tall dead grass. When the light of the torch caught his face, I saw that he looked acutely embarrassed. "What's this all about?" I said.

He lowered his head under the glance of the light. "It's not me, *Baas*. I don't know. Petrus he send me."

Irritated, I hurried him along to the huts. And there, on Petrus's iron bedstead, with its brick stilts, was a young man, dead. On his forehead there was still a light, cold sweat; his body was warm. The boys stood around as they do in the kitchen when it is discovered that someone has broken a dish — uncooperative, silent. Somebody's wife hung about in the shadows, her hands wrung together under her apron.

I had not seen a dead man since the war. This was very different. I felt like the others — extraneous, useless. "What was the matter?" I asked.

The woman patted at her chest and shook her head to indicate the painful impossibility of breathing.

He must have died of pneumonia.

I turned to Petrus. "Who was this boy? What was he doing here?" The light of a candle on the floor showed that Petrus was weeping. He followed me out the door.

When we were outside, in the dark, I waited for him to speak. But he didn't. "Now, come on Petrus, you must tell me who this boy was. Was he a friend of yours?"

"He's my brother, *Baas*. He came from Rhodesia to look for work."

The story startled Lerice and me a little. The young boy had walked down from Rhodesia to look for work in Johannesburg, had caught a chill from sleeping out along the way, and had lain ill in his brother Petrus's hut since his arrival three days before. Our boys had been frightened to ask us for help for him because we had never been intended ever to know of his presence. Rhodesian natives are barred from entering the Union unless they have a permit; the young man was an illegal immigrant. No doubt our boys had managed the whole thing successfully several times before; a number of relatives must have walked the seven or eight hundred miles from poverty to the paradise of zoot suits, police raids, and black slum townships that is their *Egoli*, City of Gold — the Bantu name for Johannesburg. It was merely a matter of getting such a man to lie low on our farm until a job could be found with someone who would be glad to take the risk of prosecution for employing an illegal immigrant in exchange for the services of someone as yet untainted by the city.

Well, this was one who would never get up again.

"You would think they would have felt they could tell *us*," said Lerice next morning. "Once the man was ill. You would have thought at least — " When she is getting intense over something, she has a way of standing in the middle of a room as people do when they are shortly to leave on a journey, looking searchingly about her at the most familiar objects as if she had never seen them before. I had noticed that in Petrus's presence in the kitchen, earlier, she had had the air of being almost offended with him, almost hurt.

In any case, I really haven't the time or inclination any more to go into everything in our life that I know Lerice, from those alarmed and pressing eyes of hers, would like us to go into. She is the kind of woman who doesn't mind if she looks plain, or odd; I don't suppose she would even care if she knew how strange she looks when her whole face is out of proportion with urgent uncertainty. I said, "Now I'm the one who'll have to do all the dirty work, I suppose."

She was still staring at me, trying me out with those eyes — wasting her time, if she only knew.

"I'll have to notify the health authorities," I said calmly. "They can't just cart him off and bury him. After all, we don't really know what he died of."

She simply stood there, as if she had given up — simply ceased to see me at all.

I don't know when I've been so irritated. "It might have been something contagious," I said. "God knows." There was no answer.

I am not enamored of holding conversations with myself. I went out to shout to one of the boys to open the garage and get the car ready for my morning drive to town.

As I had expected, it turned out to be quite a business. I had to notify the police as well as the health authorities, and answer a lot of tedious questions: How was it I was ignorant of the boy's presence? If I did not supervise my native quarters, how did I know that that sort of thing didn't go on all the time? Et cetera, et cetera. And when I flared up and told them that so long as my natives did their work, I didn't think it my right or concern to poke my nose into their private lives, I got from the coarse, dull-witted police sergeant one of those looks that come not from any thinking process going on in the brain but from that faculty common to all who are possessed by the master-race theory — a look of insanely inane certainty. He grinned at me with a mixture of scorn and delight at my stupidity.

Then I had to explain to Petrus why the health authorities had to take away the body for a post-mortem — and, in fact, what a post-mortem was. When I telephoned the health department some days later to find out the result, I was told that the cause of death was, as we had thought, pneumonia, and that the body had been suitably disposed of. I went out to where Petrus was mixing a mash for the fowls and told him that it was all right, there would be no trouble; his brother had died from that pain in his chest. Petrus put down the paraffin tin and said, "When can we go to fetch him, *Baas?*"

"To fetch him?"

"Will the *Baas* please ask them when we must come?"

I went back inside and called Lerice, all over the house. She came down the stairs from the spare bedrooms, and I said, "*Now* what am I going to do? When I told Petrus, he just asked calmly when they could go and fetch the body. They think they're going to bury him themselves."

"Well, go back and tell him," said Lerice. "You must tell him. Why didn't you tell him then?"

When I found Petrus again, he looked up politely. "Look, Petrus," I said. "You can't go to fetch your brother. They've done it already — they've *buried* him, you understand?"

"Where?" he said slowly, dully, as if he thought that perhaps he was getting this wrong.

"You see, he was a stranger. They knew he wasn't from here, and they didn't know he had some of his people here so they thought they must bury him." It was difficult to make a pauper's grave sound like a privilege.

"Please, *Baas*, the *Baas* must ask them." But he did not mean that he wanted to know the burial place. He simply ignored the incomprehensible machinery I told him had to set to work on his dead brother; he wanted the brother back.

"But, Petrus," I said, "how can I? Your brother is buried already. I can't ask them now."

"Oh, *Baas!*" he said. He stood with his bran-smeared hands uncurled at his sides, one corner of his mouth twitching.

"Good God, Petrus, they won't listen to me! They can't, anyway. I'm sorry, but I can't do it. You understand?"

He just kept on looking at me, out of his knowledge that white men have everything, can do anything; if they don't, it is because they won't.

And then, at dinner, Lerice started. "You could at least phone," she said.

"Christ, what d'you think I am? Am I supposed to bring the dead back to life?"

But I could not exaggerate my way out of this ridiculous responsibility that had been thrust on me. "Phone them up," she went on. "And at least you'll be able to tell him you've done it and they've explained that it's impossible."

She disappeared somewhere into the kitchen quarters after coffee. A little later she came back to tell me, "The old father's coming down from Rhodesia to be at the funeral. He's got a permit and he's already on his way."

Unfortunately, it was not impossible to get the body back. The authorities said that it was somewhat irregular, but that since the hygiene conditions had been fulfilled, they could not refuse permission for exhumation. I found out that, with the undertaker's charges, it would cost twenty pounds. Ah, I thought, that settles it. On five pounds a month, Petrus won't have twenty pounds — and just as well, since it couldn't do the dead any good. Certainly I should not offer it to him myself. Twenty pounds — or anything else within reason, for that matter — I would have spent without grudging it on doctors or medicines that might have helped the boy when he was alive. Once he was dead, I had no intention of encouraging Petrus to throw away, on a gesture, more than he spent to clothe his whole family in a year.

When I told him, in the kitchen that night, he said, "Twenty pounds?"

I said, "Yes, that's right, twenty pounds."

For a moment, I had the feeling, from the look on his face, that he was calculating. But when he spoke again I thought I must have imagined it. "We must pay twenty pounds!" he said in the faraway voice in which a person speaks of something so unattainable that it does not bear thinking about.

"All right, Petrus," I said, and went back to the living room.

The next morning before I went to town, Petrus asked to see me. "Please, *Baas*," he said, awkwardly handing me a bundle of notes. They're so seldom on the giving rather than the receiving side, poor devils, that they don't really know how to hand money to a white man. There it was, the twenty pounds, in ones and halves, some creased and folded until they were soft as dirty rags, others smooth and fairly new — Franz's money, I suppose, and Albert's, and Dora the cook's, and Jacob the gardener's, and God knows who else's besides, from all the farms and small holdings round about. I took it in irritation more than in astonishment, really — irritation at the waste, the uselessness of this sacrifice by people so poor. Just like the poor everywhere, I thought, who stint themselves the decencies of life in order to insure themselves the decencies of death. So incomprehensible to people like Lerice and me, who regard life as something to be spent extravagantly, and, if we think about death at all, regard it as the final bankruptcy.

The servants don't work on Saturday afternoon anyway, so it was a good day for the funeral. Petrus and his father had borrowed our donkey cart to fetch the coffin from the city, where, Petrus told Lerice on their return, everything was "nice" — the coffin waiting for them, already sealed up to save them from what must have been a rather unpleasant sight after two weeks' interment. (It had taken all that time for the authorities and the undertaker to make the final arrangements for moving the body.) All morning, the coffin lay in Petrus's hut, awaiting the trip to the little old burial ground, just outside the eastern boundary of our farm, that was a relic of the days when this was a real farming district rather than a fashionable rural estate. It was pure chance that I happened to be down there near the fence when the procession came past; once again Lerice had forgotten her promise to me and had made the house uninhabitable on a

Saturday afternoon. I had come home and been infuriated to find her in a pair of filthy old slacks and with her hair uncombed since the night before, having all the varnish scraped off the living-room floor, if you please. So I had taken my No. 8 iron and gone off to practice my approach shots. In my annoyance, I had forgotten about the funeral, and was reminded only when I saw the procession coming up the path along the outside of the fence toward me; from where I was standing, you can see the graves quite clearly, and that day the sun glinted on bits of broken pottery, a lopsided homemade cross, and jam jars brown with rain water and dead flowers.

I felt a little awkward, and did not know whether to go on hitting my golf ball or stop at least until the whole gathering was decently past. The donkey cart creaks and screeches with every revolution of the wheels, and it came along in a slow, halting fashion somehow peculiarly suited to the two donkeys who drew it, their little potbellies rubbed and rough, their heads sunk between the shafts, and their ears flattened back with an air submissive and downcast; peculiarly suited, too, to the group of men and women who came along slowly behind. The patient ass. Watching, I thought, You can see now why the creature became a Biblical symbol. Then the procession drew level with me and stopped, so I had to put down my club. The coffin was taken down off the cart — it was a shiny, yellow-varnished wood, like cheap furniture — and the donkeys twitched their ears against the flies. Petrus, Franz, Albert, and the old father from Rhodesia hoisted it on their shoulders and the procession moved on, on foot. It was really a very awkward moment. I stood there rather foolishly at the fence, quite still, and slowly they filed past, not looking up, the four men bent beneath the shiny wooden box, and the straggling troop of mourners. All of them were servants or neighbors' servants whom I knew as casual, easygoing gossipers about our lands or kitchen. I heard the old man's breathing.

I had just bent to pick up my club again when there was a sort of jar in the flowing solemnity of their processional mood; I felt it at once, like a wave of heat along the air, or one of those sudden currents of cold catching at your legs in a placid stream. The old man's voice was muttering something; the people had stopped, confused, and they bumped into one another, some

pressing to go on, others hissing them to be still. I could see that
they were embarrassed, but they could not ignore the voice;
it was much the way that the mumblings of a prophet, though
not clear at first, arrest the mind. The corner of the coffin the
old man carried was sagging at an angle; he seemed to be trying
to get out from under the weight of it. Now Petrus expostulated
with him.

The little boy who had been left to watch the donkeys dropped
the reins and ran to see. I don't know why — unless it was for
the same reason people crowd around someone who has fainted
in a cinema — but I parted the wires of the fence and went
through, after him.

Petrus lifted his eyes to me — to anybody — with distress and
horror. The old man from Rhodesia had let go of the coffin entirely, and the three others, unable to support it on their own,
had laid it on the ground, in the pathway. Already there was a
film of dust lightly wavering up its shiny sides. I did not understand what the old man was saying; I hesitated to interfere.
But now the whole seething group turned on my silence. The
old man himself came over to me, with his hands outspread and
shaking, and spoke directly to me, saying something that I could
tell from the tone, without understanding the words, was shock-
ing and extraordinary.

"What is it, Petrus? What's wrong?" I appealed.

Petrus threw up his hands, bowed his head in a series of
hysterical shakes, then thrust his face up at me suddenly. "He
says, 'My son was not so heavy.'"

Silence. I could hear the old man breathing; he kept his mouth
a little open, as old people do.

"My son was young and thin," he said at last, in English.

Again silence. Then babble broke out. The old man thundered
against everybody; his teeth were yellowed and few, and he had
one of those fine, grizzled, sweeping mustaches that one doesn't
often see nowadays, which must have been grown in emula-
tion of early Empire builders. It seemed to frame all his utter-
ances with a special validity, perhaps merely because it was
the symbol of the traditional wisdom of age — an idea so fearfully rooted that it carries still something awesome beyond reason. He shocked them; they thought he was mad, but they had
to listen to him. With his own hands he began to prize the lid off

the coffin and three of the men came forward to help him. Then he sat down on the ground, very old, very weak, and unable to speak, he merely lifted a trembling hand toward what was there. He abdicated, he handed it over to them; he was no good any more.

They crowded round to look (and so did I), and now they forgot the nature of this surprise and the occasion of grief to which it belonged, and for a few minutes were carried up in the delightful astonishment of the surprise itself. They gasped and flared noisily with excitement. I even noticed the little boy who had held the donkeys jumping up and down, almost weeping with rage because the backs of the grownups crowded him out of his view.

In the coffin was someone no one had ever seen before: a heavily built, rather light-skinned native with a neatly stitched scar on his forehead — perhaps from a blow in a brawl that had also dealt him some other, slower-working injury, which had killed him.

I wrangled with the authorities for a week over that body. I had the feeling that they were shocked, in a laconic fashion, by their own mistake, but that in the confusion of their anonymous dead they were helpless to put it right. They said to me, "We are trying to find out," and "We are still making inquiries." It was as if at any moment they might conduct me into their mortuary and say, "There! Lift up the sheets; look for him — your poultry boy's brother. There are so many black faces — surely one will do?"

And every evening when I got home, Petrus was waiting in the kitchen. "Well, they're trying. They're still looking. The *Baas* is seeing to it for you, Petrus," I would tell him. "God, half the time I should be in the office I'm driving around the back end of the town chasing after this affair," I added aside, to Lerice, one night.

She and Petrus both kept their eyes turned on me as I spoke, and, oddly, for those moments they looked exactly alike, though it sounds impossible: my wife, with her high, white forehead and her attenuated Englishwoman's body, and the poultry boy, with his horny bare feet below khaki trousers tied at the knee with string and the peculiar rankness of his nervous sweat coming from his skin.

"What makes you so indignant, so determined about this now?" said Lerice suddenly.

I stared at her. "It's a matter of principle. Why should they get away with a swindle? It's time these officials had a jolt from someone who'll bother to take the trouble."

She said, "Oh." And as Petrus slowly opened the kitchen door to leave, sensing that the talk had gone beyond him, she turned away, too.

I continued to pass on assurances to Petrus every evening, but although what I said was the same and the voice in which I said it was the same, every evening it sounded weaker. At last, it became clear that we would never get Petrus's brother back, because nobody really knew where he was. Somewhere in a graveyard as uniform as a housing scheme, somewhere under a number that didn't belong to him, or in the medical school, perhaps, laboriously reduced to layers of muscle and strings of nerve? Goodness knows. He had no identity in this world anyway.

It was only then, and in a voice of shame, that Petrus asked me to try and get the money back.

"From the way he asks, you'd think he was robbing his dead brother," I said to Lerice later. But as I've said, Lerice had got so intense about this business that she couldn't even appreciate a little ironic smile.

I tried to get the money; Lerice tried. We both telephoned and wrote and argued, but nothing came of it. It appeared that the main expense had been the undertaker, and after all he had done his job. So the whole thing was a complete waste, even more of a waste for the poor devils than I had thought it would be.

The old man from Rhodesia was about Lerice's father's size, so she gave him one of her father's old suits, and he went back home rather better off, for the winter, than he had come.

Nadine Gordimer (1923-   )   One of a remarkable group of South African writers whose work has won considerable praise in the years following World War II, Nadine Gordimer was born in South

Africa, where she still lives, and studied at the University of Witwatersrand in Johannesburg. Several of her stories were originally published in such .American magazines as *The New Yorker* and *The Virginia Quarterly Review;* her first volume of short stories, *The Soft Voice of the Serpent,* came out in 1952; a later collection, *Six Feet of the Country,* in 1956. Miss Gordimer is also the author of two novels about South Africa, *The Lying Days* and *A World of Strangers.*

Most of Miss Gordimer's stories are set in or around Johannesburg, which the author knows and understands in the way that Joyce knew and understood Dublin. Racial problems are at the very center of many of her stories; misunderstanding, perhaps, is the common chord that runs through all her work. "Six Feet of the Country," for example, is a drama of mounting suspense, tension, and misunderstanding. Against the larger area of conflict between black man and white man, between *Baas* and boy, the author effectively contrasts and counterpoints the misunderstandings between the neurotic husband-narrator and his artistic wife.

Six Feet of the Country is available in paperback (New American Library).

Questions   1. At the conclusion of the story, the narrator states: "So the whole thing was a complete waste, even more of a waste for the poor devils than I had thought it would be." Do you agree or disagree with him? What principles are at stake here — in the boy's efforts to flee from Rhodesia, in his relative's attempts to give him a "proper" funeral and burial, in Lerice's efforts to recover his body, in the narrator's interest in rectifying the error of the switched bodies? 2. What different attitudes towards the blacks are displayed by Lerice, by her husband, by the city officials? Are these attitudes in any way reminiscent of those displayed by Faulkner's characters in "That Evening Sun" and "A Bear Hunt"?   3. How would you characterize the narrator? Lerice? Petrus? The boy's father? In your opinion who is the most admirable character in the story? The least admirable?   4. Are there any attitudes towards city life which are at all reminiscent of those displayed in Cheever's "The Enormous Radio"?   5. Discuss the irony of the last sentence. What similar examples occur throughout the story?   6. Are symbols used in this story? (Notice that Miss Gordimer, like Hawthorne and Saroyan, is not averse to employing the word itself; the moustache of the boy's father is spoken of as the "symbol of the traditional wisdom of age"; the narrator reflects that he can see why the donkey "became a Biblical symbol").   7. What are the implications (social, moral, and otherwise) of the narrator's comment on the dead boy: "He had no identity in this world anyway"?